Chemical Energetics

GW00992289

Corrigenda

Page 22, footnote. For 285.9 kJ *read* -285.9 kJ.

Page 93, line 8 (and **Fig. 7.1**). For 6×10^{-3} *read* 3×10^{-4}.

Page 93, line 10. For 5.6×10^4 *read* 2.2×10^7.

Page 123, exercise 2. For $8H_2O$ *read* $4H_2O$.

Page 124, line 21. For $8H_2O$ *read* $4H_2O$.

Page 136, q. 7. For $+0.46$ V *read* $+0.346$ V. Following paragraph to read: Suggest a reason why the second of the above reactions has a more positive reduction potential than the first, although both are for the change Cu(II) to Cu(I). Is the Cu(II) ion a better or a worse oxidant in the presence of chloride ions?

Answers

Page 184, **3.14**, q. 3 (d) (ii). For 19 *read* 18.

Page 184, **3.16**, q. 5. Reverse signs throughout.

Page 186, **7.7**, q. 2. For 6.6 *read* 7.6.

      q. 4. For -14.6 *read* -11.5 and for -7.2 *read* -4.1.

      q. 5 (c). For 4.0% *read* 1.3%.

Page 189, **8.12**, q. 4. For $\log \dfrac{1}{0.002} = +0.16 - 0.08$ V *read* $\log \dfrac{10^2}{0.002} = +0.16 - 0.14$ V.

Page 189, **9.9**, q. 1 (iii). For $+10$ *read* -10.

Page 203, last line of Frequently used data. For ΔH *read* ΔG.

SELLEY: Chemical Energetics

Chemical Energetics

Nicholas J. Selley, M.A., B.Sc.

*Lecturer in Physical Chemistry, University of Ife, Nigeria,
Formerly Chemistry Master, City of London School*

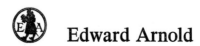

Edward Arnold

© Nicholas J. Selley 1971

First published 1971
by Edward Arnold (Publishers) Ltd.
41 Maddox Street
London W1R 0AN

ISBN: 0 7131 2348 6   BOARDS EDITION
ISBN: 0 7131 2316 8   LIMP EDITION

Printed in Great Britain by
William Clowes & Sons, Limited, London, Beccles and Colchester

Preface

Chapter 1 begins 'Why do chemical reactions occur?' Until recently it was possible for a student to complete a course in thermodynamics without ever being asked that question. Now teachers have come to see that the subject is much more attractive if it is made relevant to general chemistry right from the start. The simpler aspects of energetics *can* be taught in Sixth Forms, and a simple and satisfying answer to the question 'Why?' can be provided after a little groundwork has been done.

The book is designed for use both as the textbook for an organized course in school or college, and for individual study. In either case the student is strongly advised to *work all the exercises*. They are an integral part of the course, and serve not only to test the student's understanding of the work, but often to introduce new material. They should not be left until the end of the chapter. The Answers section will usually contain solutions to non-numerical as well as numerical problems, and clues to the method of working them. Examination and Revision Questions (without answers) are also included in the Additional Exercises section.

Some of the sections and exercises, marked thus *, are more suitable for undergraduates, and could be omitted from a school course without detracting from the logical development. No advanced mathematics is needed (O-level Additional Maths is ample) but the weaker student may find Appendix C helpful.

A word about two controversial points. I have followed Moore and many other authors in using $\Delta U = Q + W$, where $(+W)$ is work done *on* the system, which is consistent with the sign convention for all other energy terms. Physicists, engineers and some chemists are in the habit of using $(-W)$ instead. Secondly, quite early in the course ΔG is introduced as the 'driving-force of the reaction', whereas this concept is perhaps more accurately represented by $\Delta G/T$. §§5.10 and 7.5 contain a discussion of this.

SI units are used throughout.

1971   N. J. S.

Contents

Preface   v

1   Chemical reactions   1
    1.1 Why do chemical reactions occur? 1   1.2 A survey of reactions 1   1.3 Conclusion 5   1.4 Exercises 6

2   Enthalpy of reaction (ΔH)   7
    2.1 Introduction 7   2.2 Units of energy 7   2.3 Enthalpy of reaction 9   2.4 Exercises 10   2.5 The Law of Enthalpy Summation (Hess's law) 11   2.6 Definition of specified heats of reaction 13   2.7 Exercises 14   2.8 Practical work 15   2.9 The bomb calorimeter 17   2.10 The First Law of Thermodynamics 18   2.11 Obligatory work accompanying volume change 19   2.12 Variation of ΔH with T 20   2.13 Standard enthalpy of formation ($\Delta H_f^{\ominus}$) 20   2.14 Exercises 21   2.15 Ionic enthalpies 22   2.16 Exercises 22

3   Free-energy   24
    3.1 Endothermic reactions 24   3.2 Reversible reactions 25   3.3 Gibbs free-energy (ΔG) 25   3.4 Worked example 27   3.5 Exercises 28   3.6 Entropy 28   3.7 Examples 29   3.8 Exercises 30   3.9 Measurements and calculations of ΔG 31   3.10 $\Delta G = G_2 - G_1$ 32   3.11 Exercises 33   3.12 Measuring ΔG for cell reactions 33   3.13 Practical work 35   3.14 Exercises 38   3.15 Summary of principles of qualitative estimation of ΔH, ΔS and ΔG 40   3.16 Revision exercises 41

4   Enthalpy and bonding   43
    4.1 Stability 43   4.2 Covalent bond energies 43   4.3 Exercises 45   4.4 Average bond energies 45   4.5 Transferable bond energies 45   4.6 Exercises 46   4.7 The carbon–carbon bonds 47   4.8 Practical work (bond energies) 47   4.9 Delocalization energy 48   4.10 Intermolecular bonding 49   4.11 Exercises 51   4.12 Ionic compounds: the Born–Haber cycle 52   4.13 Ionic solutions 54   4.14 Exercises 55

5   Entropy and the Second Law of Thermodynamics   57
    5.1 Free-energy and spontaneous change 57   5.2 Order and
    disorder 58   5.3 Entropy and probability 59   5.4 Absolute
    entropies 60   5.5 Reaction entropy changes ΔS_r 63   5.6
    Energy and work 64   5.7 The efficiency of energy con-
    version 65   5.8 The disorder of heat 67   5.9 Heat transfer
    accompanying maximum work 68   5.10 ΔG as the criterion of
    feasibility 69   5.11 Exercises 70

6   Reaction rate   73
    6.1 Introduction 73   6.2 The dependence of reaction rate
    upon concentration 73   6.3 Order and molecularity 76   6.4
    Exercises 77   6.5 Variation of reaction velocity with tem-
    perature   78   6.6 Practical   introduction   78   6.7 The
    Arrhenius equation 80   6.8 Exercises 80   6.9 Distribution
    of molecular energies 81   6.10 Energy of activation 82   6.11
    The activated complex 83   6.12 The temperature-indepen-
    dent factor (A) 84   6.13 The principle of micro-reversibility
    85   6.14 Catalysis 86   6.15 Exercises 87

7   Equilibria   89
    7.1 Temperature effect 89   7.2 Equilibrium at constant
    temperature 90   7.3 Practical work 94   7.4 The equili-
    brium constant 95   7.5 Le Chatelier's Principle 97   7.6
    Well-known examples of equilibria 101   7.7 Exercises 104
    7.8 The free-energy expansion and dilution 105   7.9 ΔG for
    reaction with non-standard concentrations 107   7.10 The
    use of the reaction isotherm 108   7.11 Equilibrium con-
    stants and enthalpy 110   7.12 A physical interpretation of the
    van't Hoff isotherm 111   7.13 Exercises 114   7.14 Equili-
    bria in solution: dissociation constants 115   7.15 Entropy
    of dissociation of acids and bases 115   7.16 Exercises 117
    7.17 Solubility 117   7.18 Exercises 119

8   Electrochemical potentials   121
    8.1 Electron   transfer   reactions   121   8.2 Exercises   123
    8.3 Reaction at a distance 124   8.4 Cell potentials 125
    8.5 Practical work 126   8.6 Reduction potentials 126   8.7
    Addition of redox potentials 128   8.8 Application of redox
    potentials to   inorganic chemistry 129   8.9 Exercises 133
    8.10 Concentration cells 137   8.11 Non-standard redox
    potentials: the Nernst equation 138   8.12 Exercises 139
    8.13 The Ag/Ag^+: Fe^{2+}/Fe^{3+} equilibrium 140   8.14 Re-
    stricted ion concentration 142   8.15 Exercises 143   8.16
    Fuel cells 144

9   Energetics and the extraction of metals   146
      9.1 Introduction 146   9.2 The calculation of $\Delta G_r^\ominus$ for
      metallurgical reactions 146   9.3 Exercises 147   9.4 Reduc-
      tion of oxides by other metals and by hydrogen 148   9.5
      Exercise 149   9.6 The oxides of carbon 149   9.7 The
      Ellingham diagram for oxide formation 151   9.8 The ex-
      traction of metals 154   9.9 Exercises 156   9.10 Multiple
      oxidation states: disproportionation 157   9.11 Exercises 158

10 Energy considerations in biochemistry   160
      10.1 Introduction 160   10.2 The steps of metabolic processes
      160   10.3 Enzymes 162   10.4 The re-distribution of
      energy 164   10.5 Photosynthesis 166   10.6 Life processes
      167   10.7 Exercises 167

    Additional Exercises   170
      Part I Revision questions 170   Part II Examination ques-
      tions 173   Part III Miscellaneous problems 177   Part IV
      Practical projects 179

    Answers   183

    Appendix A: Energies of formation   192

    Appendix B: Standard reduction potentials at 298 K   196

    Appendix C: Glossary of terms and selected mathematical func-
      tions   198

    Bibliography   200

    Symbols   202
    Frequently-used data   203
    Selected atomic weights   203
    Logarithms   204

    Index   207

1 Chemical reactions

1.1 Why do chemical reactions occur?

A chemistry student with any curiosity will soon ask this question. He will find that there is no ready answer at an elementary level. If this stimulates him to search more deeply he will be rewarded, but there is a certain amount of preliminary work he must do before the answer can be very meaningful to him.

One of the aims of this course is to prepare the way to an answer in terms of energetics, and to show the relevance of these concepts to a general understanding of chemistry. The two final chapters show the usefulness of energetics by the two widely different examples of its application to metallurgy and biochemistry.

The question is in fact rather deceptive, and it would be well to look at it more closely. For one thing, it is not the same as '*How* do chemical reactions occur?', because this aspect, seeking the manner or mechanism of a reaction, never explains why some particles which are given the opportunity to react fail to do so.

The question 'How fast?' is relevant, and will be discussed in Chapter 7; but it is not the same as 'Why?'. Fast reactions are not necessarily the most complete; the rate of reaction does not determine its direction or eventual extent. So this raises other questions: 'How far?' and 'What conditions?'. These are all related, and will all be made clearer by a answer to our main question, which may be rephrased 'What is the driving-force behind chemical reactions?'.

1.2 A survey of reactions

It would be a sensible start to an investigation into the underlying reasons for chemical reactions to consider the observable differences in the ease with which reactions occur. These are the facts which must be accounted for by any theory of this kind.

Type A

Reactions which occur very readily, as soon as the reagents are mixed.

EXAMPLES

$$Na + H_2O \longrightarrow NaOH + \tfrac{1}{2}H_2 \qquad A\text{-}1$$
$$Mg + 2HCl \longrightarrow MgCl_2 + H_2 \qquad A\text{-}2$$
$$Na_2SO_4 + BaCl_2 \longrightarrow BaSO_4 \downarrow + 2NaCl \qquad A\text{-}3$$
$$MnO_4^- + 5Fe^{2+} + 8H^+ \longrightarrow Mn^{2+} + Fe^{3+} + 4H_2O \qquad A\text{-}4$$
$$H_2S + Cl_2 \longrightarrow 2HCl + S \downarrow \qquad A\text{-}5$$
$$2NO + O_2 \longrightarrow 2NO_2 \qquad A\text{-}6$$
$$PCl_5 + 4H_2O \longrightarrow H_3PO_4 + 5HCl \qquad A\text{-}7$$

Reactions of this kind are often between ions in solution (as *A-2* to *A-4*). They are completed immediately after mixing, in the case of gases or solutions. In the case of a liquid reacting with a solid the rate is limited only by the time taken for the reactants to meet, and the products to get away (*A-1* and *A-2*). In quite a short time these reactions go to completion, that is, they stop only when one of the reactants is completely consumed.

Type B

Reactions which proceed readily once they get started, but which go very slowly or not at all when the reactants are mixed at room temperature.

EXAMPLES

$$2H_2 + O_2 \longrightarrow 2H_2O \qquad B\text{-}1$$
$$2Mg + O_2 \longrightarrow 2MgO \qquad B\text{-}2$$
$$H_2 + Cl_2 \longrightarrow 2HCl \qquad B\text{-}3$$
$$4KNO_3 + 2C + 3S \longrightarrow 2K_2CO_3 + 3SO_2 + 2N_2 \qquad B\text{-}4$$
$$Zn + I_2 \longrightarrow ZnI_2 \qquad B\text{-}5$$
$$2Al + Fe_2O_3 \longrightarrow Al_2O_3 + 2Fe \qquad B\text{-}6$$
$$CH_3C_6H_2(NO_2)_3 \longrightarrow N_2 + CO_2 + H_2O, \text{ etc.} \qquad B\text{-}7$$

The commonest way to start these reactions is to heat at least a small part of the reactant mixture to a high temperature. Once reaction starts it spreads rapidly to the remainder of the mixture without further application of heat. In fact the amount of heat put in may be negligible, such as a single spark (*B-1*) or a single match in a keg of gunpowder (*B-4*). Once this small 'energy of initiation' has been provided, the reactions give out heat, and so sustain and propagate themselves.

Sometimes a different source of 'energy of initiation' can set the reaction off. A hydrogen + chlorine mixture can explode when exposed to ultraviolet light, (*B-3*) and some explosives can be detonated by shock (*B-7*).

In other cases a catalyst will start a reaction; e.g., a drop of water added to a dry mixture of powdered iodine and zinc, or a platinum gauze placed in a mixture of ammonia gas and oxygen. These reactions build up rapidly, once started, and can become almost explosive.

All reactions in this group go virtually to completion.

Type C

Reactions which take in heat, and are termed 'endothermic'.
In general such reactions only continue if a high temperature is maintained by an external supply of heat.

EXAMPLES

$$CaCO_3 \longrightarrow CaO + CO_2 \qquad \textit{C-1}$$
$$2NH_3 \longrightarrow N_2 + 3H_2 \qquad \textit{C-2}$$
$$C + H_2O \longrightarrow CO + H_2 \qquad \textit{C-3}$$
$$2HgO \longrightarrow 2Hg + O_2 \qquad \textit{C-4}$$
$$N_2 + O_2 \longrightarrow 2NO \qquad \textit{C-5}$$
$$2Pb(NO_3)_2 \longrightarrow 2PbO + 4NO_2 + O_2 \qquad \textit{C-6}$$

These differ from those in *Type B* in that when the supply of heat is removed, the reactions stop. The difference would be more obvious if the reactants of both types were heated to a definite high temperature *before* mixing; exothermic reactions such as those in *Type B* would proceed readily and become even hotter, whereas endothermic reactions would cause the temperature to fall, and would therefore slow up.

Endothermic reactions are often incomplete, and reach a steady state with reactants still present. This behaviour is classed as *Type E*.

Type D

Reactions which proceed slowly but steadily.
Types A and *B* were reactions with very fast speeds (after initiation). In *Type C* the speeds were difficult to assess because they were so closely linked with the rate of supply of heat. *Type D* contains slow reactions which are not appreciably endothermic.

EXAMPLES

$$Na_2S_2O_3 + 2HCl \text{ (aq)} \longrightarrow 2NaCl + H_2O + SO_2 + S \downarrow \qquad \textit{D-1}$$
$$2Na_2SO_3 + O_2 \longrightarrow 2Na_2SO_4 \qquad \textit{D-2}$$
$$2H_2O_2 \longrightarrow 2H_2O + O_2 \qquad \textit{D-3}$$
$$2HClO \longrightarrow 2HCl + O_2 \qquad \textit{D-4}$$
$$\text{sucrose} + H_2O \longrightarrow \text{glucose} + \text{fructose} \qquad \textit{D-5}$$
$$2SO_2 + O_2 \longrightarrow 2SO_3 \qquad \textit{D-6}$$
$$(COOH)_2 + KMnO_4 + H^+ \longrightarrow H_2O + CO_2 + \text{inorganic products} \qquad \textit{D-7}$$
$$C_2H_5OH + K_2Cr_2O_7 + H^+ \longrightarrow CH_3CHO + \text{inorganic products} \qquad \textit{D-8}$$

These reactions are all homogeneous—that is, between miscible liquids or gases. For these the velocity of reaction is well defined as the decrease in the molar concentration of one reactant in unit time. As mentioned above, some heterogeneous reactions between solids and liquids are slow for a different reason: the reaction conditions are 'cramped', and one reactant has to diffuse to the solid surface, while the products have to dissolve and diffuse away.

Velocities of reaction depend upon several factors, which are treated in turn in later sections.

(i) Concentration. Reaction rate is roughly proportional to concentration of reactants, as a rule.

(ii) Temperature. Rate is super-proportional to temperature, and for room-temperature reactions a rise of as little as 10K often doubles the rate.

(iii) Catalysts. Catalysts are substances which alter the rate of a reaction, sometimes from zero, without being consumed. They can accelerate reactions to a phenomenal extent, e.g. a slight trace of Cu^{2+} ion can increase the rate of *D-2* by a factor of a thousand.

Reactions can also be *autocatalytic*, that is, one of the products can be a catalyst for the reaction. Then as the reaction proceeds the rate increases, contrary to normal expectations. *D-7* is autocatalysed by Mn^{2+} ions. The following reactions are also said to be autocatalytic; but the phenomenon should not be confused with the speeding-up due to rise in temperature brought about by an exothermic reaction.

$$2Al + 3Br_2 \text{ (l)} \longrightarrow 2AlBr_3 \qquad\qquad\qquad D\text{-}9$$
$$Cu + HNO_3 \text{ (5M)} \longrightarrow Cu(NO_3)_2 + H_2O + (NO \text{ and } NO_2) \quad D\text{-}10$$

Type E

Reversible reactions: reactions which go readily enough under certain conditions, but which reverse if the conditions are changed.

EXAMPLES

$$2SbCl_3 + 3H_2S \rightleftharpoons Sb_2S_3 \text{ (s)} + 6HCl \text{ (aq)} \qquad\qquad E\text{-}1$$
$$CaCO_3 \rightleftharpoons CaO + CO_2 \qquad\qquad E\text{-}2$$
$$2Hg + O_2 \rightleftharpoons 2HgO \qquad\qquad E\text{-}3$$
$$C_2H_5OH \rightleftharpoons C_2H_4 + H_2O \qquad\qquad E\text{-}4$$
$$Al(OH)_3 \text{ (s)} + OH^- \text{ (aq)} \rightleftharpoons AlO_2^- \text{ (aq)} + 2H_2O \qquad\qquad E\text{-}5$$
$$Al^{3+} \text{ (aq)} + 2H_2O \rightleftharpoons Al(OH)^{2+} \text{ (aq)} + H_3O^+ \text{ (aq)} \qquad E\text{-}6$$

Consider *E-1*. If hydrogen sulphide gas is passed into a solution of antimony chloride in dilute hydrochloric acid, orange antimony sulphide is precipitated. But if concentrated hydrochloric acid is added to this antimony sulphide it redissolves, liberating hydrogen sulphide. The equation is then exactly the reverse of the one given, and the sign $\rightleftharpoons$ indicates the possibility of reversal.

If hydrogen sulphide were passed through a solution of antimony chloride in *moderately* concentrated hydrochloric acid, precipitation would be incomplete. The reaction would stop even though some anti-

mony chloride remained in solution, because the hydrochloric acid concentration would have been increased by the reaction to the point where
the reverse reaction was occurring as readily as the forward one. The
system would be at chemical *equilibrium.*

Some reactions reach equilibrium almost immediately, and instantly
re-establish a different equilibrium if conditions are changed. This
property is indicated by the sign $\rightleftharpoons$ (see *E-6*).

A reaction which comes to equilibrium can be taken nearer to completion if one of the products is removed. In *E-2*, if calcium carbonate is
heated in a *closed* vessel, then cooled again, the residue will always contain unchanged carbonate; but in an open vessel the carbon dioxide
escapes, and conversion to calcium oxide can be complete.

Type F

Reactions which do not proceed at all, at any temperature, without an
external supply of energy such as those shown.

EXAMPLES

$$2NaCl \longrightarrow 2Na + Cl_2 \quad \text{(electrolysis)} \qquad \qquad F\text{-}1$$
$$ZnSO_4 + Cu \longrightarrow CuSO_4 + Zn \quad \text{(electrolysis or roundabout}$$
$$\text{route)} \qquad \qquad F\text{-}3$$
$$4Ag + O_2 \longrightarrow 2Ag_2O \quad \text{(roundabout route)} \qquad F\text{-}3$$
$$6CO_2 + 6H_2O \longrightarrow C_6H_{12}O_6 \quad \text{(photosynthesis in green}$$
$$\text{plants)} \qquad \qquad F\text{-}4$$
$$H_2O \longrightarrow H + OH \quad \text{(ultraviolet light)} \qquad F\text{-}5$$

These 'unnatural' reactions can only occur when driven, either by
electrolysis or radiation, or by being coupled to other 'natural' reactions
during a roundabout route. This normally happens only by intelligent
design, or in a living cell (*F-4*).

Note that the *reverse* of all these reactions occur readily, so that the
reason why they do not go forward unaided is not the absence of any
reaction route, which might explain the impossibility of the innumerable
fantastic reactions (non-reactions) such as:

$$4K + Fe + 6C + 3N_2 \longrightarrow K_4Fe(CN)_6 \qquad F\text{-}6$$

1.3 Conclusion

This classification into six types is an arbitrary and superficial one,
based on external appearances only. There will be overlapping, and many
borderline cases. Nevertheless, the exercise shows that the differences are
profound, and suggests that such a broad range of experience requires a
broad theory to unify it.

If the theory enables the chemist, on the basis of other information, to
predict the type of some new reaction, it will do much to increase his

effectiveness. The branch of chemistry which has been most successful in this direction is that known as energetics.

1.4 Exercises

1. From your knowledge of the following reactions, classify them according to the scheme used in this chapter.

(a) $2NaHCO_3 \longrightarrow Na_2CO_3 + H_2O + CO_2$
(b) $C_2H_4 + Br_2 \longrightarrow C_2H_4Br_2$
(c) $CH_4 + Br_2 \longrightarrow CH_3Br + HBr$
(d) $CuSO_4 + H_2S \longrightarrow CuS + H_2SO_4$
(e) $2KClO_3 \longrightarrow 2KCl + 3O_2$
(f) $CuO + H_2 \longrightarrow Cu + H_2O$
(g) $Cu + H_2O \longrightarrow CuO + H_2$
(h) $C_2H_4 + H_2 \longrightarrow C_2H_6$

2. Which of these reactions are assisted by higher temperature?

3. Which are commonly assisted by a catalyst?

2 Enthalpy of reaction (ΔH)

2.1 Introduction

The material changes of chemical reactions are accompanied by heat changes. It has been remarked that when coal and oil are burned the purpose is not usually to prepare carbon dioxide. Almost from the first chemistry lesson the pupil notices that many reactions in solution, too, cause temperature changes.

Most of these will be exothermic, giving out heat. The reactions of acid with alkali, permanganate with iodide, calcium oxide with water, or aluminium with sodium hydroxide are familiar examples. The first endothermic reactions to be noticed occurring spontaneously at room temperature are the dissolution of salts such as ammonium nitrate or sodium thiosulphate in water; a fall of 10 kelvin (K) or so can result. It may be argued that these are not true chemical reactions, so for an example of a spontaneous endothermic reaction between solutions the student may like to try

$$MgSO_4 \text{ (aq)} + Na_2CO_3 \text{ (aq)} \longrightarrow MgCO_3 \text{ (s)} + Na_2SO_4 \text{ (aq)}$$

(see §2.8 for practical details).

If a reaction is reversible, the heat change will be reversible also. Copper sulphate pentahydrate loses water on heating, by an endothermic process, to become the grey monohydrate. If a little water is added to this when it is cool, the process of hydration causes the evolution of a great deal of heat. The quantity of heat evolved is equal to the heat taken in during the previous dehydration.

2.2 Units of energy

The basic SI unit of energy is the joule (J), defined as the unit $kg \times m^2 \times s^{-2}$. This rather remote construction is clearer when considered as $(kg\ m\ s^{-2}) \times m$, and since the newton (N) is the force which can accelerate a mass of 1 kg by 1 m s^{-2}, so the joule is the work done when a force of one newton moves through one metre. Since the standard gravitational acceleration is 9.81 m s^{-2}, the energy required to raise a mass of 1 kg by 1 m is 9.81 J.

When a substance undergoes a change in temperature (but no other changes) the heat transferred to or from the substance is equal to the product of total mass × specific heat capacity × temperature change. The specific heat capacity of water is approximately $4.18 \text{ J g}^{-1} \text{ K}^{-1}$, so one joule is sufficient heat to raise the temperature of 1 g water through $1/4.18 = 0.24$ kelvin.

Heat transfer is alternatively equal to amount × molar heat capacity × temperature change. Molar heat capacity at constant pressure is symbolized C_p, and can have units of $\text{J mol}^{-1} \text{ K}^{-1}$.

WORKED EXAMPLE

Calculate the mean molar and specific heat capacities of iron from the following information. When 20 g iron at 373 K was transferred (without heat loss) to 80 g water at 303.0 K, in a container of negligible heat capacity, the temperature of the water rose to 304.9 K.

Heat gained by water $= 80 \text{ g} \times 4.18 \text{ J g}^{-1} \text{ K}^{-1} \times (304.9 - 303.0) \text{ K}$
$\qquad\qquad\qquad\quad = (80 \times 4.18 \times 1.9) \text{ J}$

Heat lost by iron $\qquad = 20 \text{ g} \times c \times (373 - 304.9) \text{ K}$
$\qquad\qquad\qquad\quad = (20 \times 68) \text{ g K} \times c$

where $c =$ specific heat capacity.

Since heat loss = heat gain,

$$c = \frac{80 \times 4.18 \times 1.9}{20 \times 68} \text{ J g}^{-1} \text{ K}^{-1}$$
$$= 0.47 \text{ J g}^{-1} \text{ K}^{-1}$$

The atomic weight of iron $= 55.8$

$$\therefore \ C_p = 0.47 \text{ J g}^{-1} \text{ K}^{-1} \times 55.8 \text{ g mol}^{-1}$$
$$= 26 \text{ J K}^{-1} \text{ mol}^{-1}$$

The joule may also be approached from the direction of electrical energy. The basic unit of current is the ampere (A), and the amount of electricity which passes a given point in a wire when 1 ampere flows for 1 second is 1 coulomb (C). The unit of electrical potential difference (p.d.) is the volt (V), and it follows from the definitions that when u coulomb of electricity passes across a p.d. of v volt the electrical energy transformed is $u \times v$ joule.

The joule is rather small for measurement of chemical energy changes, and the kilojoule (kJ) is more commonly used:

$$1 \text{ kJ} = 10^3 \text{ J}$$

Other units of energy are in use, but they are not part of the International System of Units (SI), and will gradually cease to be used in accurate scientific work. These obsolescent units originally had self-sufficient definitions, which have proved to be insufficiently precise.

Therefore the units have been redefined in terms of the SI units, as follows:

Name	*Symbol*	*Definition*
thermochemical calorie	cal	4.184 J
kilocalorie (kilogram-calorie)	kcal	4.184×10^3 J
Calorie (dieticians')	Cal	as kcal
British Thermal Unit	B.Th.U. (Btu)	1.055×10^3 J
kilowatt-hour	kWh	3.6×10^6 J

The calorie is roughly equal to the heat which will change the temperature of 1 gram of water by 1 kelvin ('1 degree'), but this varies slightly according to the original temperature of the water. The B.Th.U. (Btu) is the heat which will change the temperature of 1 pound (0.4536 kg) water by one degree Fahrenheit ($\frac{5}{9}$ K). Both of these units are likely to continue for some years to be used in engineering and industry.

Several other 'units' of energy may be encountered, since any product of electrical charge $\times$ p.d., or pressure $\times$ volume, or force $\times$ distance, will have the dimensions of energy. Some conversion factors are given here.

foot-pound-force	1 ft lbf $= 1.36$ J
electron volt	$1 \text{ e V} = 1.60 \times 10^{-19}$ J
molar electronvolt	$1 \text{ e V/mol} = 96\ 487$ J mol^{-1}
($=$ Faradayvolt)	
litre-atmosphere	1 litre atm $= 101.3$ J
kilogramforce meter	1 kgf m $= 9.81$ J
horsepower hour	1 h.p.hr $= 2.68 \times 10^6$ J

The *gas constant* R has units of energy $\div$ (temperature $\times$ amount), and some of its values are:

$$R = 8.314 \text{ J K}^{-1} \text{ mol}^{-1}$$
$$= 1.987 \text{ cal K}^{-1} \text{ mol}^{-1}$$
$$= 0.0824 \text{ litre atm K}^{-1} \text{ mol}^{-1}$$

2.3 Enthalpy of reaction

The quantity of heat transferred by a chemical reaction is clearly proportional to the number of moles which react, so the *enthalpy of reaction* is defined as the heat absorbed or evolved during one gram-equation of unharnessed reaction at constant pressure, and with the final temperature of the products being equal to that of the reactants. One gram-equation of reaction occurs when the reactants, in the amount (in moles) specified by the equation, react to form products, the physical states of all substances being stated. The abbreviations (s) = solid, or (c) = crystalline, (l) = liquid, (g) = gas and (aq) = dilute aqueous solution are used in the equation for this purpose.

The enthalpy change is given the symbol ΔH (delta H) and the sign convention is that ΔH is negative for exothermic processes (i.e. when heat is given out by the system) and positive for endothermic ones (heat taken in). ΔH means 'change in H', and the sign is given by the general 'delta convention' for the change in any quantity X: $\Delta X = X_{final} - X_{initial}$. H denotes the heat content, or enthalpy, of the substances.

For example:

$$C(s) + O_2 (g) \longrightarrow CO_2 (g); \quad \Delta H = -393.5 \text{ kJ g-eqn}^{-1}$$

The enthalpy of this exothermic reaction is minus 393.5 kJ.

It may seem strange that the heat change is minus for a reaction which *produces* heat, but the emphasis is on the store of energy within the chemical system. It may be compared to a book-keeping operation at a bank, in which a sum of money paid out would be registered as a negative change to the bank account.

The value of the enthalpy change is dependent upon the amount of reaction considered. For example, if the equation is halved, so is ΔH:

$$2Al (s) + 3Cl_2 (g) \longrightarrow 2AlCl_3 (s); \quad \Delta H = -1390 \text{ kJ}$$
$$Al (s) + \tfrac{3}{2}Cl_2 (g) \longrightarrow AlCl_3 (s); \; \Delta H = \quad -695 \text{ kJ}$$

The heat evolved when one mole of a compound is formed from its elements is known as the 'heat of formation' or *enthalpy of formation* (ΔH_f) of that compound as specified by a stated formula (see also §2.13). Thus $\Delta H_f(AlCl_3) = -695 \text{ kJ mol}^{-1}$.

It follows that the heat required to decompose a compound into its elements is the reverse of the enthalpy of formation:

$$AlCl_3 (s) \longrightarrow Al (s) + \tfrac{3}{2}Cl_2 (g); \quad \Delta H = +695 \text{ kJ}$$

2.4 Exercises†

1. From the following, select (i) a strongly exothermic reaction, (ii) a strongly endothermic one, and (iii) a reaction which has little heat change.

$$CaCO_3 (s) \longrightarrow CaO (s) + CO_2 (g); \quad \Delta H = +176 \text{ kJ}$$
$$4Al (s) + 3O_2 (g) \longrightarrow 2Al_2O_3 (s); \quad \Delta H = -3340 \text{ kJ}$$
$$2Na (s) + 2H_2O (l) \longrightarrow 2NaOH (aq) + H_2 (g); \; \Delta H = -184 \text{ kJ}$$
$$BaCl_2 (aq) + K_2SO_4 (aq) \longrightarrow BaSO_4 (s) + 2KCl (aq); \Delta H = -19 \text{ kJ}$$
$$SrCl_2 (aq) + K_2CO_3 (aq) \longrightarrow SrCO_3 (s) + 2KCl (aq); \Delta H = +3.3 \text{ kJ}$$

For these reactions at 298 K (25°C):

(a) is the most exothermic reaction the most rapid?
(b) is the most endothermic reaction the least rapid?

† A question may require data given in a previous question, in the text, or in an appendix. Full answers appear at the end of the book. Questions marked * are somewhat more elaborate or advanced.

(c) it is generally true that endothermic processes are impossible at this temperature?

2. $MgO \text{ (s)} + 2H^+ \text{ (aq)} \longrightarrow Mg^{2+} \text{ (aq)} + H_2O \text{ (l)};$
$$\Delta H = -146 \text{ kJ g-eqn}^{-1}$$

Interpret this equation and explain fully what amounts and what masses of substances must react to evolve (a) 146 kJ, (b) 2920 J of heat in the reaction between magnesium oxide and hydrochloric acid.

3. $4P \text{ (white)} + 5O_2 \text{ (g)} \longrightarrow P_4O_{10} \text{ (s)}; \quad \Delta H = -2984 \text{ kJ}$

(a) What is the enthalpy change for the reaction:

$$\tfrac{1}{4}P_4O_{10} \text{ (s)} \longrightarrow P \text{ (white)} + \tfrac{5}{4}O_2 \text{ (g)}?$$

(b) What is $\Delta H_f(P_2O_5)$ in kcal? (Note that a simpler formula is specified.)

4. What mass of phosphorus would be the minimum that would have to be burned to provide the heat to raise 500 cm³ water from 20°C to 30°C? (atomic weights p. 203)

5.* $H_2SO_4 \text{ (l)} + 2H_2O \text{ (l)} + aq \longrightarrow 2H_3O^+ \text{ (aq)} + SO_4^{2-} \text{ (aq)};$
$$\Delta H = -87 \text{ kJ}$$

$$H_2O \text{ (s)} \longrightarrow H_2O \text{ (l)}; \qquad \Delta H = +6 \text{ kJ}$$

Calculate, roughly, the temperature change when cold (0°C) concentrated sulphuric acid is poured on to twice its own mass of ice at 0°C. (Assume that this ice, when melted, will provide sufficient water for complete hydration. Take the specific heat capacity of the dilute acid to be $4.2 \text{ J g}^{-1} \text{ K}^{-1}$.)

6. What mass of ice (at its melting-point) could be melted by the passage of 1 amp for 5 minutes across a p.d. of 10 V? (Latent heat given in Question 5.)

7. The heats of formation of the two oxides of carbon are:

$$\Delta H_f(CO, g) = -111 \text{ kJ mol}^{-1}$$
$$\Delta H_f(CO_2, g) = -394 \text{ kJ mol}^{-1}$$

What might be the enthalpy of the reaction:

$$2CO \text{ (g)} + O_2 \text{ (g)} \longrightarrow 2CO_2 \text{ (g)}?$$

2.5 The Law of Enthalpy Summation (Hess's Law)

Question 7 above could be solved very simply if it was assumed that the heat change for $C + O_2 \rightarrow CO_2$ was the sum of the heat changes for $C + \tfrac{1}{2}O_2 \rightarrow CO$ and $CO + \tfrac{1}{2}O_2 \rightarrow CO_2$. Two of these were known, so simple subtraction gave the answer.

This procedure depended on the assumption that *the sum of the enthalpy changes for a sequence of steps equals the enthalpy change for the straight-through reaction.* This assumption is justified, and has been very adequately proved experimentally in the years since it was proposed by Hess in 1840.

Hess's Law can also be stated as 'The heat evolved or absorbed during a chemical reaction is independent of the route taken, or the number of steps which make up the change.' This is because the enthalpy H of any given amount of substance is an intrinsic property (under stated conditions) and not dependent upon the chemical reaction in which it is taking part. Figure 2.1 shows diagrammatically the enthalpies of the chemical system containing one mole of carbon and two moles of oxygen atoms; it illustrates further the example given at the start of this section.

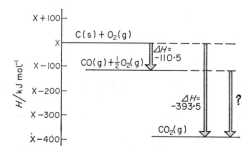

Fig. 2.1   Enthalpy diagram for the system $C + 2O$

The principle of enthalpy summation operates even if some of the steps are imaginary ones, impossible to perform in practice (these will often be the reverse of reactions which do proceed). This enables the calculation of an unknown ΔH to be done by the addition of an appropriate sequence of reaction steps. The three points to watch in this procedure are: (i) all the enthalpies must have their correct signs, (ii) reversing a reaction reverses the sign of ΔH, (iii) multiplying an equation also multiplies ΔH.

WORKED EXAMPLE

From the data given, calculate the enthalpy of formation of solid anhydrous iron(III) chloride.

(i) $Fe\ (s) + 2HCl\ (aq) \longrightarrow FeCl_2\ (aq) + H_2\ (g)$; $\Delta H = -88\ kJ$
(ii) $2FeCl_2\ (aq) + Cl_2\ (g) \longrightarrow 2FeCl_3\ (aq)$; $\Delta H = -254\ kJ$
(iii) enthalpy of hydration of $FeCl_3 = -145\ kJ$
(iv) enthalpy of formation of HCl (aq) $= -167\ kJ$

Calculation:

(i) $Fe\ (s) + 2HCl\ (aq) \longrightarrow FeCl_2\ (aq) + H_2\ (g)$ $\Delta H = -88\ kJ$

(ii ÷ 2) $FeCl_2\,(aq)+\tfrac{1}{2}Cl_2\,(g) \longrightarrow FeCl_3\,(aq);$	$-127\ kJ$
(iii reversed) $FeCl_3\,(aq) \longrightarrow FeCl_3\,(s)+aq;$	$+145\ kJ$
(iv × 2) $H_2\,(g)+Cl_2\,(g)+aq \longrightarrow 2HCl\,(aq);$	$-334\ kJ$

(unknown) $Fe\,(s)+\tfrac{3}{2}Cl_2\,(g) \longrightarrow FeCl_3\,(s);$ overall $\Delta H = -404\ kJ$

2.6 Definition of specified heats of reaction

The heat changes of certain reactions are given individual names, which imply precisely specified conditions.

Heat of combustion ΔH_c

The heat of combusion of a substance is the heat evolved when 1 mole of it is burned completely in oxygen (see Table 2.1). For hydrocarbons and other organic compounds the word 'completely' means that the products must be carbon dioxide and liquid water. If there is any ambiguity about the products of combustion the term is best avoided, and the equation written out in full. There is lack of agreement on the sign convention, and unfortunately some authors quote $-\Delta H_c$; but since the reactions are invariably exothermic, no confusion arises. Thus the heat of combustion of octane petrol is $(-)5512\ kJ\ mol^{-1}$:

$$C_8H_{18}\,(l)+12\tfrac{1}{2}O_2\,(g) \longrightarrow 8CO_2\,(g)+9H_2O\,(l); \qquad \Delta H = -5512\ kJ$$

Heat of solution ΔH_{sol}

Heat of solution is the heat change for the dissolution of one mole of solute to give a solution of specified concentration. The latter part of the definition is necessary because there is usually a further (but smaller) heat change when a concentrated solution is diluted.

The *standard state* of a solute in aqueous solution is the hypothetical ideal solution of 1 molal concentration (1 mole per kg water); it is indicated by the superscript $\ominus$. So $\Delta H_{sol}^{\ominus}$ equals the heat of solution to infinite dilution, since an ideal solution has no heat of dilution. This condition of infinite dilution is shown in an equation by the abbreviation 'aq' (for *aqua*), which means an unspecified large quantity of solvent water. In calculations, 'aq' must not be confused with 'H_2O', one mole of water as reactant or product; 'aq' has no heat of formation.

The state of hydration of the solid solute must of course be specified; for example:

$$\Delta H_{sol}^{\ominus}(Na_2CO_3) = -25\ kJ\ mol^{-1}$$
$$\Delta H_{sol}^{\ominus}(Na_2CO_3.10H_2O) = +67\ kJ\ mol^{-1}$$

Heat of neutralization

The heat of neutralization of an acid by a base is the heat change which accompanies the reaction of one mole of each, in aqueous solution of specified concentration. The amount of acid or base must be that which transfers one mole of H^+ ion under the conditions of the experiment, e.g. one mole of $\frac{1}{2}H_2SO_4$, as in:

$$NH_3 \text{ (1 M)} + \tfrac{1}{2}H_2SO_4 \text{ (1 M)} \longrightarrow \tfrac{1}{2}(NH_4)_2SO_4 \text{ (1 M)}; \qquad \Delta H = -52 \text{ kJ}$$

or

$$NH_3 \text{ (aq)} + H^+ \text{ (aq)} \longrightarrow NH_4^+ \text{ (aq)}; \qquad \Delta H^\ominus = -52 \text{ kJ}$$

Heat of formation ΔH_f

The heat of reaction in which one mole of the substance is formed from its elements in their standard states, being the forms which are stable at 298 K.† It is *not* the heat of formation from isolated atoms. (See §§2.3, 2.13 and 4.4.)

Heat of atomization ΔH_{at}

The enthalpy change for the production of one mole of separate atoms from the substance in its standard form (not necessarily one mole), e.g.

$$\tfrac{1}{8}S_8 \text{ (s)} \longrightarrow S \text{ (at)}; \qquad \Delta H = +224 \text{ kJ}$$

2.7 Exercises

1. Calculate the enthalpy change for the reaction:

$$C_2H_4 + H_2 \longrightarrow C_2H_6$$

given that the heats of combustion of ethylene, hydrogen and ethane are -1411, -286 and -1550 kJ mol^{-1} respectively. (For practice, set the calculation out fully as the addition of three equations.)

2. $C_2H_2 + 2H_2 \longrightarrow C_2H_6$; $\Delta H = -311$ kJ
      $C_2H_2 + Cl_2 \longrightarrow 2C \text{ (gr)} + 2HCl$; $\Delta H = -412$ kJ
      $H_2 + Cl_2 \longrightarrow 2HCl$; $\Delta H = -185$ kJ

Calculate the enthalpy of the reaction:

$$C_2H_6 + 3Cl_2 \longrightarrow 2C \text{ (gr)} + 6HCl$$

(All the substances are gases except the graphite.)

3. From the data given above in §2.5, together with the fact that $\Delta H_f(FeCl_2 \text{ (s)}) = -341$ kJ mol^{-1}, calculate the enthalpy of hydration of $FeCl_2$.

† Note that the standard state of phosphorus is the *white* allotrope, although the red is more stable.

4. A chemist wishes to determine the enthalpy change for the endo-thermic reaction:

$$CaCO_3 \text{ (s)} \longrightarrow CaO \text{ (s)} + CO_2 \text{ (g)}$$

ΔH for neither this reaction nor its reverse can be measured directly. Devise a set of reactions which would be suitable for calorimetric measurement, and show how the desired ΔH could be calculated from the results.

2.8 Practical work

Heats of neutralization

Prepare solutions which can supply approximately 1 mole H^+ (aq) per litre (0.5 M H_2SO_4 and 1 M for most other acids and alkalis). Standardize them, one against another.

Measure out equal volumes (say 50 cm³) of one acid and one alkali, and take their temperatures. If they are within a few Kelvins the mean may be taken as the initial temperature. The mixing should be done in a vacuum flask for preference, but a thin plastic container† (of negligible heat capacity) is suitable. The mixture must be well stirred, and the maximum temperature rise noted.

The specific heat capacity of the solutions are approx. 4.2 J K^{-1} g^{-1}. Since all the heat produced is shown by the rise in temperature of the solution, the temperature rise is independent of the *scale* of the experiment. Therefore the mixing of one litre each of the acid and alkali would cause the same temperature rise, ΔT. This simplifies the calculation, for the heat produced is then $2000 \times \Delta T \times 4.2$ J, and this is approximately equal to the heat of neutralization. Allowance must then be made for the fact that if the concentrations are not both exactly one mole/litre, the amount of reaction will be limited by the more dilute reagent.

Each student should measure the heat of the reaction between HCl and NaOH, and one other combination from HCl, HNO_3, H_2SO_4, CH_2COOH, NaOH, KOH, NH_3 (aq). When all these results are collected together from the class, and compared, they provide interesting evidence for the complete ionization of the dilute strong acids and bases (but see §7.15 for further discussion).

To compare the heats of combustion of fuels

By its nature this experiment gives less accurate results than the previous one, because it is so difficult to capture the heat from the gaseous products. With care, however, results may be obtained which are *consistently* low, and therefore valid for comparison. One substance of known

† E.g. liquid detergent bottle.

heat of combustion may be used to 'calibrate' the apparatus: indeed this is the practice with vastly more sophisticated calorimeters.

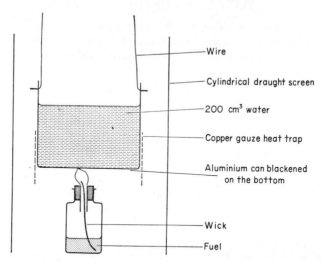

Fig. 2.2   Simple apparatus for measurement of heat of combustion

A lightweight aluminium can (about 250 cm³) has three holes drilled at the top so that it can be suspended by thin wire or thread. A strip of copper gauze is wrapped round and wired on, and extends about 1 cm below the base of the can, which is blackened with soot.

If the fuel is a solid, weigh about 1½ g of it, and support it on a wire gauze while it burns. If the fuel is a liquid, weigh a small bottle of it, fitted with metal tube and wick, and reweigh after about 5 minutes' burning. For a gas, confine it in a Winchester quart bottle and drive it out by passing in water from the tap; burn it at a micro-bunsen.

Suitable fuels are:

  (i) 'Meta-fuel' (obtainable at camping shops; it burns with a clean flame, and gives good reproducible results)
 (ii) a candle (or two of different quality)
(iii) paraffin oil (use a small flame and avoid soot)
 (iv) methanol, ethanol, butanol (obtain, by difference, the heat of combustion of $\cdot CH_2 \cdot$)
  (v) town gas, butane (bottled camping gas), propane (sold liquefied, at tobaccconists)
 (vi) hydrogen (care), carbon monoxide, H_2S (to get ΔH_f)
(vii) dried foods, e.g. potato crisps, toast, sugar cube (with a cigarette-ash catalyst)—these all need a small oxygen supply.

Table 2.1   Selected heats of combustion in $(kJ\ mol^{-1})$

methane	CH_4 (g)	-882	methanol	CH_3OH(l)	-715
ethane	C_2H_6 (g)	-1550	ethanol	C_2H_5OH (l)	-1371
propane	C_3H_8 (g)	-2202	1-propanol	C_3H_7OH (l)	-2010
-butane	C_4H_{10} (g)	-2877	ethyl ether	$(C_2H_5)_2O$ (l)	-2727
ethylene	C_2H_4 (g)	-1411	acetone	$(CH_3)_2CO$ (l)	-1786
acetylene	C_2H_2 (g)	-1305	acetic acid	CH_3COOH (l)	-876
benzene	C_6H_6 (l)	-3273	oxalic acid	$(COOH)_2$ (s)	-246
naphthalene	$C_{10}H_8$ (s)	-5157	benzoic acid	C_6H_5COOH (s)	-3227
carbon	C (gr)	-393.5	glucose	$C_6H_{12}O_6$ (s)	-2816
hydrogen	H_2 (g)	-285.8	sucrose	$C_{12}H_{22}O_{11}$ (s)	-5644

2.9 The bomb calorimeter

For accurate determinations of heats of combustion an apparatus known as the bomb calorimeter is used (Fig. 2.3). This is a strong steel vessel fitted with a small platinum crucible to hold the weighed sample of fuel (in liquid or powder form), an electrical ignition device, and a valve to admit oxygen at high pressure from a cylinder. The heat capacity of the

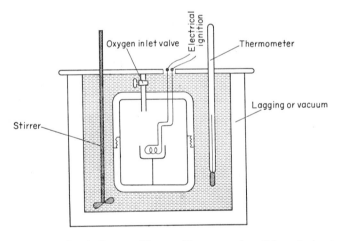

Fig. 2.3   A bomb calorimeter. The total heat capacity of the calorimeter, the water, the thermometer and the stirrer must be determined by calibration using a substance of known heat of combustion, or by electrical heating

calorimeter is known; cooling corrections are applied; and the heat evolved is calculated. This gives the heat of combustion at constant volume (ΔU) and the correction is made to convert this to ΔH, for constant pressure (see §2.11).

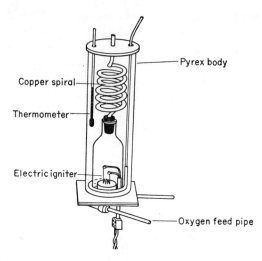

Pyrex body

Copper spiral

Thermometer

Electric igniter

Oxygen feed pipe

Fig. 2.4 The Philip Harris food/fuel calorimeter. A limited flow of oxygen is passed through, and the fuel is ignited electrically. The hot gaseous products flow through the copper spiral, where their heat is conducted to the water in the outer jacket. After stirring, the temperature increase is noted

2.10 The First Law of Thermodynamics

Our universe apparently obeys without exception a law of conservation of mass-plus-energy. Mass and energy can neither be created nor destroyed, though they may be interconverted. The relationship is given by the Einstein equation, $E = mc^2$. On Earth the only important conversion of this kind is that accompanying nuclear transformations. For all chemical reactions it is entirely negligible, and the Law of Conservation of Energy is obeyed. The interpretation of this Law is simple enough for mechanical systems, but for processes in which the final materials are different from the initial ones it is necessary to assume that these contain a greater or lesser amount of stored-up *internal energy*.

Although during naturally-occurring chemical changes the materials are often free to come and go, the chemist finds it best to concentrate his attention on the *closed system*, a collection of materials of fixed total mass. Sometimes the state of chemical combination will be specified (e.g. $\frac{1}{2}$ mole of H_2S gas) or sometimes the materials can be in any form, but in either case the closed system will contain a definite number of atoms.

If a system is sealed and thermally insulated so that no energy can enter or leave, it is called an *isolated system*. Usually a system undergoing a change of form will transfer energy to or from its *surroundings*, which are materials not included in the system. A system and its surroundings considered together will often be a large-scale isolated system.

If the internal energy of a closed system in its initial state is symbolized U_1, and that of the final state U_2, then the energy change, ΔU, is given by†

$$\Delta U = U_2 - U_1$$

These states are specified by definite temperature, pressure and volume. Of course all three variables could change at once, but it simplifies matters to keep to changes of only one or two of the conditions at a time. For example P can be kept constant while V changes, or vice-versa. If T is kept constant by transferring all the thermal energy of the change to the surroundings, the conditions are known as *isothermal*. If, at the other extreme, T is made to change as much as possible, by arranging for perfect thermal insulation so that *no* heat is transferred to the surroundings, then the conditions are said to be *adiabatic*. Actual conditions will be somewhere in between, but may be made to approximate to either isothermal or adiabatic.

Under isothermal conditions, when $T_1 = T_2$, the system must transfer the energy ΔU to the surroundings either as heat (q) or as work (w). Q and W, in capitals, represent molar quantities. The two usual forms of work to be considered are electrical and pressure-volume.

$$\Delta U = Q + W$$

This application of the Law of Conservation of Energy to material changes is known as the First Law of Thermodynamics.

2.11* Obligatory work accompanying volume change

Electrical and most other forms of work can be called *optional work* (W_{opt}) because they need to be harnessed deliberately by specially designed apparatus and will not appear otherwise. For an isothermal change at constant volume (as in the bomb calorimeter) no work is done by the system at all, so $w = 0$. The whole of the energy change ΔU is represented by the heat transferred to the surroundings.

Chemical changes very commonly occur at constant (atmospheric) pressure, and in this case some of the energy *must* be transferred as work if constant pressure conditions are to be achieved. This can be called *obligatory work*, W_{obl}. Since ΔP is to be zero, there must be a volume change of the system, ΔV; this volume change takes place against the opposition of the external pressure, P_{ext}, and work is therefore done by the system:

$$W_{obl} = -P_{ext} \Delta V \quad \text{(work transferred out is negative)}$$

ΔV is negligible for change of solids and liquids, but is appreciable for reactions in which there is a change in the number of gas molecules: then

---

† Some authors use the symbols E and ΔE for internal energy.

ΔV equals the molal volume for each extra mole of gas involved. For ideal gases the value of $P_{ext}\,\Delta V$ is RT per mole of gas formed (where R is the gas constant and T the absolute temperature); at 298 K this is 2.5 kJ. To sum up,

$$\Delta U = Q + W_{opt} + W_{obl}$$

But when no optional work is transferred,

$$\Delta U = Q_p - P_{ext}\,\Delta V$$
$$Q_p = \Delta U + P\,\Delta V \equiv \Delta H \qquad \text{by definition.}$$

Under conditions of constant pressure, the thermal energy transferred out of the system during an unharnessed reaction is measured by ΔH (negative), which is different from the total energy change ΔU by an amount equal to $P_{ext}\,\Delta V$. For many purposes this small difference is un-important.

2.12* Variation of ΔH with T

In the earlier part of this chapter, ΔH was used as if it were independent of temperature. This is not actually quite true, but ΔH does not usually vary much even over a temperature range of a thousand kelvins (unless there is a change of state of the participants). It is interesting to see how this comes about, by considering an example. The molar heat capacities C_p are given below the equation.

$$\text{Mg (s)} + \tfrac{1}{2}O_2\text{ (g)} \longrightarrow \text{MgO (s)}; \qquad \Delta H^{\ominus}_{298} = -602 \text{ kJ}$$
$$C_p: \quad 24 \qquad \tfrac{1}{2} \times 28 \qquad 37 \text{ J K}^{-1}$$

If the magnesium and oxygen are first heated to 1298 K, the heat they will absorb in the process is $1000 \times (24 + \tfrac{1}{2} \times 29)$ J $= 39$ kJ. They react, with unknown ΔH_{1298}; then the magnesium oxide on cooling back to 298 K gives up 1000×37 J. The total of all these changes must be ΔH_{298}:

$$+39 + \Delta H_{1298} - 37 = -602$$
$$\therefore \Delta H_{1298} = -604 \text{ kJ}$$

The difference is negligible for most purposes, and ΔH can be regarded as independent of T. That this is so is a result of the widely-obeyed rule that the heat capacity of a system is roughly independent of the way in which the atoms are combined. It seems that the mass and size of the atoms are more important in this case than the electronic arrangements (i.e. bonding).

2.13 Standard enthalpy of formation ($\Delta H^{\ominus}_f$)

$\Delta H^{\ominus}_f$ is defined as the heat which would be absorbed ($+$) or evolved

$(-)$ if one mole of the substance were formed from its elements (in their stable forms), the initial and final conditions being 298 K (25°C) and 101 325 N m^{-2} (1 atm) pressure.

The $\Delta H_f^{\ominus}$ values have been calculated for almost all common compounds, and are listed in tables of data (see Appendix A, and Bibliography). The great importance of them is that if the enthalpies of formation of all the substances in an equation are known, the enthalpy of the reaction can easily be calculated, since:

$$\Delta H_r = \sum \Delta H_f \text{ (products)} - \sum \Delta H_f \text{ (reactants)}$$

Enthalpy of reaction equals the algebraic sum of enthalpies of formation of products minus the sum of enthalpies of formation of reactants.

$\Delta H_f^{\ominus}$ of any *element* in its most stable form at 298 K is zero, by arbitrary convention.

WORKED EXAMPLE

Given that the values of ΔH_f for CH_4, CO_2, and H_2O (l) are -75, -394 and -286 kJ respectively, calculate the heat of combustion of methane to carbon dioxide and liquid water.

$$CH_4 + 2O_2 \longrightarrow CO_2 + 2H_2O \text{ (l)}; \quad \Delta H_r = ?$$
$$\Delta H_f: \quad \underbrace{-75 \quad 2\times 0}_{-75} \quad \underbrace{-394 \quad 2\times -286}_{-966}$$
$$\Delta H_r = -966 - (-75) = -891 \text{ kJ g-eqn}^{-1}$$

The justification for this procedure is that it is an abbreviated form of a 'Hess's Law' heat summation, which could be written out in full as follows:

$$
\begin{array}{ll}
CH_4 \text{ (g)} \longrightarrow C \text{ (s)} + 2H_2 \text{ (g)}; & \Delta H = \quad +75 \\
O_2 + C \text{ (s)} \longrightarrow CO_2 \text{ (g)} & \Delta H = -394 \\
2H_2 + O_2 \longrightarrow 2H_2O \text{ (l)}; & \Delta H = -572 \\
\hline
CH_4 \text{ (g)} + 2O_2 \text{ (g)} \longrightarrow 2H_2O \text{ (l)} + CO_2 \text{ (g)}; & \Delta H = -891 \text{ kJ}
\end{array}
$$

2.14 Exercises

1. Using the above data, calculate the heat of combustion of liquid benzene, C_6H_6, given that its $\Delta H_f = +49$ kJ.

2. Use data from Appendix A to calculate the enthalpy of the reaction:

$$2H_2S + SO_2 \longrightarrow 2H_2O \text{ (l)} + S \text{ (s)}$$

3. (a) Calculate ΔH_r for the reaction:

$$MnO_2 \text{ (s)} + 2HCl \text{ (g)} \longrightarrow MnO \text{ (s)} + H_2O \text{ (l)} + Cl_2 \text{ (g)}$$

(b) Using this and the following data:

$$MnO (s) + 2HCl (aq\ 12\ \text{M}) \longrightarrow MnCl_2 (aq) + H_2O (l); \quad \Delta H = -113\ \text{kJ}$$
$$HCl (g) + aq \longrightarrow HCl (aq\ 12\ \text{M}); \quad\quad\quad \Delta H = -59\ \text{kJ}$$

calculate the enthalpy of reaction of:

$$MnO_2 (s) + 4HCl (aq\ 12\ \text{M}) \longrightarrow MnCl_2 (aq) + 2H_2O (l) + Cl_2 (g)$$

2.15 Ionic enthalpies

When a solid crystal dissolves there is a heat change (enthalpy of solution), followed by a smaller change when the solution is diluted. So the enthalpy of formation of a compound in solution is not the same as ΔH_f for the solid. If enthalpy calculations are to be done on reactions involving dissolved ionic compounds, it would be useful to know the ΔH_f values for these dilute aqueous solutions. These could quite easily be determined, and listed alongside ΔH_f for the solids.

There is a much more economical way of giving the information, however. It can be shown that the enthalpy change for the reaction of an element (or elements) to an ion in dilute solution is a constant, and does not depend upon the nature of the oppositely-charged ion which partners it. The difficulty in obtaining these enthalpies lies in the fact that they can only be studied in pairs, and not in isolation.

For example, ΔH_f for NaCl (aq) is known, since

$$Na (s) + \tfrac{1}{2}Cl_2 (g) + aq \longrightarrow NaCl (aq); \quad \Delta H_f = -407\ \text{kJ}$$

and

$$\Delta H_f(NaCl\ (aq)) = \Delta H_f(Cl^- \ (aq)) + \Delta H_f(Na^+ \ (aq))$$

but no one knows how the -407 kJ should be divided between the Na^+ and the Cl^-. The difficulty is overcome by setting the enthalpy of formation of one ion, the hydrogen cation, at an arbitrary zero. Then all the others fall into place. The enthalpy of formation of dilute hydrochloric acid is -167 kJ mol^{-1}, for instance. With ΔH_f (H$^+$ (aq))† set at 0, ΔH_f (Cl$^-$ (aq)) becomes -167 kJ. So ΔH_f (Na$^+$ (aq)) must be -240 kJ, in order that the enthalpies of the Na^+ and Cl^- ions should add up to that of the aqueous NaCl.

Thus from quite a short list of ionic enthalpies (Appendix A) the enthalpies of hundreds of compounds in solution can be found by simple addition.

2.16 Exercises

Use ΔH_f data from Appendix A.

† Note that $\Delta H_f(H_3O^+) = \Delta H_f(H^+) + \Delta H_f(H_2O(l)) = 285.9$ kJ.

1. What transfer of heat results from one gram-equation of the following reactions (at constant pressure)?

   (a) $Ag^+ (aq) + Cl^- (aq) \longrightarrow AgCl (s) + aq$
   (b) $2Na (s) + 2H_2O (l) + aq \longrightarrow 2Na^+ (aq) + 2OH^- (aq) + H_2 (g)$
   (c) 1 mole dilute nitric acid neutralized by dilute sodium hydroxide solution, in ideal standard states.
   (d) 1 mole calcium carbonate reaction with dilute hydrochloric acid.
   (e) the dissolution of one mole of NaCl and $\frac{1}{4}$ mole of $Na_2CO_3.10H_2O$ in a litre of water.
   (f) $H_2S (g) + Cl_2 (g) \longrightarrow 2HCl (g) + S (s)$
   (g) $H_2S (g) + Cl_2 (aq) \longrightarrow 2HCl (aq) + S (s)$

2. The enthalpy of neutralization of strong (fully dissociated) acids by strong alkalis is always -58 kJ mol^{-1} (at 1 M concentration):

$$OH^- (aq) + H^+ (aq) \longrightarrow H_2O (l); \quad \Delta H = -58 \text{ kJ}$$

but for ammonia solution:

$$NH_3 (aq) + HCl (aq) \longrightarrow NH_4Cl (aq); \quad \Delta H = -54 \text{ kJ}$$

and for hydrofluoric acid:

$$HF (aq) + NaOH (aq) \longrightarrow NaF (aq) + H_2O (l); \quad \Delta H = -69 \text{ kJ}$$

Calculate the enthalpies of the reactions:

   (a) $NH_3 (aq) + H_2O (l) \longrightarrow NH_4^+ (aq) + OH^- (aq)$
   (b) $HF (aq) \longrightarrow H^+ (aq) + F^- (aq)$

3. It is desired to measure the heat of reaction for:

$$Mg (s) + CuO (s) \longrightarrow MgO (s) + Cu (s)$$

but the reaction is dangerously violent. Devise a sequence of milder reactions for which ΔH is measurable directly, which could give the required ΔH by calculation.

   As an additional exercise, use ΔH_f tables to calculate the expected enthalpy of each of your steps.

4. 2.0 g MgO (s) was dissolved in 500 cm^3 molar hydrochloric acid in a plastic container of negligible heat capacity, and caused a temperature rise of 3.5 K. By assuming the heat capacity of the solution to be 4.2 J K^{-1} cm^{-3}, calculate ΔH for the reaction and then, by comparison with the usual heat of neutralization, find ΔH for

$$MgO (s) + H_2O (l) + aq \longrightarrow Mg^{2+} (aq) + 2OH^- (aq)$$

3 Free-energy

This chapter develops a simple theory of the driving-force of chemical reactions. The suggestion was put forward by Berthelot and others around 1880 that the driving-force is the heat of reaction. This is attractive at first sight, because many vigorous reactions are highly exothermic; but it can readily by shown to be at best only part of the truth by the consideration of endothermic and reversible reactions.

3.1 Endothermic reactions

In *Type C* of §1.2, some examples of endothermic reactions were given. They normally occur only at elevated temperatures, and absorb heat as they proceed. If the supply of heat is removed, the reactants cool, and the reaction stops. Many of the reactions of this type come in the category of 'thermal decompositions', which involve the breakdown of single compounds into two or more products (see §3.6). For example,

$$2Pb(NO_3)_2 \longrightarrow 2PbO + 4NO_2 + O_2$$

There are also many 'physical' processes which occur spontaneously at normal room temperatures, and yet result in heat being taken in from the surroundings. Melting and boiling are endothermic; evaporation can take place over a wide temperature range, always with the absorption of heat. The dissolution of crystals in a solvent is usually endothermic.

There are even a few examples of endothermic chemical reactions which occur spontaneously in solution. Any theory concerning the 'driving-force' of reactions must, then, take account of endothermic processes.

PRACTICAL WORK

Some endothermic processes which provide simple class experiments have been described in other sections, particularly Chapter 2; for example, the dissolving of ammonium nitrate, ammonium thiocyanate or sodium thiosulphate crystals, or the mixing of carbon tetrachloride with benzene. A suitable chemical reaction is the precipitation of magnesium carbonate by mixing magnesium sulphate and sodium carbonate solutions. In these experiments care should be taken to ensure that the reagents are at the same steady temperature before mixing.

More spectacular is the vigorous but highly endothermic reaction between solid ammonium carbonate and concentrated acetic acid.

3.2 Reversible reactions

Some reactions can, at different temperatures or concentrations, proceed in either direction. One direction will be exothermic and the other endothermic; the latter being favoured at higher temperatures.
For example, at moderate temperatures:

$$2SO_2 \text{ (g)} + O_2 \text{ (g)} \longrightarrow 2SO_3 \text{ (g)}; \qquad \Delta H = -196 \text{ kJ}$$

whereas at very high temperatures:

$$2SO_3 \longrightarrow 2SO_2 + O_2; \qquad \Delta H = +196 \text{ kJ}$$

It follows that the 'driving-force' must involve more than the enthalpy, ΔH. It must include two factors which can operate against each other; one factor becoming more effective at high temperatures.
Further examples of reversible reactions are to be found in §1.2 (*Type E*), and §§8.1 and 8.3.

PRACTICAL WORK

$$CaCO_3 \underset{\text{cool}}{\overset{\text{heat}}{\rightleftarrows}} CaO + CO_2$$

Heat a weighed amount of calcium carbonate powder strongly for five minutes. Note any loss in weight, and compare (i) alkalinity, (ii) action of acids, and (iii) action with water, against a control sample.
Powder some strongly-heated calcium oxide, made from limestone. Show that there is little or no evolution of gas with dilute nitric acid. Pass dry CO_2 over it (or shake with a gas-jar of CO_2) and test again. (Is there a detectable temperature change for the recombination of CaO with CO_2?)

3.3 Gibbs free-energy (ΔG)

The quantity which measures the driving-force of any chemical or physical process is known as the Gibbs free-energy change, and is given the symbol ΔG. The sign convention is that ΔG is negative for processes which can proceed spontaneously.†
From a consideration of reversible reactions, it seems that ΔG must be the sum of separate and sometimes conflicting 'driving-forces'. The facts to be accounted for are:

(i) Reactions of a similar type tend to go more readily when ΔH is more negative, and need a higher temperature for their reversal, e.g.

† 'Spontaneously' in this context does not necessarily means 'instantaneously'. The reactions in *Type B* of §1.2 are 'spontaneous'.

$$H_2 + Cl_2 \text{ (g)} \longrightarrow 2HCl \text{ (g)}; \quad \Delta H = -185 \text{ kJ (explosive)}$$
$$H_2 + Br_2 \text{ (g)} \longrightarrow 2HBr \text{ (g)}; \quad \Delta H = -103 \text{ kJ (rapid and complete)}$$
$$H_2 + I_2 \text{ (g)} \longrightarrow 2HI \text{ (g)}; \quad \Delta H = -10 \text{ kJ (slow and incomplete)}$$

(ii) Reversible reactions go in the exothermic direction at lower temperatures and in the endothermic direction at higher temperatures.

From (i) it appears that ΔG must include ΔH. From (ii) it follows that the second part of ΔG must be a function of temperature. These features can be summed up by the equation:

$$\Delta G = \Delta H - T \times \text{something}$$

In the next section it will be shown that the 'something' is the entropy change, ΔS. ΔS is, like ΔH, approximately independent of temperature, and independent of the route from reactants to products.

Thus the extremely important equation showing the make-up of ΔG is:

$$\begin{array}{cccccccc} \Delta G & = & \Delta H & - & T & \times & \Delta S \\ \text{Gibbs free-energy} & & \text{enthalpy} & & \text{absolute} & & \text{entropy} \\ \text{change} & & \text{change} & & \text{temperature} & & \text{change} \end{array}$$

From this equation it is clear that, while ΔH and ΔS are approximately independent of T, ΔG is very temperature-dependent. The equation enables one to calculate the sign and value of ΔG at any temperature, and thereby to predict the effect of temperature on a chemical reaction.

The sign of ΔS can often be deduced from the chemical equation of the reaction (see §3.6); the sign of ΔH is easily found from a calorimetry experiment, or deduced from a consideration of changes of bonding (see Chapter 4); and therefore the variation of sign of ΔG can often be predicted.

When a process is at equilibrium there is no overall driving-force in either direction; then $\Delta G = 0$. This comes about when $T_{eq} \Delta S = \Delta H$, and so an equilibrium temperature is determined by the values of ΔS and ΔH.

If ΔG is negative the reaction is feasible, or 'thermodynamically favoured', or 'spontaneous', but this is no guarantee that the reaction *will* go. The rate of reaction may be effectively zero, and then no change will occur unless a suitable catalyst can be provided.

However, if ΔG is large and positive the reaction is unfeasible, and will not go (unless driven by a supply of external work, as in electrolysis).

The adjectives *exergonic* and *endergonic* apply to negative and positive ΔG respectively.

A simple case which illustrates these points is the evaporation of a liquid. The latent heat of evaporation, ΔH_{vap}, is always positive, i.e. endothermic. The entropy of evaporation of liquid to vapour at 1 atm pressure, $\Delta S^{\ominus}_{vap}$, is also positive (see §3.6).

So
$$\Delta G^{\ominus}_{vap} = \Delta H_{vap} - T \Delta S^{\ominus}_{vap}$$
$$(+ve) \qquad (+ve)$$

At low temperatures $\Delta G^{\ominus}_{vap}$ will be positive, and the liquid will not boil. At high temperatures, $T\Delta S^{\ominus} > \Delta H$, and so $\Delta G^{\ominus}$ will be negative and the liquid will boil away completely.

At one definite temperature $\Delta H = T\Delta S^{\ominus}$, and then $\Delta G^{\ominus} = 0$. This is the equilibrium temperature, i.e. the boiling point. It is equal to $\Delta H_{vap} \div \Delta S^{\ominus}_{vap}$, and is thus a fixed property of the liquid. At other pressures ΔH_{vap} is almost unchanged, but ΔS differs (§7.8); so the boiling point varies with pressure.

3.4 Worked example

The energetics of the water–gas reaction

$$C\,(s) + H_2O\,(g) \longrightarrow H_2\,(g) + CO\,(g); \qquad \Delta H = +131\ kJ$$
$$\Delta S^{\ominus} = +134\ J\ K^{-1}$$

(i) At room temperature (300 K):

$$T\Delta S^{\ominus} = 300 \times (+134)\ J$$
$$= +\frac{300 \times 134}{1000}\ kJ$$
$$\Delta G^{\ominus} = +131 - \frac{300 \times 134}{1000}\ kJ$$
$$= +131 - 40$$
$$= +91\ kJ\ g\text{-eqn}^{-1}$$

Therefore at 300 K (27°C) and 1 atm pressure the reaction is endergonic, and unfeasible.

(ii) At 1300 K:

$$\Delta G^{\ominus} = +131 - \frac{1300 \times 134}{1000}\ kJ$$
$$= +131 - 174$$
$$= -43\ kJ$$

Therefore at 1300 K the reaction is feasible and will proceed virtually to completion.

(iii) The temperature at which equilibrium will be reached, with all three gases at 1 atm pressure, is given by:

$$T_{eq} = \Delta H / \Delta S$$

since $\Delta G = \Delta H - T\Delta S = 0$ at equilibrium.

For this reaction

$$T_{eq} = \frac{+131 \times 1000}{+134}\ K = 980\ K\ (707°C)$$

So the calculation from thermodynamic data is that the reaction will go readily at temperatures above 980 K. See Figure 3.1.

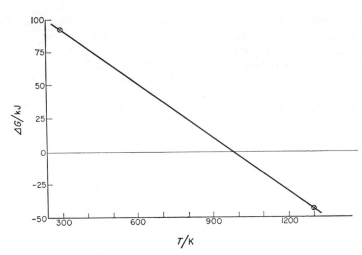

Fig. 3.1   Variation of ΔG with T, for the water–gas reaction

3.5 Exercises

1. A certain exothermic reaction has ΔS negative and small. What will be the sign of ΔG at (i) low temperatures, (ii) high temperatures?

2. The reaction $A \rightarrow B$ is endothermic, yet proceeds to completion at 1000 K.

   (i) What is the sign of ΔS?
   (ii) What is the sign of ΔG at 1000 K for the reverse reaction $B \rightarrow A$?
   (iii) What is the sign of ΔG for $B \rightarrow A$ at low temperatures?
   (iv) Could the reaction $B \rightarrow A$ possibly proceed at this lower temperature?
   (v) Will the reaction $B \rightarrow A$ necessarily proceed at this lower temperature?

3. Calculate ΔG at various temperatures from the following data, and plot a graph. Use this to find the equilibrium temperature, for which $\Delta G = 0$.

$$2CuCl\,(s) + Cl_2\,(g) \rightleftharpoons 2CuCl_2\,(s); \qquad \Delta H = -166\ kJ$$
$$\Delta S = -173\ J\ K^{-1}$$

3.6 Entropy

In §3.3 ΔS was introduced as a mysterious quantity which had the dimensions of energy ÷ temperature. A clue to the physical meaning of entropy is to be found by considering thermal decomposition reactions. These all have the following three features in common:

(i) they are endothermic; $\Delta H = +\text{ve}$;

(ii) they go more completely as the temperature is raised;

(iii) there is a net gain of gas molecules due to the reaction.

From (i) and (ii) it follows that the driving-force is in every case the $T \Delta S$ term. From $\Delta G = \Delta H - T \Delta S$ it is clear that ΔS must be positive, since ΔG becomes more negative as the temperature increases, but is positive at low temperatures.

In every case the positive entropy change is associated with the increase in the number of gas molecules. The link is that *entropy is a measure of the **disorder** of a system*, and when a system changes to one with more gas molecules the possibility of disorder increases, because gas molecules have random motion in three dimensions.

This principle is valid for all types of chemical and physical process. When liquids evaporate and when solids melt, the freedom of motion of the molecules increases, and so does the entropy (disorder). This will be discussed more thoroughly in Chapter 5.

Rules for deducing the sign of $\Delta S^{\ominus}$

The entropy change ($\Delta S^{\ominus}$) is positive when:

(1) in a gas reaction, the number of product molecules exceeds the number of reactant molecules; e.g.

$$2SO_3 \text{ (g)} \longrightarrow 2SO_2 \text{ (g)} + O_2 \text{ (g)};$$

(2) there is no change in the number of gas molecules, but H_2 is a reactant—this is a small effect, and only applies to gas reactions (see p. 63)—e.g.

$$H_2 + Cl_2 \longrightarrow 2HCl \text{ (g)};$$

(3) a solid decomposes to give a gas amongst the products; e.g.

$$MgCO_3 \text{ (s)} \longrightarrow MgO \text{ (s)} + CO_2 \text{ (g)};$$

(4) a solid melts or sublimes;

(5) a liquid boils or evaporates;

(6) liquids mix, or a solid dissolves—this rule only holds for non-electrolytes.

$\Delta S^{\ominus}$ is negative for the reverse of all these processes.

3.7 Examples

To show how energetics can be used to predict the effect of temperature on some reversible reactions:

(a) $CuSO_4 . 5H_2O \rightleftharpoons CuSO_4 . H_2O + 4H_2O \text{ (g)};$

$$\Delta H = +222 \text{ kJ g-eqn}^{-1}$$

Four extra gas molecules are produced (the steam) so ΔS is clearly positive. (In fact $\Delta S^{\ominus} = +500$ J K^{-1})

$$\Delta G = \Delta H - T\Delta S$$
$$(+\text{ve}) \quad (+\text{ve})$$

If T is small, ΔG is positive, and the reaction will not go. The hydrate is in fact stable at temperatures below about 300 K. If T is large, $T\Delta S$ becomes the more important factor, and since ΔS is positive, ΔG will become negative, and the reaction will go. Dehydration is rapid above 400 K.

It is worth noting that the reaction

$$CuSO_4.5H_2O \rightleftharpoons CuSO_4.H_2O + 4H_2O \text{ (l)}$$

though much less endothermic, shows no tendency to go, as it does not have a large positive entropy change.

(b) $N_2 + 3H_2 \rightleftharpoons 2NH_3$; $\Delta H = -92$ kJ g-eqn^{-1}

The reaction causes a decrease in the number of gas molecules so ΔS is negative. At high temperatures the term $(-T\Delta S)$ predominates over the ΔH, making ΔG positive, so the synthesis becomes unfeasible. The reaction tends to reverse. Therefore it is essential to carry out the reaction at a sufficiently low temperature for ΔG to be negative, even though this may mean that the reaction rate is slow.

(c) $3O_2 \rightleftharpoons 2O_3$; $\Delta H = +284$ kJ g-eqn^{-1}

The number of gas molecules is decreased, so ΔS is negative. Both terms, ΔH and $(-T\Delta S)$, are positive, and so ΔG is positive at all temperatures. Therefore the reaction will not proceed spontaneously. It must be driven by a supply of work, such as ultraviolet radiation, or an electric discharge.

(d) $CH_4 + 2O_2 \rightleftharpoons CO_2 + 2H_2O$ (g); $\Delta H = -800$ kJ g-eqn^{-1}

There are three gas molecules on both sides, so the sign of $\Delta S^{\ominus}$ cannot be predicted. However, when no solids or liquids are involved, a reaction with equal numbers of gas molecules has an entropy change which is very small, or zero. ΔG is then almost independent of temperature, -800 kJ in the present example. The reaction is feasible at all temperatures, and does not reverse or reach any centrally-placed equilibrium.

3.8 Exercises

1. For each of the following reactions, say whether the sign of ΔS can be inferred from the equation, and if so, what it is, and what effect increased temperature will have on the driving force.

   (a) $2CuCl \text{ (s)} + Cl_2 \text{ (g)} \rightleftharpoons 2CuCl_2 \text{ (s)}$
   (b) $CHCl_3 \text{ (l)} \rightleftharpoons CHCl_3 \text{ (g)}$

(c) SO_2 (g)$+H_2O$ (l)$+$aq $\rightleftharpoons$ H_2SO_3 (aq)
(d) $3Fe$ (s)$+4H_2O$ (g) $\rightleftharpoons$ Fe_3O_4 (s)$+4H_2$ (g)
(e) C_3H_8 (g)$+5O_2$ (g) $\longrightarrow$ $3CO_2$ (g)$+4H_2O$ (g)
(f) N_2 (g)$+O_2$ (g) $\rightleftharpoons$ $2NO$ (g)
(g) $2KNO_3$ (s) $\longrightarrow$ $2KNO_2$ (s)$+O_2$ (g)

2. $2NaOH$ (s)$+CO_2$ (g) $\longrightarrow$ $Na_2CO_3.H_2O$ (s)

This reaction proceeds despite a large negative entropy change. What is the sign of ΔH?

3. Nitrous oxide is an endothermic compound:

$$2N_2+O_2 \longrightarrow 2N_2O \text{ (g)}; \qquad \Delta H = +ve$$

Predict the feasibility of the synthesis at different temperatures (with reasons).

4. (*Revision*) How could the enthalpy of the dehydration of $CuSO_4.5H_2O$ (see §3.7) be measured calorimetrically?

3.9 Measurements and calculations of ΔG

Some idea of the value of ΔG can be obtained by inserting estimates of ΔH and ΔS into the equation $\Delta G = \Delta H - T\Delta S$. However, actual quantitative values of ΔG are more useful; they can be measured in three important ways:

(i) from equilibrium constants. (The relationship is

$$\Delta G^\ominus = -2.3 \ RT \log K,$$

see Chapter 8)
(ii) from electrode potentials (see §3.13)
(iii) from calorimetric measurements of both ΔH and ΔS (see §5.4).

These methods will be treated more fully in turn, but the immediate point is that exact measurements of ΔG can be made for most reactions. Unlike ΔH, ΔG varies with concentration or pressure (as well as temperature), so these must be specified. Chemists have found it valuable to work with a quantity known as the *standard free-energy change* ($\Delta G^\ominus$), which is the ΔG for the change from reactants in standard concentrations to products in standard concentrations. The specified standard concentrations (indicated by the superscript $^\ominus$) are:

(i) solids and liquids in sufficient quantity to be in effective contact with any other phases;
(ii) gases in the state equivalent to an ideal gas at one atmosphere ($101 \ 325 \ Nm^{-2}$) partial pressure;
(iii) solutes in the state equivalent to an ideal solution (i.e. zero enthalpy of dilution) containing 1 mole solute per kg solvent.

For elementary work (ii) and (iii) may be replaced by: 'Gases at 1 atm partial pressure' and 'solutes at 1 mol litre^{-1}.'

ΔH changes very little with concentration, and will be regarded as constant, with $\Delta H = \Delta H^\ominus$. ΔG does vary with concentration (§3.13) and ΔG can be calculated from $\Delta G^\ominus$ (§7.9) but the difference is often relatively unimportant except with large excess or deficiency of participating substances.

Standard free-energies of formation $\Delta G_f^\ominus$ are defined and used in an exactly similar way to enthalpies of formation (§2.13 and Appendix A), and the free-energy of reaction is given by:

$$\Delta G_r^\ominus = \text{sum of } \Delta G_f^\ominus \text{ for products} - \text{sum of } \Delta G_f^\ominus \text{ for reactants}$$

The convention for aqueous ions is the same as for $\Delta H_f^\ominus$, namely that

$$\Delta G_f^\ominus(\text{H}^+\,(\text{aq})) = 0$$

3.10* $\Delta G = G_2 - G_1$

ΔG for a reaction is the difference between the free-energy content of the products (G_{prod}) and that of the reactants (G_{react}). When a reaction proceeds spontaneously it is because G_{prod} is lower than G_{react}; the system moves to one of lower free-energy, i.e. one of greater thermodynamic stability at the temperature specified. The value of G will depend on concentration and pressure, and if these are standard it will be $G^\ominus$. For any change:

$$\Delta G = G_{\text{prod}} - G_{\text{react}}$$

Since G is an intrinsic property of a system of chemical substances, the difference between G_{prod} and G_{react} has a fixed value, which is independent of the *route* of the reaction. Therefore ΔG for a sequence of reactions is equal to the algebraic sum of the ΔG values of the individual steps. The procedure is exactly similar to that used for the summation of enthalpy changes (see §2.6).

EXAMPLE

From $\Delta G^\ominus$ data for the oxidation of copper to copper(I) and copper(II) oxides, calculate $\Delta G^\ominus$ for the reaction

$$2Cu_2O + O_2 \longrightarrow 4CuO$$

(ii) $Cu + \frac{1}{2}O_2 \longrightarrow CuO$; $\Delta G^\ominus$ (at 298 K) $= -127$ kJ
(ii) $2Cu + \frac{1}{2}O_2 \longrightarrow Cu_2O$; $\Delta G^\ominus = -146$ kJ

Re-writing:

$2Cu_2O \longrightarrow 4Cu + O_2$; $\Delta G^\ominus = +292$ kJ
$4Cu + 2O_2 \longrightarrow 4CuO$; $\Delta G^\ominus = -508$ kJ

adding: $2Cu_2O + O_2 \longrightarrow 4CuO$; $\Delta G^\ominus = -216$ kJ

3.11 Exercises

Use the thermochemical data tables, Appendix A.

1. Calculate $\Delta G_r^{\ominus}$ at 298 K for the following reactions. Use the results to predict whether the reactions are (a) unfeasible, (b) feasible, or (c) appreciably incomplete in either direction. Also deduce the signs of $\Delta S^{\ominus}$ by means of the disorder concept.

(i) $2NO\ (g) + O_2\ (g) \longrightarrow 2NO_2\ (g)$
(ii) $Cl_2\ (g) + 2HI\ (g) \longrightarrow I_2\ (s) + 2HCl\ (g)$
(iii) $I_2\ (g) + H_2S\ (g) \longrightarrow 2HI\ (g) + S\ (s,\ rhombic)$
(iv) $3NO\ (g) \longrightarrow N_2O\ (g) + NO_2\ (g)$
(v) $CuCO_3\ (s) \longrightarrow CuO\ (s) + CO_2\ (g)$
(vi) $CuSO_4\ (anh) \longrightarrow CuO\ (s) + SO_3\ (g)$

2. For reactions (i), (v) and (vi) above calculate ΔH. From this and $\Delta G^{\ominus}$ calculate $T\Delta S^{\ominus}$ at 298 K and from this obtain $\Delta S^{\ominus}$. Check that the signs agree with those inferred from the equations.

Assuming that ΔH and $\Delta S^{\ominus}$ remain constant over the temperature range, calculate $\Delta G^{\ominus}$ for these reactions at 400 K and 2000 K. It is likely that feasible reactions will proceed rapidly at these elevated temperatures, so your results will show the actual effect of temperature on the direction of reaction.

3. When hydrogen chloride, mixed with oxygen or air, is passed over a hot copper(I) chloride catalyst it is oxidized to chlorine (Deacon's process):

$$4HCl\ (g) + O_2\ (g) \longrightarrow 2H_2O\ (g) + 2Cl_2\ (g)$$

Would you expect this reaction to be reversible in the gas phase? (In sunlight chlorine *solution* gives off oxygen.) Could you test your prediction experimentally? Before doing so, calculate $\Delta G^{\ominus}$ for the reaction, and see what the chances are.

4. Calculate the standard free-energy of the following reactions at 298 K. Use the results as in Question 1 above.

(i) $Zn\ (s) + 2Ag^+\ (aq) \longrightarrow Zn^{2+}\ (aq) + 2Ag\ (s)$
(ii) $Ca(OH)_2\ (s) + aq \longrightarrow Ca^{2+}\ (aq) + 2OH^-\ (aq)$
(iii) $2Fe^{3+}\ (aq) + 2I^-\ (aq) \longrightarrow 2Fe^{2+}\ (aq) + I_2\ (aq,\ as\ KI_3)$
(iv) $LiH\ (s) + H_2O\ (l) \longrightarrow Li^+\ (aq) + OH^-\ (aq) + H_2\ (g)$

See also Additional Exercises (Parts I and II) at the end of the book.

3.12 Measuring ΔG for cell reactions

Although ΔG of a reaction is generally more difficult than ΔH to measure experimentally, it can be found quite easily for reactions which can take place in an electrochemical cell. The theory will be treated in more detail in Chapter 8 but the basic outline is as follows.

ΔG measures the maximum *work*, as opposed to heat, that can be obtained from a reaction. ΔH measures the heat evolved (or absorbed) when the reaction takes place without being harnessed to do any optional work; but if the reaction is made to take place in an apparatus designed to make it do work, the heat evolved will be less than ΔH be an amount equal to the work done (§2.11)

$$\begin{array}{ccc} \text{total energy transfer} & = & \text{heat transfer} + \text{work transfer} \\ \Delta H & & Q_p \qquad\qquad W_{opt} \end{array}$$

The two most common ways of harnessing the work of a reaction are:

(i) reactions which involve an expansion can be made to push a piston against an applied pressure;
(ii) reactions which can occur as a pair of electrode reactions can be made to develop an electromotive force (e.m.f., or 'voltage') and send an electric current through a circuit.

The amount of work actually transferred by one gram-equation of reaction can range from zero (unharnessed) to a maximum, equal to ΔG, when the reaction is constrained so that it can only proceed infinitely slowly—a state of affairs known as 'reversible conditions'. (The word has a different meaning here from that in 'reversible reaction'.)

In the case of work harnessed by an electrochemical cell, the work obtainable per gram-equation of reaction is equal to nFE, where $F =$ the faraday, $n =$ the number of moles of electrons transferred during one g-eqn of reaction, and $E =$ the voltage developed by the cell. The voltage is at a maximum when the cell is on open circuit, so that no current is being drawn from it. When the cell has electrolytes in molar ionic concentrations, this maximum 'reversible' voltage is designated $E^\ominus$, the *standard cell potential*. So:

$$\Delta G^\ominus = -nFE^\ominus$$

Inserting units (J = joule, C = coulomb, V = volt):

$$\Delta G^\ominus/\text{J g-eqn}^{-1} = -(n/\text{mol g-eqn}^{-1})\,(F/\text{C mol}^{-1})\,(E^\ominus/\text{V})$$

$$\text{or}\quad \Delta G^\ominus/\text{kcal g-eqn}^{-1} = -\frac{(n/\text{mol g-eqn}^{-1})\,(F/\text{C mol}^{-1})\,(E^\ominus/\text{V})}{4.18 \times 10^3/\text{J kcal}^{-1}}$$

EXAMPLE

For the cell consisting of Cd in 1.0 M Cd^{2+} connected by a salt bridge to 1.0 M Hg_2^{2+} with a mercury electrode the maximum cell potential is 0.119 V (cadmium electrode negative). Calculate $\Delta G^\ominus$ for the reaction.

The reaction is

$$Cd + Hg_2^{2+} \longrightarrow Cd^{2+} + 2Hg$$

Inserting values into $\Delta G^\ominus = -nFE^\ominus$:

$$\Delta G^\ominus = -2\,\frac{\text{mol}}{\text{g-eqn}} \times 96\,500\,\frac{\text{C}}{\text{mol}} \times 0.119\,\text{V}$$

$$= -22\,900\,\frac{CV}{\text{g-eqn}} = -22\,900\,\text{J g-eqn}^{-1}$$
$$= -22.9\,\text{kJ g-eqn}^{-1}$$

3.13 Practical work

To measure ΔH and $\Delta G^{\ominus}$ for the reaction:

$$Cu\,(s) + 2Ag^+\,(aq) \longrightarrow Cu^{2+}\,(aq) + 2Ag\,(s)$$

(*a*) *The enthalpy*

Required: 15 cm³ 0.30 M silver nitrate solution
0.5 g (approx.) copper powder (reduced CuO)
small polythene bottle with bung and thermometer

The thermometer should be 0–50°C if available; if, in order for the mercury thread to be visible, the bulb must be only just inside the bung, the whole bottle should be inverted when readings are taken.

Procedure: Put 15.0 cm³ silver nitrate solution in the bottle, shake, and record the temperature. Add about 0.5 g copper powder (excess) and shake well. Record the highest temperature reached.

Calculate the heat evolved, assuming that the heat capacity of the apparatus is negligible, and the heat capacity of the dilute solution is the same as that of water (4.2 J cm^{-3} K^{-1}).

Also calculate the amount of reaction which occurred (in g-eqn) and hence, by proportion, ΔH.

(*b*) *The free-energy from the standard cell potential, E^{Φ}*

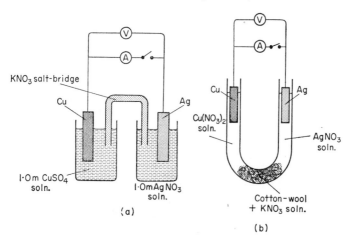

KNO₃ salt-bridge
Cu   Ag
1·0m CuSO₄ soln.   1·0mAgNO₃ soln.
(a)

Cu   Ag
Cu(NO₃)₂ soln.   AgNO₃ soln.
Cotton-wool + KNO₃ soln.
(b)

Fig. 3.2

Set up a pair of half-cells, connected by a potassium nitrate salt bridge (KNO_3 solution immobilized either by gelatine or cotton wool). The milliammeter should show a small current of electrons from copper to silver. Now disconnect the milliammeter, so that the resistance of the circuit becomes high, and the reading on the voltmeter rises to near the maximum e.m.f. of the cell, $E^\ominus$. Calculate $\Delta G^\ominus$ as shown in §3.12, noting that for this reaction $n = 2$.

(c) Checking

Check your result for ΔH by the ΔH_f table for aqueous ions; and check $E^\ominus$ from the standard redox potentials of the two half-reactions.

What is the *least* quantity of heat evolved during one gram-equation of reaction in the cell under load?

Calculate $\Delta S^\ominus$ for the reaction. Is the sign what you would have predicted from inspection of the equation? (Explain.)

(d) A more accurate method of measuring $E^\ominus$

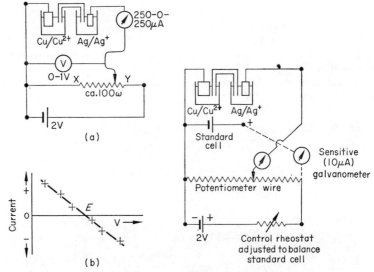

Fig. 3.3 Bridge circuit with counter-voltage

Fig. 3.4 Potentiometer circuit

Set up the potentiometer circuit shown in Fig. 3.2 or 3.3. The copper–silver cell can be opposed by a counter-voltage, and the current flowing through the cell (and its direction) can be found for various values of the counter-voltage, as the rheostat or resistance-wire tapping is changed from low (X) to high (Y).

Note that when the counter-voltage is greater than $E^\ominus$ the reaction is being *driven* in the endergonic direction; i.e.

$$2Ag + Cu^{2+} \longrightarrow 2Ag^+ + Cu; \qquad \Delta G^\ominus = +ve$$

Determine the e.m.f. exerted by the cell when the current from it is zero: this is the maximum (reversible) cell potential, E. Since the concentrations are standard, it is denoted $E^\ominus$.

With circuit 3.3 (a), a graph of current versus voltage for several rheostat settings near to the null-point (Fig. 3.3(b)) will assist the exact determination of $E^\ominus$.

(*e*) *To show the qualitative variation of ΔG with concentration*

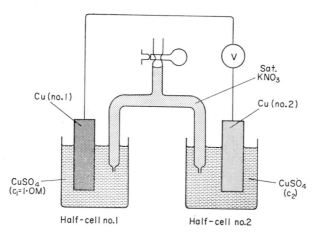

Fig. 3.5 A simple concentration cell

Set up two half-cells as in Fig. 3.5, and connect the two copper-foil electrodes to a sensitive millivoltmeter (or microammeter). Fill both half-cells with approx. 1 M $CuSO_4$ solution, and place the salt-bridge† in position. There should be no potential difference between the two identical half-cells; if the voltmeter does register a p.d. it should be noted and regarded for the present purpose as a 'zero error'.

Remove the salt-bridge, and change the electrolyte in the right-hand

† The salt-bridge may take several forms: (i) a narrow glass tube as in Fig. 3.1(a) filled with a gel containing the electrolyte; (ii) a specially-made bridge as shown in Fig. 3.5, with very small openings to the lower limbs. With these openings immersed in the chosen electrolyte, the bridge is filled by suction at the top, which is then sealed with a clip; (iii) a simple U-tube fitted at each end with a cork and short length of capillary tube. It is filled and corked when vertical, then inverted; (iv) a strip of filter-paper soaked in electrolyte, and discarded after being used once.

cell (no. 2) to approx. 0.1 M CuSO₄. Replace the salt-bridge and read the p.d., being particularly careful to observe the *polarity* correctly. The terminals of the voltmeter will be marked + (or red) and − (or black): a clockwise deflection of the instrument needle indicates that the electrodes have the polarity of the terminals to which they are connected.

Repeat with very dilute (approx. 10^{-3} M) CuSO₄ in half-cell no. 2.

DISCUSSION

The only electrode reaction which can occur in either half-cell is the reversible change:

$$Cu\,(s) \rightleftharpoons Cu^{2+}\,(aq) + 2e^-$$

If a potential difference exists (after allowance for the 'zero error' of the circuit) it must be due to this reaction taking place in one direction at electrode 1, and in the other direction at electrode 2. Therefore the free-energy of the reverse reaction is not, in this experiment, exactly equal-but-opposite to the free-energy of the forward reaction (otherwise the net free-energy change would be zero, and no p.d. would appear). The only difference between the two half-cells is the concentration. Therefore ΔG of a reaction involving dissolved substances will depend upon their concentrations. (This is taken further in §7.8 and §8.10.)

TREATMENT OF RESULTS

1. Complete the table:

Concentrations		Meter readings		Polarity of electrodes	
c_1	c_2	Observed	Corrected	No. 1	No. 2
1.0	1.0		±0		
1.0	0.1				
1.0	0.001				

2. How does the p.d. vary with the concentrations? Does it increase with increasing ratio c_1/c_2? Is the p.d. *proportional* to c_1/c_2?

3. Write the equations for the electrode reactions which must occur to give the observed polarity; include the concentrations in the equations by writing Cu^{2+} (1 M) and Cu^{2+} (dilute) where appropriate.

4. Add the two half-equations together to obtain the equation for the net reaction. This reaction is spontaneous, and has negative ΔG.

5. By comparing the p.d. due to concentration differences with the p.d. of the Cu/Ag cell (§3.13(a)), decide whether the variation of ΔG_r due to *small* differences in concentration is of practical importance.

3.14 Exercises

1. In an experiment similar to that described in §3.13(d), a student measured the cell potential at two temperatures, 323 K and 363 K:

$$Cu\ (s) + 2Ag^+\ (aq) \longrightarrow Cu^{2+}\ (aq) + 2Ag\ (s); \qquad \begin{aligned} E^{\ominus}_{323} &= 0.438\ V \\ E^{\ominus}_{363} &= 0.402\ V \end{aligned}$$

(i) Calculate $\Delta G^{\ominus}$ for the two temperatures.

(ii) Is the reaction favoured or opposed by the rise in temperature?

(iii) Substitute values for $\Delta G^{\ominus}$ and T in the equation

$$\Delta G^{\ominus} = \Delta H^{\ominus} - T\,\Delta S^{\ominus},$$

at both temperatures, then solve the simultaneous equations to obtain the constants $\Delta H^{\ominus}$ and $\Delta S^{\ominus}$. Compare the answer for $\Delta H^{\ominus}$ with that calculated from $\Delta H^{\ominus}_f$ data.

(iv) Can you account for the sign of $\Delta S^{\ominus}$, from consideration of the equation?

2. The cell potential for the following cell is 1.10 V:

$$Zn/ZnSO_4\ (1\ \text{M}):\text{salt-bridge}:CuSO_4\ (1\ \text{M})/Cu$$

The reaction is:

$$Zn\ (s) + Cu^{2+}\ (aq) \longrightarrow Zn^{2+}\ (aq) + Cu\ (s); \qquad \Delta H = -218\ kJ$$

Calculate:

(a) $\Delta G^{\ominus}$ in kJ;

(b) the amount of heat evolved or absorbed when the cell undergoes 1/100 gram-equation of reaction under maximum e.m.f. conditions;

(c) the heat transferred by 1/100 g-eqn reaction when the cell is providing a substantial current, and is developing 75% of its maximum e.m.f.

3. (a) Use energies of formation to calculate $\Delta G^{\ominus}$ and ΔH for the reaction:

$$2Ag\ (s) + Hg_2Cl_2\ (s) \longrightarrow 2AgCl\ (s) + Hg\ (l)$$

(b) Will the reaction occur spontaneously, or will it reverse?

(c) If the reaction could take place in an electrochemical cell, calculate the reversible cell potential, $E^{\ominus}$, at 298 K.

(d) What heat is transferred to or from the surroundings when:

(i) the cell is short-circuited, and is producing no external work;

(ii) the cell is under load, and is developing 90% of its maximum voltage as it charges a large capacitor.

4. From the experiment in §3.13(*e*) it was found that the process of dilution is exergonic; e.g.

$$Cu^{2+}\ (1\ \text{M}) + aq \longrightarrow Cu^{2+}\ (\text{dilute}); \qquad \Delta G = -\text{ve}$$

Show that this result is consistent with, and helps to explain: (a) the spontaneous diffusion of solute into a region of lower concentration; (b) osmosis; (c) the relative vapour pressures of solutions of different concentrations.

5. The free-energy of the reaction:

$$Cu\,(s) + 2Ag^+\,(aq,\ 1\ \text{M}) \longrightarrow 2Ag\,(s) + Cu^{2+}\,(aq,\ 1\ \text{M})$$

is $\Delta G_r^{\ominus}$ (see §3.9), and it is negative. Use the information given in the previous question to determine whether ΔG_r (non-standard) for the following reaction is more or less negative than $\Delta G_r^{\ominus}$:

$$Cu\,(s) + 2Ag^+\,(aq,\ 1\ \text{M}) \longrightarrow 2Ag\,(s) + Cu^{2+}\,(aq,\ 10^{-3}\ \text{M})$$

3.15 Summary of principles of qualitative estimation of ΔH, ΔS and ΔG

ΔH is predicted by consideration of bonding. Reactions in which bonds are formed are invariably exothermic, e.g.

$$I + I\,(\text{atoms}) \longrightarrow I_2\,(g); \qquad \Delta H = -\text{ve}$$

Usually, however, some bonds are formed while others are broken. Then the reaction in which *more* and *stronger* bonds are formed is exothermic. The additional general (but not invariable) rule which helps here is that bonds between atoms of two different elements are usually stronger than bonds between two identical atoms. So in the reaction:

$$H_2\,(g) + Cl_2\,(g) \longrightarrow 2HCl\,(g); \qquad \Delta H = -\text{ve}$$

one H—H and one Cl—Cl bond must be broken, but the two H—Cl bonds are stronger, so the reaction is exothermic. Similarly, in:

$$CH_3CH_2OH\,(g) \longrightarrow CH_2{:}CH_2\,(g) + H_2O\,(g)$$

one C—H and one C—O are broken, and one H—O forms; so as all three are of comparable strength, the formation of fewer bonds makes the reaction endothermic.

ΔS is predicted by consideration of the change in the number of moles of gas. Reactions in which more gas is formed lead to a state of greater disorder, and ΔS is positive. Reactions with gases among the products but none among the reactants have a large positive entropy change, e.g.

$$2Pb(NO_3)_2\,(s) \longrightarrow 2PbO\,(s) + 4NO_2\,(g) + O_2\,(g); \qquad \Delta S = +\text{ve}$$

Less certainly, the rule would predict a negative entropy for:

$$2PbO\,(s) + 2Cl_2\,(g) \longrightarrow 2PbCl_2\,(s) + O_2\,(g)$$

If the number of moles of gas does not change, the sign of ΔS cannot be predicted, but is probably small:

$$N_2\,(g) + O_2\,(g) \longrightarrow 2NO\,(g); \qquad \Delta S\ \text{small}$$

ΔG is calculated from the equation $\Delta G = \Delta H - T\,\Delta S$, where T is the absolute temperature. While ΔH and ΔS are almost independent of temperature, the equation shows that ΔG changes greatly. ΔG also depends upon concentration; in this section standard concentrations are assumed. The value of the prediction of at least the *sign* of ΔG is that if it is negative (exergonic) the reaction is feasible, and will proceed as soon as it has been initiated (if this is necessary); whereas if ΔG is positive (endergonic) the reaction cannot proceed (though if ΔG is *small* and positive the reaction may sometimes go some way before coming to equilibrium).

If ΔH and ΔS are of the same sign (the usual case) ΔG will change sign on going from low to high temperature. *At low temperature*, the $-T\Delta S$ term will be less important than ΔH, so the sign of ΔG will be the same as ΔH: the exothermic reaction will go. *At high temperature* the $-T\Delta S$ term, which grows larger with increasing T, becomes the more important, so ΔG takes on the sign *opposite* to ΔS: the reaction with positive entropy will go.

Thus for the reaction:

$$CH_3CH_3 \text{ (g)} \longrightarrow CH_2CH_2 \text{ (g)} + H_2 \text{ (g)}$$

the predictions are: ΔH positive (fewer bonds), ΔS positive (more moles of gas), so ΔG negative at high temperature. At low T, ΔG positive, and this means that the *reverse* reaction will then be feasible.

3.16 Revision exercises

1. The following reactions can occur, with suitable catalysts, and in the correct temperature range. By considering bond breaking and forming predict ΔH; and by inspection of the equation predict ΔS. Hence decide whether the suitable temperature for each reaction is (i) low, such as 300 K, (ii) high, such as 1000 K, or (iii) both.

    (a) $CH_4 \text{ (g)} + \frac{1}{2}O_2 \text{ (g)} \longrightarrow CH_3OH \text{ (g)}$
    (b) $C_2H_6 \text{ (g)} \longrightarrow C_2H_4 \text{ (g)} + H_2 \text{ (g)}$
    (c) $C_2H_4 \text{ (g)} + Cl_2 \text{ (g)} \longrightarrow CH_2ClCH_2Cl \text{ (g)}$
    (d) $C_2H_4 \text{ (g)} + Cl_2 \text{ (g)} \longrightarrow CH_2CHCl \text{ (g)} + HCl \text{ (g)}$

2. What conditions of temperature and pressure will favour each step in the following sequence of reactions used in the petrol industry?

    (a) $n\text{-}C_4H_{10} \text{ (g)} \longrightarrow (CH_3)_2{:}CH_2 \text{ (g)} + H_2 \text{ (g)}$
    (b) $2(CH_3)_2C{:}CH_2 \longrightarrow (CH_3)_3C.CH_2.C(CH_3){:}CH_2 \text{ (g)}$
    (c) $(CH_3)_3C.CH_2.C(CH_3){:}CH_2 + H_2 \longrightarrow$
                                              $(CH_3)_3C.CH_2CH(CH_3)_2 \text{ (g)}$
                                                iso-octane

3. Which of the following decompositions of formic acid is the more exergonic? (In fact both can be brought about by different catalysts.)

    (a) $HCOOH \text{ (g)} \longrightarrow H_2 + CO_2$
    (b) $HCOOH \text{ (g)} \longrightarrow CO + H_2O \text{ (g)}$

4. For the following reactions, which direction is favoured at 298 K, forward or reverse? Make an intelligent guess, then check by calculation.

(a) I_2 (s) $+$ KClO$_3$ (s) $\longrightarrow$ KIO$_3$ (s) $+$ Cl$_2$ (g)

(b)   KCl (s) $+$ KBrO$_3$ (s) $\longrightarrow$ KClO$_3$ (s) $+$ KBr (s)

(c)   CCl$_4$ (l) $+$ H$_2$ (g) $\longrightarrow$ CHCl$_3$ (l) $+$ HCl (g)

5. For the reaction:

$$\text{KIO}_3 \text{ (s)} \longrightarrow \text{KI (s)} + \tfrac{3}{2}\text{O}_2 \text{ (g)}$$

find $\Delta G^{\ominus}$ at 298 K and 1000 K, and plot a graph of $\Delta G^{\ominus}$ against T, and read off the minimum temperature for decomposition to occur in an atmosphere of oxygen. Will T_{eq} for decomposition of KIO$_3$ in *air* be higher or lower?

4 Enthalpy and bonding

4.1 Stability

The products of an exothermic change are said to be more *stable* than the reactants at low temperatures, and this corresponds to the formation of more and stronger bonds between the atoms. At higher temperatures, or if energy is supplied as radiation, the bonds are broken, or replaced by weaker ones, thus giving a 'less stable' system. An enquiry into the incentive for this will be found later in the book.

The terms 'strong bonds' and 'weak bonds' are no more than convenient labels for bonds which require respectively large and small amounts of energy (enthalpy) for their breaking. For any chemical or physical change at constant pressure,

$$+\Delta H = \left\{ \begin{array}{c} \text{sum of energies of} \\ \text{bonds broken} \end{array} \right\} - \left\{ \begin{array}{c} \text{sum of energies of} \\ \text{bonds formed} \end{array} \right\}$$

4.2 Covalent bond energies

In the case of the dissociation of diatomic gases the enthalpy of reaction is interpreted simply as the energy required to break one mole of the bond in question, e.g.

$$H_2 \text{ (g)} \longrightarrow H \text{ (g)} + H \text{ (g)}; \qquad \Delta H_D = +436 \text{ kJ}$$

This bond dissociation enthalpy, ΔH_D, is a quantitative measurement of the strength of the H—H bond. When hydrogen atoms re-combine 436 kJ is evolved as heat (per mole of H_2 formed). This is the principle of the atomic hydrogen torch, in which a stream of hydrogen is atomized by an electric arc and directed onto the object to be heated. It also provides a calorimetric means of measuring ΔH_D.

Some bond dissociation enthalpies are given in Table 4.1(a). Many of them will have been calculated from spectroscopic data, one of the most accurate methods.

When hydrogen and chlorine react, the products are more stable by 184 kJ per mole $H_2 + Cl_2$, and clearly this is the difference between the enthalpy of breaking one H—H plus one Cl—Cl bond, and the enthalpy of forming two H—Cl bonds.

$$H_2 \text{ (g)} + Cl_2 \text{ (g)} \longrightarrow 2HCl \text{ (g)}$$
$$\begin{aligned}
\Delta H_r &= \Delta H_D(H\!-\!H) + \Delta H_D(Cl\!-\!Cl) - 2\Delta H_D(H\!-\!Cl) \\
&= 436 + 242 - 2 \times 431 \\
&= -184 \text{ kJ g-eqn}^{-1}
\end{aligned}$$

Table 4.1(a)   Bond dissociation enthalpies for some diatomic molecules

Molecule	H_2	O_2	N_2	F_2	Cl_2	Br_2(g)	I_2(g)	HCl	HI	NO
ΔH_D/kJ mol^{-1}	436	496	946	158	242	193	151	431	299	630

Table 4.1(b)   Average bond dissociation enthalpies ('transferable bond energies') (See §4.5)

Bond	C—C	C=C	C≡C	C—H	C—O	C=O	O—H	C—Cl
ΔH_D/kJ mol^{-1}	348	615	839	414	358	745	463	329

The thermal stability of HCl compared to HI can be explained by examining the relevant bond enthalpies. Considering the bond-breaking aspect, $\Delta H_D(I-I)$ is smaller than $\Delta H_D(Cl—Cl)$, so it is easier to atomize iodine. But the energy evolved from the combination of $H+I$ atoms is less than that from $H+Cl$. Only a look at the actual figures can decide which factor will be the more important.

The bond dissociation enthalpies are, in kJ mol^{-1}:

Cl—Cl	I—I	difference		H—Cl	H—I	difference
242	151	+91		431	299	+132

So it is the bond enthalpies of the *compounds* which are decisive in this case, and ΔH_f for HCl is greater than that for HI (Fig. 4.1).

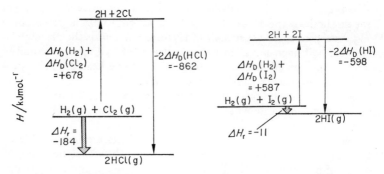

Fig. 4.1   Enthalpy diagrams for the formation of HCl and HI

4.3 Exercises

1. Use data from Table 4.1(a) to construct diagrams, similar to Fig. 4.1, for these reactions:

   (i) $2HI + Cl_2 \longrightarrow 2HCl + I_2$ (g)
   (ii) $N_2 + O_2 \longrightarrow 2NO$

2. $2HBr(g) + Cl_2(g) \longrightarrow 2HCl(g) + Br_2(g)$; $\Delta H_r = -82$ kJ g-eqn^{-1}
Use data from Table 4.1(a) to find $\Delta H_D(H\!-\!Br)$.

4.4 Average bond energies

In polyatomic molecules of compounds of two elements there will usually be two or more identical bonds, e.g. the two O—H bonds in H_2O, and the four C—H bonds in CH_4. The *total* bond energy of such molecules can be calculated from the enthalpy of formation. By dividing this by the number of bonds, the *average bond dissociation enthalpy* is obtained. This will not be equal to the energy required to rupture just the first one of the bonds, but the difference is unimportant for many purposes.

WORKED EXAMPLES

The calculation of average $\Delta H_D(C\!-\!H)$ in CH_4

$$CH_4\,(g) \longrightarrow C(s,\,gr) + 2H_2\,(g); \quad \Delta H = +\quad 75\text{ kJ }(= -\Delta H_f)$$
$$C(s,\,gr) \longrightarrow C(g,\,atoms); \quad\quad\quad \Delta H = +\;718\text{ kJ}$$
$$2H_2\,(g) \longrightarrow 4H\,(atoms); \quad\quad\quad\quad \Delta H = +\;872\text{ kJ}$$

adding: $CH_4\,(g) \longrightarrow C\,(g) + 4H\,(g); \quad\quad \Delta H = +1665$ kJ

$$\therefore\; \Delta H_D(C\!-\!H) = \tfrac{1}{4} \times 1664 = 416\text{ kJ}$$

Compare this with the enthalpy of breaking just one of the bonds (found from spectra):

$$CH_4 \longrightarrow CH_3 + H; \quad\quad \Delta H = +432\text{ kJ}$$

For the 2nd, 3rd and 4th bonds the enthalpies are, successively, 372, 523 and 342 kJ.

4.5 Transferable bond energies

With organic compounds, particularly, the same bond may appear in many different molecules, and it does not necessarily follow that ΔH_D will be the same in each case. However it is found that there is usually agreement to within 2 or 3% unless there is some good reason. In fact, the study of deviations from the normal covalent bond energies can often reveal some interesting abnormality in the structure of the molecule.

By combining ΔH_D values from diatomic molecules with the ΔH_f of some polyatomic molecule, further bond dissociation enthalpies can be calculated. For example, $\Delta H_f(C_2H_6\ (g)) = -85$ kJ; the enthalpy of atomization of $2C + 6H = (2 \times 718 + 6 \times 218)) = 2744$ kJ. Therefore the total bond energy in C_2H_6 must be the sum of $2744 + 85 = 2829$ kJ. If the average $\Delta H_D(C—H)$ is the same as it was in CH_4, the six C—H bonds will contribute $6 \times 416 = 2496$ kJ to this total, leaving 333 kJ for the bond energy of C—C. This value carries over remarkably well to other organic compounds, though the accepted value which gives the best fit in most cases is 348 kJ. This and other transferable bond energies appear in Table 4.1(b).

4.6 Exercises

1. (a) Show that the combination of dissociation enthalpies of H_2 and O_2 (from Table 4.1(a)) with the enthalpy of formation of gaseous water $(-242$ kJ mol$^{-1})$ leads to a value of 463 kJ for the average bond dissociation enthalpy of O—H.

(b) $\Delta H_f(CCl_4\,(l)) = -139$ kJ mol^{-1}; ΔH of vaporization $(CCl_4\,(l)) = +32$ kJ mol^{-1}. Calculate the average $\Delta H_D(C—Cl)$.

(c) Draw an enthalpy diagram (showing reactants, free atoms, and products) for the following reaction, and so calculate ΔH_r.

$$CH_4\ (g) + Cl_2\ (g) \longrightarrow CH_3Cl\ (g) + HCl\ (g)$$

2. (a) Assuming that all the bonds have their normal dissociation energies, calculate the enthalpies of formation of:

(i) C_3H_7OH (g);   (ii) cyclohexane (g),   (iii) cyclohexene (g).

```
   H2C —CH2                H2C—CH
  /        \              /       \\
H2C        CH2         H2C        CH
  \        /              \       //
   H2C—CH2                H2C —CH2
```

(b) Compare your answer to (i) with that calculated from the enthalpy of combustion of liquid propanol $(-2010$ kJ) and the value of $+33$ kJ mol^{-1} for the vaporization. (See also Appendix A.)

(c) From your answers to (ii) and (iii) calculate the enthalpy of hydrogenation of cyclohexene.

3.* (a) Construct a bond enthalpy diagram to illustrate the argument presented in the previous section for obtaining $\Delta H_D(C—C)$ in C_2H_6. Include levels for (i) 2C (s) $+ 3H_2$ (g), (ii) 2C (g) $+ 6H$ (g), (iii) $2CH_3$ (g), and (iv) C_2H_6 (g).

(b) Is this value for $\Delta H_D(C—C)$ consistent with the fact that the enthalpy of atomization of graphite is $+718$ kJ per mole of atoms, even though each carbon atom is held by *four* covalent bonds?

4.7 The carbon–carbon bonds

The bond dissociation enthalpies of single, double and triple carbon–carbon bonds are:

$$C\!-\!C \quad 348\ kJ$$
$$C\!=\!C \quad 615\ kJ \quad (348+267)$$
$$C\!\equiv\!C \quad 839\ kJ \quad (348+267+224)$$

It is sometimes stated that the double bond is 'weaker' than the single, but this is clearly not so, since 267 kJ *more* is needed to break it. It would be true, though, to say that it is a more reactive bond, since it can 'open' (not 'break') and add on other atoms, e.g.

$$H_2C\!=\!CH_2 + H_2 \longrightarrow H_3C\!-\!CH_3$$
$$\text{ethene} \qquad\qquad\qquad \text{ethane}$$

In this reaction 267 kJ is absorbed as a result of the change from double to single bond, and 436 kJ is absorbed in atomizing the H_2; but two extra C–H bonds are formed, releasing 414 kJ each, so the overall enthalpy of the reaction equals $+703-828 = -125$ kJ (exothermic). (In fact with a suitable nickel catalyst the reaction takes place readily at very moderate temperatures.)

It could be said that the 'second half' of a double $C\!=\!C$ bond is weaker than another single bond; so in the polymerization of ethylene there is a gain in stability of 80 kJ per mole of C_2H_4 as a result of the change from one double to two single bonds:

$$n\ CH_2\!=\!CH_2 \longrightarrow (-CH_2\!-\!CH_2\!-)_n$$

Acetylene is an endothermic compound. Heat is evolved if it reverts to graphite and hydrogen. The total bond energy of C_2H_2 is

$$(839+2\times414) = 1667\ kJ,$$

whereas the energy of atomization of $2C+2H$ is $(2\times718+436)=$ 1872 kJ. So ΔH for the decomposition is -205 kJ mol^{-1}.

4.8 Practical work (bond energies)

Set up a small-scale acetylene generator, consisting of a boiling-tube, one-holed cork, and right-angled delivery-tube. Use about 8 g calcium carbide in hard lumps, and when all is ready, add about 10 cm^3 water. Allow the acetylene to escape for a minute or so, then collect two boiling-tubes half-full, over water.

Clamp the two tubes in a vertical position in a fairly full dish of water, so that the clamps can be near the open ends; and mark the initial volume of gas.

Heat one of the tubes gently all over the exposed region, for about five minutes, then let it cool back to room temperature. The gas will be found to have contracted, due to partial polymerization to benzene and other aromatic hydrocarbons, e.g.

$$3C_2H_2\ (g) \longrightarrow C_6H_6\ (l); \qquad \Delta H = -629\ kJ$$

An oily layer can sometimes be seen, and the aromatic smell is unmistakeable.

The second half-tube of acetylene is treated differently. Heat one point strongly with a roaring bunsen flame, and observe the interior of the tube closely through a perspex safety screen. A remarkable red flash and trail of smoke will be seen, as some of the acetylene decomposes to its elements:

$$C_2H_2 \text{ (g)} \longrightarrow 2C \text{ (s)} + H_2 \text{ (g)}; \qquad \Delta H = -205 \text{ kJ}$$

Draw enthalpy diagrams showing the bond energy changes in these two reactions, and interpret the results. Which reaction is the more favoured by the following factors: (i) enthalpy, (ii) entropy, (iii) energy of initiation.

4.9* Delocalization energy

Sometimes the experimental total bond dissociation enthalpy of a molecule is significantly greater than the sum of the individual bond enthalpies calculated from other molecules. The substance is then more stable than expected, and has a smaller enthalpy of combustion than would be predicted from a comparison with other substances.

For example, $\Delta H_D(C{=}O)$ calculated from aldehydes and ketones is 745 kJ; but the average $\Delta H_D(C{=}O)$ in the CO_2 molecule is 829 kJ. The accepted interpretation is that the carbon dioxide is 'stabilized by delocalization of electrons'. The total bond enthalpy is 168 kJ mol^{-1} greater than predicted, and this is referred to as the 'delocalization energy'. (It is worth noting that this is the additional energy which the molecule has *not* got.)

The most satisfactory explanation of this phenomenon, which is also known as 'mesomerism', is given by the theory of molecular orbitals, which it would be out of place to discuss here.

The degree of delocalization stabilization can also be measured by the shortening of bond lengths. The bond lengths of $C{=}O$ in aldehydes and ketones is 0.122 nm (1.22 Å), whereas that in CO_2 is 0.115 nm (1.15 Å).

The last exercise of §4.6 was the calculation of the enthalpy of hydrogenation of one isolated $C{=}C$ bond in cyclohexane, and the answer was $\Delta H = -125$ kJ. Benzene is C_6H_6, and the classical structural formula for it (right) has three single C—C and three double $C{=}C$ bonds. From this it would be expected† that the enthalpy of hydrogenation of benzene to cyclohexane would be $3 \times -125 = -375$ kJ mol^{-1}. In fact the experimental result is only -208 kJ mol^{-1}, a difference of 168 kJ mol^{-1} delocalization energy. The enthalpy of combustion leads to a similar value.

† If bond-angle changes are ignored.

This extra stability shows that the bonds between the carbon atoms are not the usual single and double bonds: the explanation is perhaps a delocalized orbital extending round the whole ring, or alternatively, six three-electron bonds with reduced electron repulsion.

4.10* Intermolecular bonding

In contrast to the covalent bonds within molecules there are comparatively weak forces *between* molecules, even those which are chemically inert. These intermolecular attractions are responsible for the liquefying and freezing of gases. Substances with strong intermolecular forces (ionic attractions, metallic bonds, or covalent bonds in giant molecules) have very high boiling-points. Other substances, with weak intermolecular forces, and hence low enthalpies of vaporization, have low boiling-points.

Van der Waals forces

Van der Waals forces are the weakest of the intermolecular attractions, but they are always present between molecules within a certain distance of each other. These forces are believed to arise from sympathetic oscillations of the electron clouds (Fig. 4.2): the electrons can move rapidly relative to the heavy nuclei, and if the electron clouds on two adjacent molecules move in phase, the potential energy is lowered by the temporary electrostatic attraction.

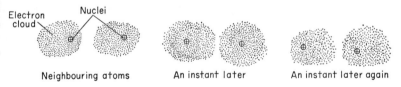

Fig. 4.2 A model for the origin of van der Waals forces

Van der Waals forces are non-directional and non-specific, that is, they arise between any adjacent molecules, different or identical, regardless of their chemical nature. The forces are roughly proportional to the number of electrons taking part, which is the sum of the atomic numbers. For this reason van der Waals attractions increase with increasing molecular weight. Thus Ar has almost the same boiling-point as the iso-electronic F_2 (18 electrons), but one much higher than that of He (2 electrons). The point can be illustrated quantitatively by comparing the ratio of the number of electrons in benzene C_6H_6 and naphthalene $C_{10}H_8$ with the ratio of their boiling-points (353 K and 491 K respectively). Both are roughly 2:3.

Molecules with about 20 electrons have van der Waals forces totalling about 6 kJ mol^{-1}. Compare this with the enthalpies of vaporization of ionic salts, which are usually over 120 kJ mol^{-1}; and the covalent bond dissociation enthalpies listed earlier in this chapter.

Permanent dipoles (and hydrogen-bonding)

It may be helpful to preface this section with a note about *electronegativity*. This measures the relative ability of atoms to attract shared electrons, and it can vary greatly from one element to another.

In any row of the periodic table the atoms do not alter greatly in size, but the nuclear charge increases from left to right. This results in an increase in the electrostatic attraction on the electrons, and the non-metallic character increases until the halogen is reached, at the end of the row.

For elements in the same group, the electronegativity generally *decreases* with increasing size; for although the atomic number goes up by 8 or 18 units each time, the effective pull of the nucleus on outer electrons is reduced by the 'screening' effect of the additional full inner shell of electrons, and by the greater radius.

In general, then, electronegativity increases towards the top right-hand corner of the periodic table.

A covalent bond between atoms of different electronegativity will be *polar* because the more electronegative element will attract the electrons closer to itself. The result of this is that unless the molecules are geometrically symmetrical (e.g. CCl$_4$), compounds have a *permanent dipole* of a strength proportional to the difference in the electronegativities of the elements.

The interaction of these electrical dipoles causes intermolecular bonding, and hence an increase in the enthalpies of fusion and evaporation, and a rise in the melting-point and boiling-point.

There is one kind of permanent dipole attraction which is particularly strong, uniquely so amongst non-metal compounds. This is the *hydrogen bond*, which can exist between a bonded hydrogen atom and an electronegative atom in another molecule, thus:

$$\overset{\delta-}{Y}-\overset{\delta+}{H}\cdots\overset{\delta-}{Z}-$$

where both Y and Z are one of the elements of highest electronegativity: N, O or F, and $\delta+$ and $\delta-$ show the partial charges on the atoms. The small size and low electron density of the hydrogen atom are the contributing factors to the peculiar effectiveness of this polar attraction.

The existence of hydrogen bonding in hydrogen fluoride, ammonia, water, alcohols, amines, etc. explains the abnormally high boiling-points of these substances. The enthalpy of vaporization of water is 41 kJ mol^{-1}, whereas that of the iso-electronic molecule methane is only 8 kJ. This difference of 31 kJ must be attributed mainly to hydrogen bonding in water; so with about two moles of hydrogen bonds per mole of H_2O molecules, the strength of the hydrogen bond appears to be about 15 kJ (4 kcal) per mole.

Table 4.2 Selected enthalpies of vaporization

Molecule	B.pt/(K)	ΔH_{vap}/(kJ mol^{-1})	No. of electrons
He	4.2	0.08	2
H_2	20.4	0.92	2
CH_4	111.7	8.2	10
H_2O	373.15	40.7	10
F_2	85	6.3	18
Ar	87	6.5	18
HCl	188	16.2	18
C_6H_6	353	34	42
$C_{10}H_8$ naphthalene	491	40	68

[Trouton's Rule† states that for many liquids:

$$\Delta H_{vap} \div T_b \approx 88 \text{ J K}^{-1} \text{ or } 21 \text{ cal K}^{-1}$$

where T_b is the boiling-point in kelvins.]

† *Phil. Mag.* **18**, 54 (1884).

4.11* Exercises

1. Discuss the intermolecular bonding in (i) argon, (ii) methane, (iii) ammonia, (iv) quartz (SiO_2).

2. Comment upon the following facts:

dimethyl ether $(CH_3)_2O$, b.pt=248 K ($-25°C$), $\Delta H_{vap}=+24$ kJ mol^{-1}
ethanol C_2H_5OH, b.pt = 352 K (79°C), $\Delta H_{vap} = +43$ kJ myl^{-1}

3. Test Trouton's Rule (Table 4.2) on some common liquids. Does it apply to very low and very high boiling points? (e.g. NaCl, b.pt 1738 K, $\Delta H_{vap} = 170$ kJ mol^{-1}). Is there a simple theoretical explanation for the Rule?

4. PRACTICAL INVESTIGATION

Find out, approximately, the enthalpies of mixing equal amounts of various pairs of liquids, and interpret the results in terms of breaking and forming of intermolecular bonds. (Water, ethanol, acetone, benzene, chloroform.)

4.12* Ionic compounds: the Born–Haber cycle

A valuable approach to the understanding of inorganic chemistry is through a comparison of the stabilities of compounds as measured by their enthalpies of formation. For example, the ΔH_f values for the oxides and chlorides of zinc, iron(II) and copper(II) are (in kJ):

$$
\begin{array}{llll}
\text{ZnO} & -348; & \text{ZnCl}_2 & -416 \\
\text{FeO} & -265; & \text{FeCl}_2 & -341 \\
\text{CuO} & -155; & \text{CuCl}_2 & -218
\end{array}
$$

These values are clearly linked with the decreasing chemical reactivity from zinc to copper. It was shown in Chapter 3 that strictly the free-energies rather than enthalpies should be compared; but for comparisons between reactions involving similar numbers of atoms, and equal numbers of gas molecules, the enthalpies are as good a guide.

Naturally one wants to interpret these enthalpies in terms of the properties of the atoms and ions; but there are several variables, and it would be unwise to explain a set of ΔH values by just one feature of the reaction process.

For example, it is sometimes said that the reactivity of a metal is due to its readiness to lose electrons, and that while sodium, zinc, etc., readily give up one or two electrons, the less active metals hold theirs more tenaciously. This is misleading in two ways. For one thing, *all* ionizations of free atoms are endothermic; even the sodium atom does not 'readily give out an electron', but has to be given 494 kJ/mol to make it do so. Secondly, the ionization energy is an important factor, but by no means the only one. The enthalpies of ionization of gaseous Zn, Fe and Cu to the divalent gaseous ion are $+2638$, $+2322$ and $+2705$ kJ mol^{-1} respectively. On this basis iron, with the least endothermic ionization, should be far more reactive than zinc, which would be hardly better than copper (see Table 4.5).

The significance of enthalpies of formation becomes much clearer if the data are analysed by means of the *Born–Haber thermochemical cycle*. The formation of an ionic compound from its elements is imagined to take place in a series of steps, as follows:

Table 4.3 Steps in the formation of ionic compounds

Process	Energy change	Usual sign of ΔH
1. Metal vaporized to metal atoms	enthalpy of vaporization (atomization)	+
2. Non-metal vaporized and dissociated to atoms	$\frac{1}{2}\Delta H_D$ for diatomic molecules	+
3. Ionization of metal to cation	ionization energy	+

Process	Energy change	Usual sign of ΔH
4. Ionization of non-metal anion	electron affinity	— (for 1 electron) + (for 2 or 3 electrons
5. Formation of crystal from gaseous ions *or*	lattice energy	—
Formation of hydrated ions in solution	hydration energy	—

The cycle can be set out diagrammatically, and to illustrate this the enthalpy of formation of sodium chloride will be analysed.

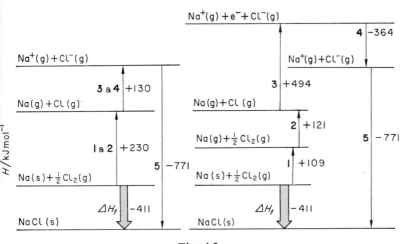

Fig. 4.3

The data for the single steps are obtained as follows.

1. The enthalpy of vaporization of the metal, by direct calorimetry.

2. The ionization energy from spectroscopy.

3. The bond dissociation energy of the non-metal, directly or from enthalpies of reaction (by Hess's Law).

4. Electron affinities. Difficult to measure directly, and usually estimated from the Born–Haber cycle for a completely ionic compound. Once obtained, though, they can be used in calculations on any other compound. (See Table 4.4.)

5. Lattice energy. Again difficult to measure directly (it is not merely the enthalpy of sublimation of the solid crystal, because the vapour of a salt consists of ion pairs, not separate ions). Theoretical calculations based on the size and charge of the ions, and Coulomb's Law of electrostatic attraction give lattice energies which are consistent with Born–Haber cycle results for many crystals, including the alkali halides; but in other cases there are deviations which are interpreted as indicating 'polarization' or 'partial covalent character'. This deviation from fully ionic behaviour is found particularly when the cation is small, with a multiple charge (e.g. Be^{2+}, Mg^{2+}, Al^{3+}) or when the anion is a large single atom (e.g. I^-).

Indeed, one of the most fruitful uses of the Born–Haber cycle is the calculation of lattice energies from heats of formation and other data, as this gives evidence about the type of bonding in the crystals.

Table 4.4   Electron affinities

Reaction	$\Delta U/(kJ\ mol^{-1})$
$H + e \rightarrow H^-$	-72
$F + e \rightarrow F^-$	-348
$Cl + e \rightarrow Cl^-$	-364
$Br + e \rightarrow Br^-$	-342
$I + e \rightarrow I^-$	-314
$O + e \rightarrow O^-$	-142
$O + 2e \rightarrow O^{2-}$	$(+700)$
$S + 2e \rightarrow S^{2-}$	$+332$

Table 4.6   Enthalpies of atomization

Element	$\Delta H_{at}/(kJ\ mol^{-1})$
H	218
C (gr)	716
N	473
O	248
Na	109
Mg	150
Al	314
Si	439
P (wh)	314
S (rh)	(224)
Ca	193
Fe	418
Cu	339
Zn	130

Table 4.5   Ionization energies

Atom	$\Delta U/(kJ\ mol^{-1})$		
	1st e	2nd e	3rd e
H	1310		
He	2370	5250	
Li	519	7300	11 800
Be	900	1760	14 800
B	800	2420	
C	1090	2350	
N	1400	2860	
O	1310	3390	
F	1680	3370	
Ne	2080	3950	
Na	494	4560	6940
Mg	736	1450	7740
Al	577	1820	2740
K	418	3070	
Ca	590	1150	
Mn	716	1510	3250
Fe	762	1560	
Cu	745	1960	
Zn	908	1730	
Ag	732	2070	

4.13* Ionic solutions

If a solution of an ionic salt contained separate free ions of the kind postulated in the Born–Haber treatment, then the dissolution of a crystal would be endothermic to the extent of many hundred kilojoules per mole, equalling the lattice energy. This is far from being true for aqueous solutions, and heats of solution are generally less than ± 80 kJ. It follows that there must be a large release of energy accompanying the change from free gaseous ions to ions in dilute solution; this is the 'energy of hydration'. It is comparable in size to the lattice energy, but is usually a little smaller.

If the crystal lattice is particularly stable, so that the lattice energy greatly exceeds the hydration energy, then the crystal will be virtually insoluble—e.g. most oxides and sulphides.

The enthalpy of solution of a salt can be found from tables of ΔH_f for the solid and for the ions. E.g. ΔH_f (NaCl (s)) $= -411$; ΔH_f (Na$^+$(aq)) $= -240$; ΔH_f (Cl$^-$(aq)) $= -167$. Therefore ΔH of solution $= -240 -167+411 = +4$ kJ mol.

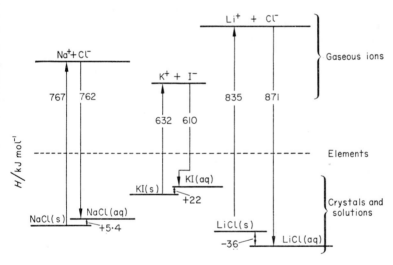

Fig. 4.4   Lattice and hydration enthalpies for some alkali halides

4.14*   Exercises

1. Draw a sketch diagram of a Born–Haber cycle for the formation of a solid salt such as calcium chloride. List out the stages in order, and state which of these are obtainable by physical measurement, and which by theoretical calculation. One step can neither be measured nor calculated except as the last remaining unknown in the cycle itself: which step is this? How is it that this limitation does not make the whole procedure useless as a means of predicting new information?

2. Calculate the enthalpies of solution (with correct sign) of caesium fluoride and chloride from the data below, and from these predict the relative solubility of the two salts.

	Lattice energy kJ mol^{-1}	*Hydration energy* kJ mol^{-1}
CsF	720	757
CsCl	648	632

In the case of CsF, write thermochemical equations to show exactly what processes have enthalpies of $+720$ and $+757$ kJ mol^{-1}.

3. (a) The lattice energy of NaF is 900 kJ mol^{-1}, and the enthalpy of atomization of sodium is 109 kJ. Use this and other data from this chapter to construct a Born–Haber cycle diagram, and find the enthalpy of formation of the salt.

(b) Using data from this chapter and from the appendix, calculate the lattice energy of NaI. How are the lattice energies of NaI and NaF connected with the sizes of the anions?

See also Additional Exercises.

5 Entropy and the Second Law of Thermodynamics

In Chapter 3 the two-part nature of free-energy was deduced empirically, and ΔG was used to determine the feasibility of chemical changes. The present chapter aims to uncover reasons why this is so. The first approach is through an examination of entropy and disorder, distinguishing two kinds of entropy, and showing that when the Second Law of Thermodynamics ('Entropy must increase') is applied to chemical systems, two terms $T\Delta S$ and $-\Delta H$ must be combined to give the overall increase in disorder.

The second half of the chapter makes a similar journey, but by a different route. The concepts of 'work' and 'degradation of energy' are discussed in the context of reversible and irreversible transfer of energy, to show that ΔG measures maximum available work. If this work is *not* harnessed it is degraded to heat, thereby increasing the disorder of the universe. So ΔG is a quantitative measure of the 'driving-force' of a reaction.

It is a matter of individual taste how much time should be spent on this chapter. To some it may be the most fascinating aspect of energetics. Others may be impatient to get back to practical applications of the theory. Some of the sections (marked *) are not strictly essential to a first reading, and students or course supervisors who are pressed for time could shorten the course by omitting them.

5.1 Free-energy and spontaneous change

In Chapter 3 the driving-force of physical and chemical processes was discussed, and it was pointed out that although exothermic reactions seem to be favoured at low temperatures, the energy which is transferred in or out of the system as heat is not sufficient to determine whether a reaction is feasible. This is not surprising, since energy is something which is *conserved*: the system and surroundings between them have exactly the same total energy after the reaction as they had before. It would be more persuasive to propose that when a reaction proceeds spontaneously and 'irreversibly' (see §5.7) something is irretrievably *lost*. This would explain the definite one-way direction of a freely-running chemical reaction before it approaches equilibrium. Free-energy satisfies this requirement, for when a system changes spontaneously to a condition of lower free-energy, ΔG is negative, representing a loss. Unlike ΔH it is not transferred to the surroundings, but just disappears. It is not conserved, and so ΔG is not really an 'energy' at all; rather it is a measure of the organization of energy (§5.8).

In an isolated system, that is a closed system plus its surroundings, two laws of thermodynamics are obeyed:

First Law: the total energy is unchanged by any change in materials;

Second Law: the total free-energy decreases with every spontaneous change.

5.2 Order and disorder

In the large-scale world we conceive of order as the quality which a house has which is missing from the same materials lying in a heap after an explosion; or something possessed by an army marching on parade, or a harmonious musical chord. Order is something to do with symmetry, fixed spatial relationships, uniformity of velocities, mathematical connections between a set of frequencies. Order is a restriction of choice, a limitation on random variation. Its opposite, disorder, can therefore be measured in terms of the number of different ways of arranging the components of a system. This definition enables one to consider partial disorder. For example, a class of 30 pupils sitting in their own desks has a high degree of order; but if each pupil is allowed to sit in any desk, the total number of possible arrangements is large. However, no one is in a position which does not correspond to one of the desks, and this places a severe limitation on the degree of disorder. The disorder increases if the pupils are allowed to walk about, but still not to the maximum extent, because each one has only the choice of positions within the classroom walls.

Molecular spatial disorder

The same considerations apply on an atomic scale. A pure crystalline solid has a very high degree of order, because there is a very limited number of positions available to any atom, ion or molecule. In a liquid the crystal lattice has broken down, and the molecules have greater freedom for variation in position, so there is much more disorder. There are still some restrictions though: the molecules must remain within the volume occupied by the bulk liquid; and certain transient patterns of molecules ('short-range order') are continuously being established and destroyed.

In a gas the only restriction on position is the containing vessel, and within this volume the molecules have complete freedom to move. A low-pressure gas has virtually complete spatial disorder.

Mixtures of substances have greater disorder than the same substances

purified and separated. In solutions the solute is in a much greater state
of disorder, but the molecules of the solvent may *gain* order because they
become attached to the solute, and lose some of their freedom of movement. This applies particularly to aqueous solutions of electrolytes, and
the hydration of the ions can even cause the dissolution of a crystal to
result in an overall decrease of disorder (see §7.15).

Disorder of energy distribution

Imagine a number of atoms at rest, well-spaced in regular positions.
Provide one atom with a definite amount of kinetic energy, and watch
the result. The atom will collide with the others and set them moving,
and soon the regular spatial arrangement will be destroyed. That is not
the only kind of disorder, though. The total kinetic energy remains the
same, but it is no longer concentrated in one atom: the collisions soon
lead to high disorder in the *distribution* of the energy.

Thermal energy is actually quantized, and even kinetic energy can be
held only in multiples of definite units, or quanta, Therefore the total
number of ways of distributing the thermal energy between the atoms,
though very large, is finite.

5.3* Entropy and probability

The **entropy** (S) of a system is the thermodynamic property which
measures the degree of disorder. It is a state function (like H, G and U)
and depends only on the present thermodynamic state of the system, and
not on the nature of any changes which it may be undergoing.

The total number of ways that a system has of arranging its components
with regard to position and energy distribution (§5.2) is given the symbol
Ω. This is sometimes called the 'thermodynamic probability' because
the system is Ω times more likely to be found in one of its Ω disordered
arrangements than in a hypothetical state of complete order.

The entropy of a system is a function of Ω, but it cannot be directly
proportional to it. For consider a system consisting of two unmixed parts,
A and B. The entropy of the whole must equal the sum of the entropies
of the parts; but the thermodynamic probability of the whole, Ω_{whole} is
the *product* $\Omega_A \times \Omega_B$ (as illustrated in Fig. 5.1). Therefore the entropy
must be proportional to log Ω, so that

$$\underset{\substack{\text{disorder of whole}\\\text{system}}}{\log \Omega_{whole}} = \log \Omega_A \Omega_B = \underset{\substack{\text{sum of disorder}\\\text{of parts}}}{\log \Omega_A + \log \Omega_B}$$

It can be shown that the relationship is actually:

$$S = k \ln \Omega \text{ (per molecule)}$$
$$S = R \ln \Omega \text{ (per mole)}$$

(where k = Boltzmann's constant and R = the gas constant).

Figure 5.1 also illustrates the point that while the entropy of a system which has two separate distinguishable parts A and B is the sum $S_A + S_B$, the entropy increases to a greater value if parts A and B are mixed.

<table>
<tr><td>

A_1 A_2
A_2 A_1

Part A: Two particles.
Two arrangements:

$\Omega_A = 2$
$S_A = k \ln 2 = 0.7k$

</td><td>

B_1 B_2 B_3
B_1 B_3 B_2
B_2 B_1 B_3
B_2 B_3 B_1
B_3 B_1 B_2
B_3 B_2 B_1

Part B: Three particles
Six arrangements:

$\Omega_B = 6$
$S_B = k \ln 6 = 1.8k$

</td></tr>
<tr><td>

A_1 A_2 B_1 B_2 B_3
A_1 A_2 B_1 B_3 B_2
A_1 A_2 B_2 B_1 B_3
A_1 A_2 B_2 B_3 B_1
A_1 A_2 B_3 B_1 B_2
A_1 A_2 B_3 B_2 B_1
A_2 A_1 B_1 B_2 B_3
A_2 A_1 B_1 B_3 B_2
A_2 A_1 B_2 B_1 B_3
A_2 A_1 B_2 B_3 B_1
A_2 A_1 B_3 B_1 B_2
A_2 A_1 B_3 B_2 B_1

Whole system (systems A and B taken together). Twelve arrangements:

$\Omega_{total} = 2 \times 6 = 12$
$S_{total} = k \ln 2 + k \ln 6 = 2.5k$

</td><td>

A_1 B_1 B_2 A_2 B_3
A_1 B_1 B_3 B_2 A_2
B_3 A_2 B_2 A_1 B_1
·   ·   ·   ·   ·

Parts A and B mixed. Some of the 120 arrangements:

$\Omega = 120; \quad S = 4.8k$

</td></tr>
</table>

Fig. 5.1   Thermodynamic probabilities of some very simple systems

5.4* Absolute entropies

The total entropy of a system can be regarded as the sum of (i) the configurational entropy, S_{config}, due to disorder of spatial arrangement, and (ii) thermal entropy, S_{therm}, due to disorder of energy distribution.

$$S_{total} = S_{config} + S_{therm}$$

S_{config} is fairly constant for a given phase, but increases greatly with melting or vaporization. S_{therm} increases steadily with temperature, since as T rises not only is there more thermal energy to be distributed, but also more energy quantum levels become accessible. The changes of these component entropies with temperatures are shown in Fig. 5.2.

The configurational entropy change accompanying melting or boiling is easily measured. If the latent heat of vaporization is measured at the

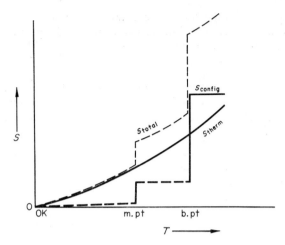

Fig. 5.2   Variation of entropy with temperature

boiling point T_b it is the enthalpy change for a process carried out at equilibrium, for which $\Delta G = 0$. Therefore

$$\Delta G = 0 = \Delta H_{vap} - T_b \Delta S_{vap}$$

$$\Delta S_{vap} = \Delta H_{vap}/T_b$$

(So Trouton's Rule, p. 51, is really a suggestion that the entropy of vaporization of many liquids is roughly constant. This is so because the molal volumes of the vapours are large compared to the molal volumes of the liquids. See §5.11, Question 9.)

The thermal entropy change is found as follows. If a small quantity of heat q is transferred to the system reversibly and at constant pressure, so that the temperature increases by a small increment δT,

$$\Delta G = 0 = \Delta H - T \Delta S_{therm}$$

$$\Delta S_{therm} = \frac{\Delta H}{T} = \frac{q}{T} = \frac{C_p \, \delta T}{T}$$

where C_p is the molar heat capacity at constant pressure. The entropy change for a larger temperature change is obtained by integration:

$$\Delta S_{therm} = \int_{T_1}^{T_2} \frac{C_p \, dT}{T} = \int_{T_1}^{T_2} C_p \, d(\ln T)$$

The integration can be performed if C_p is known as a function of T, or obtained from the area under a graph of C_p against $\ln T$.

The **Third Law of Thermodynamics** states that the entropy of a crystalline solid at 0 K is zero (with a few predictable exceptions). Therefore the absolute entropy S of any substance at a temperature T is the sum of the thermal entropy integrals from 0 to T K, plus any phase-change configurational entropies.

WORKED EXAMPLE

To calculate the absolute entropy of Cl_2 gas at its boiling-point 239 K.

The variation of heat capacity of chlorine up to its boiling-point is shown in Fig. 5.3(a) and ΔS_{therm} is given by the areas under the graph in Fig. 5.3(b).

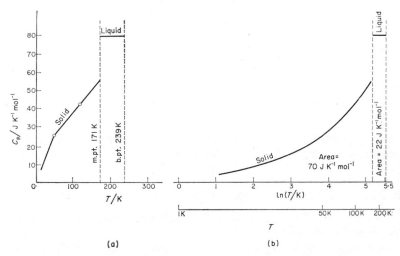

(a)   (b)

Fig. 5.3 Graphs of heat capacity of Cl_2 versus **(a)** T **(b)** $\ln T$

The absolute entropy of Cl_2 (g) at the b.pt. is the sum of the following:

$$\Delta S_{therm} \text{ at m.pt} = \int_0^{171} C_p \, d(\ln T) = 70 \text{ J mol}^{-1} \text{ K}^{-1}$$

$$\Delta S_{config} \text{ (fusion)} = \Delta H_{fus}/171 \text{ K} = 38 \text{ J mol}^{-1} \text{ K}^{-1}$$

$$\Delta S_{therm} \text{ (liquid)} = \int_{171}^{239} C_p \, d(\ln T) = 22 \text{ J mol}^{-1} \text{ K}^{-1}$$

$$\Delta S_{config} \text{ (vaporization)} = \Delta H_{vap}/239 \text{ K} = 85 \text{ J mol}^{-1} \text{ K}^{-1}$$

$$\text{Total} = S_{239}(Cl_2 \text{ (g)}) = 215 \text{ J mol}^{-1} \text{ K}^{-1}$$

By such means the standard absolute entropies at 298 K have been calculated for most common substances, and are listed in tables of data (see Table 5.1).

From these data $\Delta S^{\ominus}$ for any reaction can be calculated, since:

$$\Delta S_r^{\ominus} = \sum S^{\ominus} \text{ (products)} - \sum S^{\ominus} \text{ (reactants)}$$

Table 5.1   Absolute entropies $S^\ominus$ (J mol^{-1}K^{-1}) at 298 K

Gases				Liquids		Solids	
He	126	HCl	187	H_2O	70	C(di)	2.4
Ne	146	H_2O	189	Hg	77	C(gr)	5.7
Xe	170	NH_3	193	Br_2	152	Fe	27
H	115	SO_2	248	C_6H_6	173	Cu	33
H_2	131	O_3	238	CH_3OH	127	S(rh)	32
F_2	203	CH_4	186			Ca	42
Cl_2	223	C_2H_6	230			CuO	43
N_2	192	C_2H_4	219			CaO	40
O	161	C_2H_2	201			$CaCO_3$	93
O_2	205	C_6H_6	269				
CO	198	Br_2	245				
CO_2	214						
NO	211						

For other compounds use $\Delta S_f^\ominus = \dfrac{\Delta H_f^\ominus = \Delta G_f^\ominus}{298}$

Note the low entropy of $H_2(g)$, which is less than three-quarters of the value of other diatomic or polyatomic gases. This is the basis of Rule 2 in §3.6.

WORKED EXAMPLE

To calculate

$$3H_2\,(g) + N_2\,(g) \longrightarrow 2NH_3\,(g); \quad \Delta S_{298}^\ominus = ?$$

Data given: $S_{298}^\ominus = 3 \times 131 \quad 192 \quad\quad 2 \times 193$

$$\therefore \Delta S_r^\ominus = +386 - (393 + 192)$$
$$= -199 \text{ JK}^{-1}\text{g-eqn}^{-1}$$

This agrees with the result obtained from the difference between $\Delta G_f^\ominus$ and $\Delta H_f^\ominus$ of ammonia.

5.5* Reaction entropy changes ΔS_r

(a) It is found that, to a rough approximation, all substances have entropy/temperature curves of the same shape (Fig. 5.4). An important feature is always the large increase in S at the boiling-point, and this means that, for comparable numbers of atoms, the entropy of any gas will almost certainly be greater than that of any liquid or solid at the same temperature. This is the basis of the rule which predicts $\Delta S^\ominus$ positive for any chemical reaction which produces a gas from solids or liquids (§3.6).

(b) The thermal entropy of a substance depends upon the number of ways it has of holding thermal energy, and for a gas molecule the most numerous ways are those for translational kinetic energy. The breaking of a gas molecule into two must increase this number, and result in a positive entropy change. E.g.

$$N_2O_4 \text{ (g)} \longrightarrow 2NO_2 \text{ (g)}; \quad \Delta S^\ominus = +\text{ve}$$

(c) The entropy/temperature curves for different substances are roughly parallel (except at phase changes). $\Delta S_r^\ominus$ is a difference between several $S^\ominus$ values at a given temperature, and since these differences remain fairly constant, $\Delta S_r^\ominus$ will not vary greatly with temperature (Fig. 5.4).

Thus both ΔH and ΔS for a reaction are approximately independent of temperature, as long as the components remain in the phases specified by the equation.

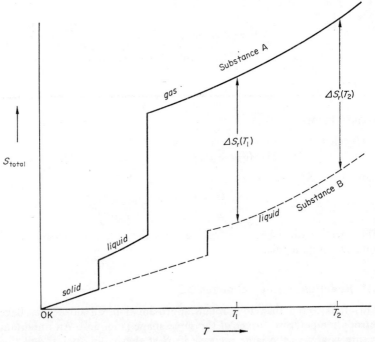

Fig. 5.4 Entropy/temperature curves for two different substances

5.6 Energy and work

Energy shares with the Deity the property of not being observable directly, but only by its effects. Indeed, it requires an act of faith to believe in energy at all, because it is supposed to change from one form to another, from kinetic energy to gravitational potential energy, to electricity or radiation, and yet remain the same.

It is now possible to measure different kinds of energy in the same units (joules) and it is found that quantitatively no energy is lost or gained by a conversion of form. But this does *not* mean that any form of energy can necessarily be completely converted into any other.

All forms of energy can be completely converted into heat, but heat can not be completely converted back. It would be useful to have a label for the forms of energy which can be converted into other forms completely (if practical difficulties such as friction can be overcome). The word *work* serves this purpose. To say that electricity is work means, then, that it can be turned into any other chosen type of energy. Kinetic and potential energy, and radiation, also come into the category of work.

Heat, though, is not work, and cannot be completely converted into work; the restriction is a sound theoretical one (§8.18), and not merely due to the lack of a suitable engine.

Heat is low-grade energy. Its grade depends upon the temperature difference across which it can flow, so the lowest grade of all energy is heat in a system at the same temperature as its surroundings.

The conversion of high-grade energy ('work') into heat can be called the *degradation of energy*. The transfer of heat from a high temperature to a lower is a further degradation.

The degrading of part of the supply of heat energy can result, in a suitable machine, in the up-grading of some of the heat to work. The mathematical theory of heat engines was of enormous historical importance in the development of thermodynamics, and was until recently the usual approach to the subject. However, although it is a discipline of great elegance, it is rather too indirect a route to chemical thermodynamics, and will not be used in this book. The essential point is that the concept of the unavailability of work led to the idea of entropy.

Entropy was first defined as the quality possessed by energy which is not available as work. When high-grade energy is converted into heat, there is a gain in entropy. When high-temperature heat is used to drive an engine, there is an entropy loss associated with the work done, but a greater entropy gain associated with the flow of the rest of the heat to the lower temperature. Under no circumstances can there be an overall loss of entropy in an isolated system.

This idea is behind the various forms of the Second Law of Thermodynamics, two of which are:

The total entropy of the Universe is increasing.
The ultimate fate of all energy is its conversion into heat.

5.7 The efficiency of energy conversion

Ideally, any high-grade energy can be completely converted into work. In practice the conversion may be less than 100% for two different reasons.

(a) Friction or air resistance can hinder complete conversion; but as well-built machines, well lubricated, can reduce friction near to zero; this is not an important *theoretical* hindrance.

(b) The imperfect harnessing of the energy can result in the process 'running away with itself', with the ultimate waste of energy as heat. This is best explained by a mechanical example.

Consider a mass of one kilogram situated ten metres above ground level. It has potential energy of 10 kilogramforce-metres (kgf-m), and it is desired to make this do the work of lifting another load. We can assume that a simple frictionless pulley is available, and the weight is connected up to the load as in Fig. 5.5.

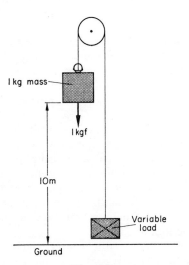

Fig. 5.5

There are three possibilities:

1. If the load is greater than 1 kgf it will not be lifted, and the 10 kgf-m will remain unused.
2. If the load is less than 1 kgf it will be lifted readily though 10 m, but then the falling 1 kg mass will hit the ground. Part of the original 10 kgf-m will now be stored as potential energy of the load, but part will be wasted as heat.
3. If the load is exactly 1 kgf it will balance, and if it is given a start will be raised up slowly, and the whole 10 kgf-m will be harnessed.

In this third case the change takes place in a slow controlled manner. A slight increase in the load would reverse the process, and cause the load to fall again, slowly. For this reason the conditions are said to be *reversible*. The system could be made to revert to its former state without any appreciable extra supply of work.

The less the load is than 1 kgf, the further the conditions are from reversibility, and the less the amount of available energy which is used as work. The limit is when the load is zero, and the weight falls freely; then *all* the energy is degraded to heat. The process is 'unharnessed' and the conditions are totally *irreversible* in the sense that as none of the work is stored, the change cannot be even partly reversed without the supply of external work.

5.8* The disorder of heat

Consider a 1 kg mass of lead on a shelf 3 metres above the ground: it has 3×9.81 J potential energy. The mass slips, gains speed as it falls, then hits the ground and comes to rest. The 3×9.81 J of potential energy is converted into heat, and the lead (and eventually the surroundings) gets a little hotter. This is a perfectly natural process—but what about its reverse? If the lead mass were suddenly to jump 3 metres into the air to land on the shelf, at the same time getting colder by the conversion of 3×9.81 J of heat energy into potential energy, the law of conservation of energy would not be violated. What is it, then, which forbids this reverse change?

An answer might be sought from the Second Law: 'Changes must occur in such a way as to increase the total disorder (entropy) of the universe'. But in what way has the conversion of potential energy to heat increased disorder? Heat is, after all, the kinetic/potential energy of translation, vibration etc of atoms. How does it differ from the kinetic/potential energy of the lead weight?

It differs in the degree of organization of the energy. The falling lead weight had organized kinetic energy, because all the atoms had the same velocity component. When it hit the ground this energy was disorganized into motions in all possible directions, at random speeds.

The lead weight and the surroundings increased their thermal entropy as a result of the fall, and the degradation of work into heat. That is why the second Law forbids the reversal.

The above example was very straightforward because it was a mechanical system. In the case of chemical reactions both internal and external entropy changes must be considered. The increase in the disorder of the surroundings by the degradation of chemical energy into heat is given by $-q/T$, and this will favour exothermic processes. For unharnessed reactions at constant pressure $Q = \Delta H$, so $-\Delta H/T$ measures the external entropy increase.

The other kind of entropy change is that due to the changes of the materials within the system, the 'chemical entropy' ΔS_r.

For a reaction to occur spontaneously the total entropy change must be an increase, but either term might be a decrease if it were more than compensated by the other. Thus the external entropy might decrease (endothermic process) as long as the 'chemical entropy' were to increase. The idea of free-energy is to take account of both terms at once. The introduction of $-\Delta G/T$ as the driving force, measuring the net increase in disorder, gives the familiar relationship:

$$\frac{-\Delta G}{T} \quad = \quad \frac{-\Delta H}{T} \quad + \quad \Delta S$$

| net move towards disorder (="driving force") | increase in disorder of surroundings by heat | increase in disorder within the closed system |

5.9 Heat transfer accompanying maximum work

Unharnessed reactions (recapitulation)

In Chapter 2 the following equations were used, in discussing the First Law:

$$\Delta U = W + Q \qquad\qquad 1$$

$$\Delta U = W_{\text{opt}} + W_{\text{obl}} + Q \qquad\qquad 2$$

ΔU is the change in internal energy; W is the work (optional or obligatory) done by the system during the change; Q is the heat transferred per gram-equation. For all three terms, a negative sign represents energy transferred out of the system.

For an adiabatic change ($Q = 0$), unharnessed ($W_{\text{opt}} = 0$), and at constant volume ($P\,\Delta V = -W_{\text{obl}} = 0$) it follows that $\Delta U = 0$.

For an isothermal change, unharnessed and at constant volume, $\Delta U = Q_{\text{V}}$. That is, the heat of reaction at constant volume equals the total internal energy change ΔU (sometimes alternatively symbolized ΔE).

For *constant pressure* conditions (the most usual) the obligatory work equals the applied external pressure multiplied by the volume change:

$$-W_{\text{obl}} = P_{\text{ext}}\,\Delta V \qquad\qquad 3$$

(where the positive ΔV represents an expansion, so that work is done *by* the system, hence $-W$).

Substituting this into **2** gives:

$$\Delta U + P_{\text{ext}}\,\Delta V = Q + W_{\text{opt}} \qquad\qquad 4$$

Enthalpy is defined as $U + PV$, and so, for constant P_{ext}:

$$\Delta U + P_{\text{ext}}\,\Delta V \equiv \Delta H \qquad\qquad 5$$

This gives:

$$\Delta H = Q + W_{\text{opt}} \qquad\qquad 6$$

And so for an unharnessed reaction at constant pressure:

$$\Delta H = Q_{\text{p}} \qquad\qquad 7$$

Harnessed reactions

If the reaction takes place in an apparatus designed to obtain work from it, $W_{\text{opt}} \neq 0$. ΔH is constant for a given reaction, but W_{opt} and Q can vary according to the manner in which it is carried out, as long as they satisfy **6**. The heat transferred out is *less than* ΔH for a harnessed reaction, by the amount of work:

$$Q = \Delta H - W_{\text{opt}} \qquad\qquad 8$$

The value of W_{opt} varies with the efficiency of the harnessing, and can range from zero to a definite maximum. The maximum transfer of work is not achieved in practice, because it comes about only under *reversible conditions*, when the reaction is exactly balanced by an opposing force (§5.7). But this opposing force can be measured (e.g. $E^{\ominus}$ for a cell) and so the maximum reversible work W_{rev} can be measured. Under these conditions the heat transferred out $-Q_{rev}$ is a minimum and the reaction is at its most endothermic.

Under reversible conditions the net increase in the disorder of the universe is zero (§5.8) and so the increase the external entropy $-Q_{rev}/T$ will exactly balance the decrease in 'chemical entropy' $-\Delta S$.

$$\therefore \; Q_{rev} = T \Delta S \qquad\qquad 9$$

$T \Delta S$ is that part of the enthalpy which *must* be transferred out as heat even when maximum work is being demanded, so it is sometimes known as the 'unavailable energy'.

$$\Delta G = \Delta H - T \Delta S$$
$$= \Delta H - Q_{rev}$$
$$\Delta G = W_{rev} \qquad\qquad 10$$

The maximum available work of the reaction equals the free-energy change.

5.10 ΔG as the criterion of feasibility

This important idea can perhaps bear repetition. A change will only occur if it causes an increase in the entropy of the universe. This increase can be the net sum of (1) the change within the system and (2) the change in the surroundings. Within the system the disorder increase is measured by $+\Delta S$; in the surroundings it is measured by $-Q/T$, which is equal to $-\Delta H/T$ for an unharnessed process at constant pressure. These two are contained in the composite quantity ΔG:

$$\frac{-\Delta H}{T} + \Delta S = \frac{-\Delta G}{T}$$

which rearranges to:

$$\Delta G = \Delta H - T \Delta S$$

As the efficiency of the harnessing of the work of reaction is made more efficient, the net gain of entropy is reduced. The limit is when, under reversible conditions, maximum work is transferred and the net change of entropy is zero. Then $W_{rev} = \Delta G$ as shown in the previous section.

So the free-energy change ΔG measures that part of the energy which *could* be transferred as work, but which in a spontaneous unharnessed reaction is actually degraded to heat. Therefore ΔG is often regarded as the driving-force of a reaction (as in Chapter 3), but this can lead to difficulties in the rare case of a reaction for which ΔH and $\Delta S^{\ominus}$ are not of the same sign (§7.5). More strictly, as shown in §5.8, the driving-force is $\Delta G/T$, which measures the maximum net disorder of the universe which can result from the process.

5.11 Exercises

1. (a) Explain the following terms carefully: system, surroundings, closed system, isolated system, open system.

(b) State the First and Second Laws of Thermodynamics in forms useful to chemists. For which of the three systems mentioned in (a) are these laws obeyed?

2. Use the general ideas of the two laws to explain the following:

(a) When a liquid evaporates into a vacuum the vapour and remaining liquid become cooler.

(b) The reaction $2H_2 + O_2 \rightarrow 2H_2O$ is spontaneous even though it results in a decrease in the entropy of the system.

(c) When a cloud rises to a region of lower pressure it cools; this cooling causes rain. (A cloud consists of minute water droplets in water-saturated air. It may be considered as an isolated system.)

3. Use absolute entropies from Table 5.1 to calculate $\Delta S_r^{\ominus}$ for the following reactions and hence find $\Delta G_r^{\ominus}$ at 300 K and 1200 K.

  (i) $CaCO_3$ (s) $\longrightarrow$ CaO (s)$+CO_2$ (g); $\Delta H = +178$ kJ
  (ii) C_2H_4 (g)$+H_2$ (g) $\longrightarrow$ C_2H_6 (g); $\Delta H = -137$ kJ
  (iii) $3C_2H_2$ (g) $\longrightarrow$ C_6H_6 (l); $\Delta H = -629$ kJ

4. 'A plant is a machine for decreasing entropy.' Discuss.

5.   Explain the term 'degradation of energy'.

Is it possible for heat energy to do work? If so, how is this reconciled with the principle that energy tends to change to a degraded form?

6. Consider the efficiency of conversion of the potential energy of a loaded spring-operated gun into the kinetic energy of projectiles of various masses. The mass of the spring and moving parts is *not* negligible: it is equivalent to a mass m at the moving end of the spring. What proportion of the energy is transferred to projectiles of masses $\frac{1}{2}m$, m, $2m$, $3m$? (The spring accelerates both the projectile and its own effective mass to a certain velocity; then the spring is stopped while the projectile travels on.)

Discuss the results in terms of 'reversible' and 'irreversible' processes.

7. The potential energy of compression of a given mass of an ideal gas is equal to pressure × volume. Thus the potential energy of one mole of nitrogen at STP will be 22.4 litre × 1 atm = 22.4 litre-atm; while the

potential energy of 1 mole N_2 at 11.2 atm pressure (and hence a volume of 2 litres) is also 22.4 litres-atm at 0°C.

(a) Is the potential energy of compression of these two samples of nitrogen equal in grade? If not, which is the higher grade?

(b) Which sample would be more effective in accelerating a missile (i) under normal atmospheric conditions, and (ii) in the vacuum of inter-planetary space?

(c) Discuss the 'grade' of the potential energy of the two gas samples in terms of 'degree of organization'.

(d) Consider 2 litres of N_2 at 11.2 atm changing to 22.4 litres at 1 atm, assuming ideal-gas behaviour.

(i) Under what conditions would the process be entirely irreversible? What transfer of heat would accompany such a change?

(ii) Is it possible that the process could be used to do work? If so, what heat change would there be?

(iii) Is it likely that the reverse process could do work?

8.* Consider a gas expending isothermally against a load almost equal to its own pressure. The lifting of the load is being done reversibly, so the work done is w_{rev}. The work done in pushing a pressure p through a small volume increase δV is $p \, \delta V$. What is the maximum reversible work which can be obtained from the expansion of an ideal gas from $p_1 V_1$ to $p_2 V_2$?

Show that for this process $\Delta G = -RT \ln (p_1/p_2)$.

9.* Consider the evaporation of one mole of a liquid to a gas at 1 atm pressure. If the thermodynamic probabilities Ω_l and Ω_g of the two states are simply proportional to their volumes, calculate the entropy change for the evaporation of one mole of a liquid of molecular weight M_r, density ρ and boiling point T_b. Then, for the particular case of methane (CH_4, $T_b = 112$ K, $\rho = 0.8 \, \text{g cm}^{-3}$) calculate ΔS_{vap} and ΔH_{vap} from first principles, and compare with the values in Table 4.2.

Discuss Trouton's Rule in the light of your calculations.

10.* Re-arrange the equation $\Delta G = \Delta H - T \Delta S$ to the form which corresponds most closely with the statement:

'The total internal energy decrease (at constant pressure) must equal the sum of the available energy (which can be converted to work) and the unavailable energy (which _must_ be converted to heat).'

Also explain why some of the total energy is unavailable; and why it is sometimes possible for the maximum available energy to _exceed_ the total internal energy decrease.

11. PRACTICAL INVESTIGATION

In a boiling tube take about 5 cm³ water and 10 g sodium thiosulphate crystals. Warm the mixture until the crystals have completely dissolved, then cool to about 15°C. The solution will not usually crystallize, and is now supersaturated. With a thermometer in the liquid, add one small crystal of the salt: this will 'seed' the solution, and bring about rapid crystallization. Note the temperature change.

Problem: This crystallization might have come about spontaneously in time (particularly with other, less stable supersaturated solutions) even in a sealed and thermally insulated vessel. Yet the entropy of the crystals is probably lower than that of the solution. A supercooled pure liquid would undoubtedly lose entropy during spontaneous 'irreversible' solidi-fication. Explain why these phenomena do not violate the Second Law.

6 Reaction rate

6.1 Introduction

The question 'Will a certain chemical reaction occur?' must be considered in two parts: (1) 'Haw far will it go before reaching equilibrium?' and (2) 'How fast will it go?' The properties of reactants and products lead to the free-energy change for the reaction, and this may be used to find whether the reaction is forbidden or allowed by energetics. Chapters 5 has shown that a reaction is feasible as long as it is capable of doing work.

But the second question, 'How fast?', is *not* answered by energetics—or at least, not by the energetics of reactants or products alone.

Chemical kinetics, as the study of reaction rates is called, leads to a knowledge of reaction pathways, and is an important subject in its own right. Therefore there is no room in this book for more than a brief summary of the simpler aspects, in preparation for a look at the area in which energetics and kinetics overlap—the theory of energy of activation.

6.2 The dependence of reaction rate upon concentration

Rate of reaction can be defined in terms of the rate of change of the amount of any reactant or product, as follows:

$$\text{Rate}_n = \frac{1}{\nu_B} \frac{dn_B}{dt}$$

where n_B = the amount of substance B

dn_B = change in n_B in time interval dt (note: dn_B is negative if B is a reactant)

ν_B = stoichiometric coefficient of B in the equation (negative if B is a reactant).

For a system of constant volume, $n_B \propto [B]$. So a second definition of rate is possible, and commonly used for reactions in solution:

$$\text{Rate}_c = \frac{1}{\nu_B} \frac{d[B]}{dt}$$

where $[B]$ = the concentration of B. For example, in the reaction:

$$PCl_5 + 4H_2O \longrightarrow H_3PO_4 + 5HCl$$

$$\text{Rate}_c = \frac{d[H_3PO_4]}{dt} = \frac{1}{5} \frac{d[HCl]}{dt} = -\frac{1}{4} \frac{d[H_2O]}{dt}$$

In practice the rate of reaction is found either by observing the rate of change of some physical property such as volume, refractive index, or light absorption, or by frequent withdrawals of small samples to be analysed chemically.

It is helpful to distinguish between *homogeneous* reactions, in which all the reactants are miscible, and *heterogeneous* reactions, in which the reactants are in different phases and cannot mix completely. Many of the familiar slow reactions are heterogeneous, and the rate depends upon the area of contact, the roughness of the surface, the state of division, and the efficiency of stirring.

Reaction rates are almost always a function of concentration (for gases, pressure). The exact form of the dependence will vary from one reaction to another, but it can usually be expressed as a direct proportionality between rate and the product of the concentrations of the reactants, each raised to the power of a small integer. Thus, for the general reaction

$$\nu_A A + \nu_B B + \cdots \longrightarrow \nu_Y Y + \nu_Z Z$$
$$\text{Rate} = k[A]^\alpha [B]^\beta \cdots$$

where [A] represents the effective concentration of A, etc. The exponents α, β are *not* necessarily equal to the coefficients ν_A, $\nu_B \ldots$ from the equation. The value of α is often referred to as the *order* of reaction with respect to A, and will often be 1 or 2, and more rarely 0, 3 or a fraction. The sum of all the exponents $\alpha + \beta +$ in the rate equation is known as the overall order. The constant of proportionality k is called the *rate constant*.

ILLUSTRATION

$$2I^- + AsO_4^{3-} + 2H^+ \longrightarrow AsO_3^{3-} + I_2 + H_2O$$

For this reaction the rate equation, obtained by timing the appearance of a certain concentration of I_2 for various initial reagent concentrations, is (over a certain pH range):

$$\frac{d[I_2]}{dt} = k[I^-][AsO_4^{3-}][H^+]$$

Thus the reaction is first-order for each reactant individually (despite the different stoichiometric coefficients) and third order overall. The rate is measured in units of mol litre^{-1} s^{-1}, and the concentrations are in mol litre^{-1}, so the units of the third-order rate constant are litre^2 mol^{-2} s^{-1}.

Processing experimental results

A well-known example of a simple reaction suitable for experimental investigation is the saponification of an ester, e.g.

$$CH_3COOC_2H_5 + OH^- \longrightarrow CH_3COO^- + C_2H_5OH$$

This can be followed by periodic sampling, and estimation of residual OH^- by back-titration against standard acid. Initially the concentrations of ester and alkali are equimolar, and this remains so while the reaction proceeds. Temperature is kept constant.

Typical results are as follows:

time/(min)	4	7	10	13	16	19	22	25	28	31
$[OH^-]$/(cm³ acid)	36.0	29.1	25.1	21.7	19.0	16.8	15.0	13.6	12.6	12.0

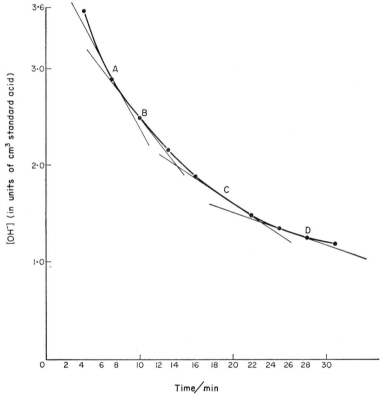

Fig. 6.1

In Fig. 6.1 these results are plotted graphically, and the curve shows the steady slowing-up of the reaction as the reactants are used up. Four tangents to the curve are shown, since the slope of the curve gives the rate of reaction $-d[OH^-]/dt$ (in arbitrary units).

Table 6.1 and Fig. 6.2 show how the rate of reaction (the slope from Fig. 6.1) varies with time and with $[OH^-]$.

The graph in Fig. 6.2(a) shows that the rate falls off rapidly with time; but so does $[OH^-]$. Fig. 6.2(b) shows that the rate decreases more rapidly than $[OH^-]$, and is in fact proportional to $[OH^-]^2$ (Fig. 6.2(c)).

Table 6.1

time/(min)	6.6	10.0	18.6	28.0
rate	1.76	1.22	0.60	0.32
$[OH^-]$	29.5	25.0	17.0	12.6
$[OH^-]^2$	870	625	290	160

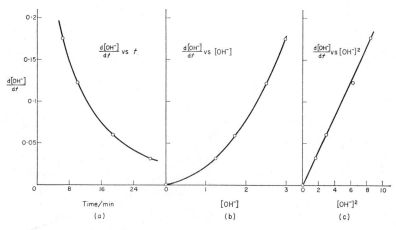

Fig. 6.2

Thus in this experiment:

$$\text{Rate} = k[OH^-]^2$$

i.e. a second-order reaction.

Since it was ensured that $[OH^-] = [CH_3COOC_2H_5]$, this agrees with the more general rate equation:

$$\text{Rate} = k[OH^-][CH_3COOC_2H_5]$$

6.3 Order and molecularity

The number of particles which must meet in order for a given reaction step to take place is known as the *molecularity* of that step. A few processes take place in a single step; for example, natural radioactivite disintegrations are unimolecular and first-order:

$$^{226}_{88}\text{Ra} \longrightarrow {}^{222}_{86}\text{Rn} + {}^{4}_{2}\text{He}$$

The great majority of reactions are complex, however, and occur as a sequence of elementary reaction steps. Then the rate of reaction is often determined by the slowest of these, known as the rate-determining step. The order of reaction will generally be equal to the molecularity of the slowest step, and *not* to the number of particles on the left-hand side of the equation. Remember that the order is found experimentally, while the molecularity is a feature of a step in a hypothetical reaction pathway.

The reaction between hydrogen and iodine obeys a second-order rate law:

$$\text{Rate} = \tfrac{1}{2} \cdot \frac{d[HI]}{dt} = k[I_2][H_2]$$

and was for a long time thought to occur as a single bimolecular step:

$$I_2\,(g) + H_2\,(g) \longrightarrow 2HI\,(g).$$

However it has now been shown (Sullivan, 1967)† that the reaction is essentially a termolecular combination of $H_2 + 2I$. So

$$\tfrac{1}{2} \cdot \frac{d[HI]}{dt} = k[H_2][I]^2,$$

but since the concentration of iodine atoms is determined by the equilibrium:

$$I + I + M \rightleftharpoons I_2 + M; \qquad [I]^2 = K_{eq}[I_2]$$

the overall rate law is the same for both pathways.

6.4 Exercises

1. A quantity of acetic anhydride, initially 0.325 mole, was reacted with water, and the quantity of anhydride consumed at various times was determined volumetrically:

time/s	0	100	400	550	800
amount consumed/mol	0	0.073	0.223	0.252	0.285

By using the graphical method shown in §6.2, find the order of reaction and the rate constant (with units).

† John H. Sullivan, *J. Chem. Phys.* **46** (1) 73–9. In the investigation iodine atoms were generated photochemically, but the previous results at high temperatures were also considered. The rate-determining step may be either:

$$H_2 + 2I \longrightarrow 2HI$$

or the second of the two steps:

$$H_2 + I + M \longrightarrow H_2I + M$$
$$H_2I + I \longrightarrow 2HI$$

2. Sodium methoxide reacts with bromoethane (in ethanol solution) thus:

$$C_2H_5Br + CH_3O^-Na^+ \longrightarrow C_2H_5OCH_3 + Na^+Br^-$$

The reaction obeys a second-order rate equation. The extent of reaction may be followed by sampling and titration against standard acid (the methoxide acts as an alkali). Draw a sketch graph of rate (dv/dt) against v (where $v =$ titre) for the two cases: (i) when initial concentrations were equimolar; (ii) when the bromoethane was in large excess.

3. The gas phosphine decomposes into its elements on heating:

$$2PH_3 \text{ (g)} \longrightarrow 2P \text{ (g)} + 3H_2 \text{ (g)}$$

Design an apparatus for measuring the rate of reaction at 650 K (377°C). It is found that the time taken for one-tenth of the phosphine to decompose is the same, whatever the initial pressure of phosphine. What can you deduce regarding (a) the order, (b) the molecularity of the reaction?

It has been suggested (Hinshelwood) that the reaction is heterogeneous What does this mean in this case, and how could the theory be tested?

6.5 Variation of reaction velocity with temperature

An increase in temperature almost always increases the rate of reaction, often very greatly for quite a small rise. It is a matter of common experience that if a reaction is very slow in the cold, warming is often sufficient to get it going (refer to Chapter 1, *Type D*).

In the case of reversible reactions, the forward and backward rate are both increased (though not equally) by a rise in temperature, and so equilibrium is reached more rapidly. The increase in the rate of attainment of equilibrium must be clearly distinguished from the change in the position of an equilibrium.

EXERCISE

In terms of the simple theory that chemical reactions occur only during collisions, write down some ways in which increased temperatures might affect reaction rates.

6.6 Practical introduction

Apparatus

    50 cm³ measuring cylinder
    conical flask
    burette
    stopclock
    thermometer (0–100°C)
    2 M hydrochloric acid (in the burette)
    1% sodium thiosulphate solution

Procedure

Measure out 50 cm³ 1% thiosulphate solution into the conical flask and warm it gently to a little over 30°C. Run 5 cm³ 2 M hydrochloric acid into the test-tube, then add it to the flask, at the same time starting the clock.

Swirl the mixture, and record its temperature. Place the flask over a distinctive pencil mark on a sheet of white paper, and watch for the moment when the mark becomes obscured. The reaction is:

$$S_2O_3^{2-} (aq) + 2H^+ (aq) \longrightarrow H_2O\ (l) + SO_2\ (aq) + S\ (s)$$

The suspension of sulphur grows steadily thicker until, at a fairly definite concentration, it hides the pencil mark.

Stop the clock, and record the time (t seconds) along with the initial temperature of the mixture.

Repeat the experiment at the same initial temperature to check on its reproducibility. Then repeat at different temperatures: 40°C, 50°C, 20°C, 60°C, 25°C. Tabulate the results thus:

Initial temperature $\theta/(°C)$ T/K	time t/s	$\frac{s}{t} \times 10^3\ (= k)$

Discussion

The time taken for the mark to disappear measured in each case the time for the reaction to proceed to the same arbitrary point. Therefore the reciprocal of this time, $1/t$, is in each case proportional to the average velocity of the reaction; and further, as the concentrations were constant, $1/t$ is proportional to the velocity constant (regardless of the order of reaction).

As $1/t$ is a small number, it is more convenient to take $1/t \times 10^3$ as k, the velocity constant in arbitrary units.

Treatment of results

(a) Plot a graph to show the variation of k with temperature. For many reactions the curve is approximately exponential (Fig. 6.3(a)).

(b) Find out from your graph the temperature rises which cause: (i) a 50% increase in reaction rate, and (ii) a doubling of reaction rate, over various sections of the curve. Are these values constant? They would be if the curve were truly exponential, i.e. if $k \propto e^T$ and $\log k = T + \text{const.}$

(c) Tabulate: | θ in (°C) | T in K | $\frac{1}{T} \times 10^3$ | t | $k \left(= \frac{t}{1} \times 10^3\right)$ | $\log_{10} k$ |

(d) Plot a graph of $\log k$ versus T. This will probably appear to be a straight line, within the limits of the errors of the experiment (Fig. 6.3(b)).

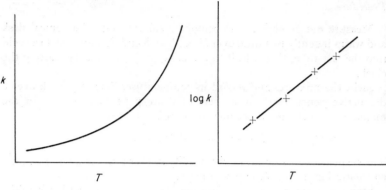

Fig. 6.3

However, precise work over greater temperature ranges has shown that for most reactions this line is a slight curve, and it is a graph of $\log k$ against the *reciprocal* of the absolute temperature that gives a straight line.

(e) Plot $\log k$ versus $1/T \times 10^3$. Note that the slope is negative. In §6.7 it will be shown that from this graph the 'energy of activation' of the reaction can be obtained.

6.7 The Arrhenius equation

$$k = A\,\mathrm{e}^{-E_a/RT}$$

The rate constant (k) of most reactions varies with temperature according to this equation proposed by Arrhenius, in which E_a is a constant for the reaction, known as the 'energy of activation'; R is the gas constant, T the absolute temperature, and A another constant for the reaction. Sometimes $\Delta H^{\ddagger}$, symbolizing enthalpy of activation, replaces E_a.

These factors are discussed in turn in later sections. Factor A is almost independent of temperature, and the change in rate with temperature change is almost entirely due to the second term.

Taking logarithms:

$$\ln k = \ln A - E_a/RT$$

$$\log k = \text{const} - \frac{E_a}{2.303\,RT}$$

So a graph of $\log k$ versus $1/T$ is a straight line of slope $-E_a/2.30R$.

6.8 Exercises

1. A reaction **1** has an energy of activation which is 4 kJ greater than that

of reaction **2**, although the constant A is the same. Which reaction is the faster at 25°C, and by how much?

2. Two reactions of a similar kind have the same value for A, but the energy of activation of one reaction is double that of the other. Can you find the relative rate constants at 0°C?

3. For the reaction:

$$2HI \longrightarrow H_2 + I_2 \text{ (g)}, \qquad \text{Rate} = k(p_{HI})^2$$
$$k = 3.5 \times 10^{-7} \text{ atm}^{-1} \text{ s}^{-1} \text{ at 560 K}$$
$$1.4 \times 10^{-5} \text{ atm}^{-1} \text{ s}^{-1} \text{ at 620 K}$$

Calculate the energy of activation.

6.9 Distribution of molecular energies

The molecules of gases and liquids are in constant random motion, resulting in collisions of various degrees of violence. The great majority of such collisions cause no change in the molecules, and the total momentum and kinetic energy are both conserved ('perfectly elastic collisions'). Occasionally, however, an inelastic collision will occur, resulting in an activated molecule—either an ordinary molecule with an abnormally high internal energy, or a new, unstable complex. Activated molecules are believed to be essential intermediates in chemical reaction, so the rate of reaction is closely tied to their rate of formation.

The frequency and force of collisions can be calculated quite accurately for gases; the situation is more complicated for liquids, but the conclusions are roughly the same.

An understanding of temperature is important to the argument. The temperature of matter is a measure of the average energy in each thermal energy level. In crystalline solids the thermal energy is oscillational; in liquids the molecules have translational energy, and potential energy as they approach their neighbours, and rotational energy; there is constant interplay between the various kinds. Gases have predominantly translational and rotational energy. Two material systems have the same temperature when their average thermal energies are equal.

Consider the translational kinetic energy of gas molecules: if a molecule of mass m is moving with a speed u, its kinetic energy is equal to $\frac{1}{2}mu^2$, while its momentum is mu. The sum of the kinetic energies of two molecules is unchanged by their collision, though it will be differently distributed between them. Therefore the total kinetic energy of one mole of gas (E_K) is constant for any given temperature, regardless of the nature of the molecules. Heavier molecules will move more slowly than light ones; e.g. the mean (RMS) speed of hydrogen molecules will be four times that of oxygen at the same temperature, since $\frac{1}{2}mu^2$ is the same for each, but the molecular weights are 2:32. This fact can easily be demonstrated by diffusion and effusion experiments, and is the basis of Graham's Law.

The mean kinetic energy E_K is directly proportional to the absolute temperature T. But since random collisions cause a wide range of velocities at any given temperature, there are always present molecules with velocities far less (right down to zero) and far greater than the mean. Hence there is also a widespread of individual kinetic energies, even though the mean value is constant.

The spread of energies is given by Maxwell's Distribution Law, as shown graphically in Fig. 6.4. It can be shown that the fraction of molecules with energies greater than a given value E is inversely exponential, and equal to $e^{-E/RT}$.

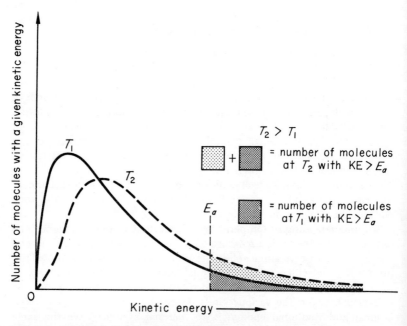

Fig. 6.4 Maxwell–Boltzmann distribution of energies of molecules, at two different temperatures

6.10 Energy of activation

The variation of the rate of constant with temperature has been interpreted by means of the collision theory of Arrhenius and Lindemann. It is supposed that there is a minimum kinetic energy (KE) which molecules must have in order to react: it is known as the activation energy, E_a. Particles which collide with an average of less than this energy merely bounce off unchanged. For gas reactions the theory can be worked out precisely, since the fraction of molecules with kinetic energy greater than E_a is, by the Maxwell–Boltzmann Law, $\exp\left(-E_a/RT\right)$. Therefore if k is the rate constant (§6.2) for a reaction,

$$k = A \exp\left(-E_a/RT\right)$$

which is the equation introduced in §6.7.

Figure 6.4 shows that most molecules have kinetic energies around the mean value; but there is an appreciable number with three or four times this value. Occasionally collisions can give molecules exceptionally high speeds, and since $KE = \frac{1}{2}mu^2$, these will have exceptionally high energy, and be capable of chemical reaction.

6.11 The activated complex

The concept of activation energy explains why 'thermodynamically favoured' reactions are slow, even infinitely slow, at low temperatures. It is assumed that in the course of the reaction the atoms must pass through a temporary, unstable arrangement, half-way between reactant and product, known as the 'activated complex'. The energy of activation is the energy which is absorbed in the formation of this complex. This energy is less than that needed to break completely the bonds which are eventually broken, so it seems that the new bonds start to form while the old ones are still partially operating.

Unless the colliding molecules have the thermal energy needed for the formation of the activated complex, they cannot react. If, however, they succeed in reacting, the activation energy absorbed in the formation of the complex is released again when the complex breaks down into the products of reaction. It appears as KE of the products, with the addition (for exothermic reactions) or subtraction (endothermic) of the enthalpy of reaction. This can be represented diagrammatically, as in Fig. 6.5.

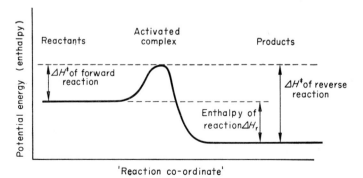

Fig. 6.5   Energy pathway for an exothermic reaction step

6.12 The temperature-independent factor (A)

The frequency of collisions between gas molecules can be calculated for any given temperature and pressure, so the probability of a collision of two reactant molecules can be known exactly. The number of collisions per second is given the symbol Z.

If we define 'sufficiently energetic collisions' as those in which the molecules have, between them, the activation energy, then there will be $Z \exp(-E_a/RT)$ sufficiently energetic collisions per second. If every sufficiently energetic collisions led to reaction, then in a system containing one mole of each reactant, the velocity would be equal to $Z \exp(-E_a/RT)$ g-equation s^{-1}. In fact it rarely is. The equation is, in general,

$$k = PZ \exp(-E_a/RT),$$

where the factor P can be as low as 10^{-6}.

It seems, therefore, that collisions can be very inefficient, even when the activation energy is available. In some cases the factor P can be interpreted as a 'steric factor', representing the need for collisions to occur in a certain way, perhaps with particular atoms of the molecules meeting in a more or less precise manner. For example the reaction $2NOCl \rightarrow 2NO + Cl_2$ *may*† proceed via an activated complex as follows:

If so, collisions of the type

would be ineffective.

The steric factor P can also be considered as representing the decrease of entropy accompanying the formation of the complex intermediate. If $\Delta S^{\ddagger}$ denotes 'entropy of activation', then $P = \exp(\Delta S^{\ddagger}/R)$. Note that, unlike the exponential term for the enthalpy of activation, this term is independent of temperature. Also, since $\Delta S^{\ddagger}$ is normally negative, $P < 1$.

So the Arrhenius equation can be written:

$$\text{Rate constant } k = Z \exp(\Delta S^{\ddagger}/R) \exp(-\Delta H^{\ddagger}/RT)$$
$$= Z \exp(T\Delta S^{\ddagger} - \Delta H^{\ddagger})/RT$$
$$= Z \exp(-\Delta G^{\ddagger}/RT)$$

† $NO + NOCl_2$ has been postulated as an intermediate.

where $\Delta G^{\ddagger}$ is the free-energy of activation, and Z the collision frequency.

The collision frequency is only slightly dependent upon temperature (it can be shown that $Z \propto T^{1/2}$). At moderate temperatures a 10 K rise causes Z to increase by less than 2%, whereas reaction rate can double. So the factor A is virtually independent of T, and the change of rate is almost entirely due to the activation enthalpy requirements.

6.13* The principle of micro-reversibility

(This section may profitably be re-read after Chapter 7.)

If we consider a chemical system from the point of view of individual colliding molecules (rather than bulk concentrations) we see that all possible collisions are occurring to some extent, with a wide range of collision force. Therefore all reactions are possible; but because of the different free-energy of activation requirements, not all equally probable. No system is static at any temperature above 0 K, but the rate of change is proportional to $e^{-1/T}$. If the temperature is high enough for reactions to proceed reasonably quickly, the system will change in the direction for which ΔG is negative. However, as soon as any product molecules have been formed, the reverse reaction becomes a possibility.

The energy diagram for a thermodynamically-favoured reaction will be like Figure 6.6. (The enthalpy diagram for an exothermic reaction is similar in form; see Fig. 6.5.) $\Delta G_1^{\ddagger}$ is the free-energy of activation of the forward reaction, and is lower than $\Delta G_2^{\ddagger}$, for the reverse reaction, since $\Delta G_2^{\ddagger} = \Delta G_1^{\ddagger} + \Delta G_r^{\ominus}$. The more negative the free-energy of reaction $(\Delta G_r^{\ominus})$ is, the greater is the difference between $\Delta G_2^{\ddagger}$ and $\Delta G_1^{\ddagger}$, and the less likely to succeed are the reverse-reaction collisions.

A postulate of the theory is that when a reaction has come to equilibrium, every reaction step is itself at equilibrium. An elementary reaction step occurs during a single collision of molecules, so the rate equations for both forward and reverse reactions have orders equal to the molecularities.

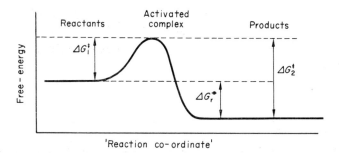

Fig. 6.6   Free-energy pathway for an exergonic reaction step

For the reaction step:

$$aA + bB \rightleftharpoons yY + zZ$$

the forward rate $= k_1[A]^a[B]^b$

and   the reverse rate $= k_{-1}[Y]^y[Z]^z$

where a, b etc. are the stoichiometric coefficients from the equation. (Rate laws for overall reaction rates, measured away from equilibrium, can *not* usually be derived from the equation in this way, because they are dependent upon the rate-determining step.)

At equilibrium the forward and reverse rates must be equal for every step. So:

$$k_1[A]^a[B]^b = k_2[Y]^y[Z]^z$$

$$\frac{[Y]^y[Z]^z}{[A]^a[B]^b} = \frac{k_1}{k_{-1}} = K_{eq}, \text{ the equilibrium constant.}$$

If this is done for every reaction step in the sequence which makes up the overall reaction, a set of equilibrium constants is obtained, each being a function of the concentrations of the species involved. If these elementary-step equilibrium constants are multiplied together, an overall equilibrium constant is obtained, and most of the concentration terms cancel out, leaving only those of the initial reagents and the final products. (The student should satisfy himself that this is so.)

Therefore this derivation of the equilibrium constant from the equality of forward and reverse rates is valid if it is remembered that k_1 and k_{-1} are not the measurable macro-rate constants.

By replacing rate constants by the Arrhenius expressions as developed in §6.12, one can derive the relationship between the equilibrium constant and the standard free-energy of reaction $\Delta G_r^{\ominus}$.

$$k = A \exp\left(-E_a/RT\right) = Z \exp\left(\Delta S^{\ddagger}/R\right) \exp\left(-\Delta H^{\ddagger}/RT\right)$$
$$= Z \exp\left(-\Delta G^{\ddagger}/RT\right)$$

Let subscripts 1 and -1 indicate forward and backward reaction steps:

$$K_{eq} = \frac{k_1}{k_{-1}} = \frac{Z \exp\left(-\Delta G_1^{\ddagger}/RT\right)}{Z \exp\left(-\Delta G_{-1}^{\ddagger}/RT\right)} = \exp\left(\frac{\Delta G_{-1}^{\ddagger} - \Delta G_1^{\ddagger}}{RT}\right)$$
$$= \exp\left(-\Delta G_r^{\ominus}/RT\right)$$

Taking logs and rearranging:

$$-\Delta G_r^{\ominus} = RT \ln K_{eq}$$

6.14 Catalysis

Catalysis is the increasing of the rate constant of a reaction, at constant temperature, by the presence of materials which are not consumed by the reaction. Often a catalyst will bring about a reaction that would not otherwise have occurred to any measurable extent: organic chemistry can provide many important examples of this. The working of catalysts is not well understood, and there must be a number of very different mechanisms. However, the following points, connected with energetics, are common to most catalysed reactions:

(1) The catalyst cannot alter the stoichiometry of the reaction; the total, final yield of product will be unaffected in the case of a single reaction. However, a catalyst may disturb the balance between various competing reactions, and lead to different predominant products.

(2) The catalyst cannot alter the enthalpy or free-energy changes.

(3) Since $\Delta G_r^{\ominus}$ is unchanged, it follows that the equilibrium constant is also unchanged. The reaction may reach equilibrium sooner, but it will be the same equilibrium.

(4) The catalyst alters forward and backward rates to precisely the same extent. So the principle of micro-reversibility also leads to point 3.

(5) Catalysts change the rate of reaction by providing an alternative reaction pathway, with a lower energy of activation (Fig. 6.7).

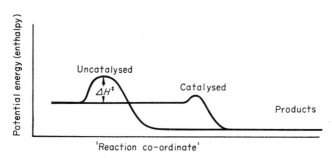

Fig. 6.7   Reaction diagram for catalysed and uncatalysed pathways

6.15 Exercises

1. Trace Fig. 6.4 accurately, and measure the proportion of the shaded area to the total area under the curve, for both temperatures. This can be done either by copying the curves on to graph paper, and counting the squares; or by copying on to stiff paper, followed by the cutting out and weighing of the areas.

Then use your results for T_1, which is 300 K, to calculate the value of the enthalpy of activation, E_a, by means of the Maxwell–Boltzmann Law.

How many times faster will reaction be at T_2 compared to T_1? From this and your result for E_a, calculate what temperature T_2 must be.

2. (a) It is often stated that some reactions double in rate for a 10 K rise at room temperature. For what enthalpy of activation is this true?

4—C.E.

(b) The reaction: $O_3 + NO \rightarrow O_2 + NO_2$ has $E_a = 10.5 \text{ kJ mol}^{-1}$. By what factor will its rate change, for a 10 K rise from 27°C to 37°C?

3. Plot graphs of $\exp(-E_a/RT)$ versus T for (a) $E_a = 40 \text{ kJ}$; (b) $E_a = 8 \text{ kJ}$, over the range 250 K to 400 K.

Use the graphs to calculate the rate constants, at 300 K and 330 K, for a reaction for which the constant A is $10^6 \text{ mol litre}^{-1} \text{ s}^{-1}$, and E_a is 40 kJ mol^{-1}.

(The following log scale may be useful for the graphs, if no log graph paper is available).

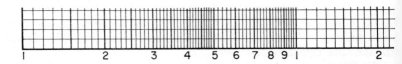

4. The two common crystalline modifications of solid sulphur (S_8) are in thermodynamic equilibrium at the 'transition point' 369 K (96°C):

$$\alpha\text{-sulphur} \rightleftharpoons \beta\text{-sulphur}$$
$$\text{(rhombic)} \qquad \text{(monoclinic)}$$

Above 369 K α-sulphur slowly changes into β, and below 369 K the reverse occurs. By considering the variation of ΔG with T, show that the change is endothermic as written.

Draw reaction diagrams (similar to Fig. 6.6) for both enthalpy and free-energy changes with time, at 369 K, 365 K and 375 K. Suggest a reason why the enthalpy of activation is large.

5. (a) The mean (RMS) speed of a CO_2 molecule at 0°C is 386 metres per second. Calculate the mean speeds of molecules of N_2, H_2O and H_2 at 0°C; also the speeds of CO_2 and H_2 at -100°C and 1000°C.

(b) In the upper atmosphere of a planet, molecules which happen to be moving vertically have a chance of leaving the planet without further collision, so long as they have sufficient speed to overcome the pull of gravity. This 'escape velocity' is the same for all objects, regardless of mass; for Earth it is 11 kms^{-1} (7 miles per second), for the moon, 2.4 kms^{-1} and for Jupiter 59 kms^{-1}.

Which gases have mean velocities in excess of these escape velocities at the temperatures referred to above?

It is believed that almost all gases have left the moon, and that hydrogen and helium, at least, are leaving the Earth, at temperatures not much above 0°C. How can this be reconciled with your calculations?

7 Equilibria

A system is said to be in equilibrium when it shows no tendency to change its composition with time. Almost all chemical reactions are reversible to some extent, and even reactions which seem to go to completion actually stop when the concentrations of the reactants have fallen to a small, but non-zero, value. Similarly, a reaction which appears to show no tendency to go does in fact produce a small, perhaps undetectable, concentration of products. Between these extremes are reactions which proceed to a fairly centrally-placed equilibrium, with all reagents and products present in comparable quantities.

Equilibrium is attained when the free-energy change, ΔG, is zero. There is then no driving-force in either direction. The *standard* free-energy, $\Delta G^{\ominus}$, is normally not zero, except at one temperature, T_{eq}. This is the temperature at which the equilibrium position is central, that is, with reactants and products all present in standard concentrations (§ 3.9).

At other temperatures than T_{eq}, $\Delta G^{\ominus}$ is not zero, and §§ 7.2 and 7.9 will show how a 'concentration correction' enables ΔG (for non-standard concentrations) to be calculated from $\Delta G^{\ominus}$; and also how certain concentrations of reactants and products result in ΔG being zero, even though $\Delta G^{\ominus}$ is not. These will be equilibrium concentrations, at a constant temperature.

Equilibrium depends upon both temperature and concentration, but fortunately these can be considered separately, as independent variables. With concentration fixed at standard, the effect of temperature on $\Delta G^{\ominus}$ is calculated. Then, with temperature fixed, the concentration term is added to convert $\Delta G^{\ominus}$ to ΔG.

7.1 Temperature effect

$\Delta G^{\ominus}$ can vary very greatly with temperature, and will often change its sign, leading to the reversal of the reaction. Many reactions have been mentioned (in Chapter 2) which have $\Delta G^{\ominus}$ positive at low temperatures, and hardly proceed at all, but which change over to $\Delta G^{\ominus}$ negative at high temperatures, and proceed almost to completion. This occurs because the driving-force of the reaction is composed of two separate terms, which often act against each other. To recapitulate, since:

$$\Delta G^{\ominus} = \Delta H - T \Delta S^{\ominus},$$

reaction is favoured by a large negative ΔH, which results from the formation of more or stronger bonds; and also, at higher temperatures, by a large positive $\Delta S^{\ominus}$, which results from the increase in disorder accompanying the breaking of bonds, and especially the creation of more gas molecules.

As an example:

$$BaO + \tfrac{1}{2}O_2 \longrightarrow BaO_2; \qquad \Delta H = -72 \text{ kJ}$$
$$\Delta S^{\ominus} = -105 \text{ J K}^{-1}$$

The forward reaction takes place if BaO is heated in air to moderate temperatures (c. 550 K). At higher temperatures the barium peroxide decomposes, liberating oxygen. This effect was used in the now obsolete Brin process for isolating oxygen from air.

The forward reaction occurs when the enthalpy (-72 kJ) is numerically greater than $T \Delta S^{\ominus}$. The entropy term, containing T, increases with rising temperature, and eventually equals -72 kJ when $T = 680$ K. At this temperature T_{eq}, the system will be in equilibrium with oxygen present at a pressure of 1 atm.

At 298 K the forward reaction would theoretically be even more complete than at 550 K, but the energy of activation (§6.10) would not be available, and the reaction would be extremely slow.

Other well-known examples of reactions which have equilibrium temperatures like this are

$$C_2H_6 \xrightleftharpoons{\quad} C_2H_4 + H_2 \qquad CaCO_3 \xrightleftharpoons{\quad} CaO + CO_2$$
$$N_2O_4 \xrightleftharpoons{\quad} 2NO_2 \qquad NH_4Cl\,(s) \xrightleftharpoons{\quad} NH_3\,(g) + HCl\,(g)$$
$$\underset{\text{pink}}{Co\,(H_2O)_4^{2+}} + 4Cl^- \xrightleftharpoons{\text{heat}} \underset{\text{blue}}{CoCl_4^{2-}} + 4H_2O$$

and the reversible decomposition of the starch-iodine complex by heat. In each case high temperature favours the forward direction, which is endothermic. This is simply because ΔH and $\Delta S^{\ominus}$ usually have the same sign, and if ΔH is positive (endothermic) $T \Delta S^{\ominus}$ will usually be positive also. Then $\Delta G^{\ominus} (= \Delta H - T \Delta S^{\ominus})$ becomes more negative as T rises and the equilibrium moves forward.

It is strictly $\Delta G^{\ominus}/T$, not $\Delta G^{\ominus}$ alone, which is the driving-force of the reaction (§5.10). If ΔH and $\Delta S^{\ominus}$ are both positive, both $\Delta G^{\ominus}$ and $\Delta G^{\ominus}/T$ become more negative as T increases; if ΔH is positive but $\Delta S^{\ominus}$ is negative, $\Delta G^{\ominus}/T$ becomes *less positive* at high temperature, and the reaction equilibrium moves foward. In either case a rise in T favours the endothermic direction, as Le Chatelier's Principle (§7.5) predicts.

7.2 Equilibrium at constant temperature

Variation of ΔG with concentration

In general, the change of ΔG with temperature is greater than the change with concentration, so (as in Chapter 2) the distinction between ΔG and $\Delta G^{\ominus}$ may largely be ignored, without too much distortion of the truth, as long as no substance is in great excess or deficiency. In the BaO_2 reaction discussed above, the oxygen pressure would have to be increased to 10^5 atm in order to bring about the same change in ΔG as results from a drop in temperature from 680 K to 480 K.

However, now that we come to examine more closely the effects of concentration on the free-energy of reaction, the terms must be defined.

Standard concentrations §3.9 are:

     gases: 1 atm partial pressure
     solutes: molal (1 mole per kg solvent)
     solids or liquids: sufficient for effective contact.

The standard free-energy change, $\Delta G^{\ominus}$, is the free-energy change for the reaction taking place with all reactants *and products* maintained in standard concentrations.

For **non-standard concentrations** ΔG will differ from $\Delta G^{\ominus}$. If the reactants are more concentrated, or products less concentrated than standard, ΔG will be more negative than $\Delta G^{\ominus}$, and reaction will be more favoured. The reverse is also true.

Consider for example the water–gas reaction:

$$C \text{ (s)} + H_2O \text{ (g)} \rightleftharpoons CO \text{ (g)} + H_2 \text{ (g)}; \qquad \Delta G^{\ominus}_{298} = +91.4 \text{ kJ}$$

In §3.4 the variation of $\Delta G^{\ominus}$ with T was investigated, and it was found that $T_{eq} = 980$ K, that is, $\Delta G^{\ominus}_{980} = 0$. At 980 K coke is in equilibrium with 1 atm each of CO, H_2 and steam. At a lower temperature $\Delta G^{\ominus}$ is positive, e.g. $\Delta G^{\ominus}_{930} = +8$ kJ, so if coke at 930 K were in contact with 1 atm of the three gases, the reaction would reverse. However, if the concentrations of CO and H_2 were kept low by pushing a stream of steam through the hot coke, the reaction would go forwards. This would be because ΔG is more negative than $\Delta G^{\ominus}$ if the product concentrations are low.

The relationship between ΔG and the gas concentrations is, empirically:

$$\Delta G = \Delta G^{\ominus} + bT \log \frac{[CO][H_2]}{[H_2O \text{ (g)}]}$$

where $b = $ a constant, and square brackets denote molar concentrations.†

     † For the purpose of concentration quotients Q_c and K_c, square brackets must be taken to mean 'concentration relative to the standard concentration'. The standard concentration $= 1.0$ M, so if the concentration of B is 0.32 M, [B] $= 0.32$, a pure number. Thus Q_c and K_c are pure numbers, without units.

     Similarly, partial pressure p_B must mean $\dfrac{\text{pressure of B}}{\text{standard pressure} = 1 \text{ atm}}$.

So if $[H_2]$ and $[CO]$ are kept to 0.01 atm by the streaming,

$$\Delta G = \Delta G^{\ominus} + bT \log \frac{0.01^2}{1}$$

substituting the value $b = 19.2$ J K^{-1} and $T = 930$ K gives:

$$\Delta G = \{+8 + 19.2 \times 10^{-3} \times 930 \times (-4)\} \text{ kJ g-eqn}^{-1}$$
$$= -63 \text{ kJ g-eqn}^{-1}$$

Therefore the reaction can proceed at these low product concentrations, even though $\Delta G^{\ominus}$ is positive.

In general if $\prod[\ \ ]$ denotes the product of the concentrations of substances each raised to the power of the stoichiometric coefficient, then, as will be shown in §7.9:

$$\Delta G = \Delta G^{\ominus} + bT \log \frac{\prod [\text{products}]}{\prod [\text{reactants}]} \qquad \textbf{7.1a}$$

(The concentrations are not necessarily those at equilibrium. See §7.4.) It can be shown that the constant $b = R \ln 10$, where $R =$ the gas constant. If one writes Q_c for the concentration quotient, and reverts to natural logarithms, one obtains the most basic form of the equation:

$$\Delta G = \Delta G^{\ominus} + RT \ln Q_c \qquad \textbf{7.1}$$

On the other hand, the substitution of $T = 298$ K, and actual values for b, gives the practical forms:

$$\Delta G_{298} = \Delta G^{\ominus}_{298} + 5.7 \text{ (kJ)} \log Q_c \qquad \textbf{7.1b}$$

and

$$\Delta G_{298} = \Delta G^{\ominus}_{298} + 1.36 \text{ (kcal)} \log Q_c \qquad \textbf{7.1c}$$

The concentrations of solids and pure liquids are standard, and may be set equal to 1, and omitted from the concentration quotient.

In a reaction in which gases are the only variable substances the concentrations may conveniently be measured by the partial pressures (which are proportional to concentrations at constant volume). The quotient is then symbolized Q_p.

ILLUSTRATION

$$2NH_3 \text{ (g)} + 3CuO \text{ (s)} \rightarrow 3Cu \text{ (s)} + N_2 \text{ (g)} + 3H_2O \text{ (g)}$$

$$Q_p = \frac{p_{N_2} \cdot p_{H_2O}^3}{p_{NH_3}^2}$$

Equilibrium concentrations

Consider the case of a reaction with a negative $\Delta G^{\ominus}$, for example:

$$\left. \begin{array}{l} NH_4Cl \text{ (aq)} + NaOH \text{ (aq)} \rightleftharpoons NH_3 \text{ (aq)} + NaCl \text{ (aq)} + H_2O \text{ (l)} \\ NH_4^+ \text{ (aq)} + OH^- \text{ (aq)} \rightleftharpoons NH_3 \text{ (aq)} + H_2O \text{ (l)} \end{array} \right\}$$

$$\Delta G^{\ominus} = -42 \text{ kJ}$$

When equal volumes of 4 M reagents are first mixed, the initial concentrations are: $[NH_4^+] = [OH^-] = 2$ M; $[NH_3 (aq)]$ very low; so ΔG is very negative, and the reaction proceeds readily. (A in Fig. 7.1)

As the concentrations of NH_4^+ and OH^- fall to 1 M and the concentration of $NH_3 (aq)$ rises to 1 M, ΔG becomes $\Delta G^{\ominus}$. This is still negative, and reaction continues (B). [Products] increases and [reactants] decreases; the last term in equation **7.1a** is now positive, and growing. Eventually, when $[NH_4^+]$ and $[OH^-]$ have fallen to 6×10^{-3} each, and $[NH_3 (aq)] = 2$,

$$\Delta G_{298}/(kJ) = -42 + 5.7 \log (5.6 \times 10^4) = -42 + 42 = 0$$

So ΔG becomes zero, and when the driving force is zero, no further reaction occurs. The system is at equilibrium, with certain concentrations of reactants and products (C).

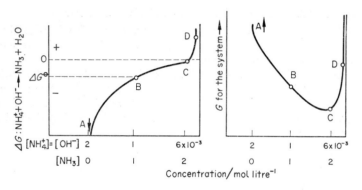

Fig. 7.1   Variation of G and ΔG with concentration (See §7.2 p. 90)

If at this point some acid is added it will react with and destroy some of the OH^- ions, and the equilibrium will be disturbed. With $\prod$ [reactants] now momentarily decreased, ΔG becomes positive, and the reaction will reverse (D). Some aqueous ammonia will react with water (thereby diminishing the smell of ammonia) until $[NH_3 (aq)]$ is small enough and $[NH_4^+]$ large enough to make ΔG zero once more. The system will again be at equilibrium, but with different concentrations than first time.

The changes in ΔG from the moment of mixing (A) to the first attainment of equilibrium (C) are shown in Fig. 7.1. The corresponding changes in G, the free-energy of the system, are also shown. Note that the sign of ΔG in the left-hand diagram is the sign of the *slope* $dG/d[NH_3]$ of the right-hand curve. At equilibrium ΔG is zero and G is a minimum.

7.3 Practical work

EXPERIMENT 1

Take about 10 cm³ aqueous bromine solution in each of two test-tubes (one to be kept for comparison).

Add two drops of dilute sodium hydroxide solution and stir. Note the colour change. Add some dilute acid, and compare again.

Dissolved bromine is the only coloured component, so the colour changes are due to the shifting of the equilibrium:

$$Br_2 \, (aq) + H_2O \, (l) \rightleftharpoons Br^- \, (aq) + OBr^- \, (aq) + 2H^+ \, (aq)$$

(a) Use data from Appendix A to calculate $\Delta G_r^\ominus$. If all the participating substances were momentarily present in standard concentrations, in which direction would reaction occur? In what form is the greater part of the bromine present in the initial solution?

(b) In what way does the addition of OH^- alter ΔG_r? Are the observed results consistent with this answer?

EXPERIMENT 2. The formation and hydrolysis of an ester.

(a) Take exactly 10.0 cm³ of approx 0.1 M H_2SO_4, warm it to about 305 K (32°C), then add about 1 cm³ ethyl acetate. Let the mixture stand for ten minutes, shaking frequently.

Meanwhile titrate 10.0 cm³ of the acid against 0.1 M NaOH with phenolphthalein indicator. Then titrate the acid + ethyl acetate mixture against the same alkali. Any sodium hydroxide required in excess of that for the sulphuric acid alone measures the acetic acid formed by the hydrolysis reaction:

$$CH_3COOC_2H_5 + H_2O \xrightarrow{\text{H}^+ \text{ catalysed}} CH_3COOH + C_2H_5OH$$

The reaction does not go to completion, and ethyl acetate can be detected even after several hours of reaction time.

(b) Mix 1 cm³ ethanol with 1 cm³ concentrated acetic acid and a few drops of concentrated sulphuric acid. Warm it in a hot water bath for a few minutes, then pour the mixture into a dish of cold dilute sodium hydroxide solution, which reacts instantly with the unchanged acetic acid. The sweet smell of ethyl acetate is then clearly detectable.

Thus the reversible reaction has been made to go both ways:

$$CH_3COOH + C_2H_5OH \rightleftharpoons CH_3COOC_2H_5 + H_2O$$

EXPERIMENT 3

Take about one third of a test-tubeful of 1 M $CuSO_4$ solution. Use a teat pipette to add M aqueous ammonia by drops, stirring frequently. Observe the changes. Then reverse the process by adding $\frac{1}{2}$ M H_2SO_4 by drops, stirring well.

$$\underset{\text{pale blue}}{Cu^{2+} \, (aq)} \underset{H_3O^+}{\overset{NH_3(aq)}{\rightleftharpoons}} \underset{\substack{\text{blue-white} \\ \text{precipitate}}}{Cu \, (OH)_2 \, (s)} \underset{H_3O^+}{\overset{NH_3(aq)}{\rightleftharpoons}} \underset{\text{deep blue}}{Cu(NH_3)_4^{2+} \, (aq)}$$

EXPERIMENT 4

(a) Take about 0.5 g bismuth oxychloride or bismuth trichloride and dissolve it in 2 cm³ concentrated hydrochloric acid, to give a clear solution of $BiCl_3$. Add distilled water by drops until the liquid is distinctly cloudy, then add one or two drops of concentrated hydrochloric acid. The equilibrium is:

$$BiCl_3 \text{ (aq)} + H_2O \text{ (l)} \rightleftharpoons BiOCl \text{ (s)} + 2HCl \text{ (aq)}$$

(b) Re-write the equation to show the *soluble* electrolytes as ions, and cancel those which appear on both sides. Then try the effect of adding other acids and other chlorides to the equilibrium mixture.

(c) Adjust the system to the point of faint but permanent cloudiness, then find the effect of temperature on the equilibrium, and thence deduce the sign of the enthalpy change.

EXPERIMENT 5

An effective demonstration of the equilibrium

$$Cl_2 \text{ (g)} + ICl \text{ (l)} \rightleftharpoons ICl_3 \text{ (s)}$$

is described in the Sample Scheme of the Nuffield O-level Chemistry Course.

Discussion

Consideration of the reactions carried out as practical work shows that they can be explained by the alteration of the sign of ΔG by changes in concentrations of participants. For example, in Experiment 2(a) the aqueous conditions keep $[H_2O]$ high and $[CH_3COOH]$ and $[C_2H_5OH]$ low. The reverse reaction is brought about by making $[CH_3COOH]$ and $[C_2H_5OH]$ high, and by using concentrated H_2SO_4 to keep $[H_2O]$ low. By these means ΔG is made negative, and reaction occurs until ΔG is again zero.

The number of reversible reactions which can be brought to an obvious equilibrium in this way is rather small; but there is good reason to believe that *all* reactions do in fact proceed to an equilibrium, even though this may be so far to the right that the residual reactants are undetectable, so that the reaction appears to have gone to completion.

7.4 The equilibrium constant

At constant temperature, equilibrium is reached when the concentrations of all reactants and products are such that ΔG is zero. Equation 7.1, which gives ΔG for any chosen concentrations, can be applied to the concentration conditions which result in equilibrium. If these are denoted by the subscript $_{eq}$,

$$\Delta G_{eq} = 0 = \Delta G^{\ominus} + RT \ln \frac{\prod [\text{products}]_{eq}}{\prod [\text{reactants}]_{eq}} \qquad \textbf{7.1d}$$

Re-arranging gives:

$$\frac{\prod [\text{products}]_{\text{eq}}}{\prod [\text{reactants}]_{\text{eq}}} = e^{-\Delta G^{\ominus}/RT} = \text{a constant, } K \qquad \textbf{7.2}$$

This equation, usually in the form:

$$\Delta G^{\ominus} = -RT \ln K \qquad \textbf{7.3}$$

is extremely important, and is known as the van't Hoff isotherm (§7.9). Note that it contains K, referring to the equilibrium state, together with $\Delta G^{\ominus}$ for *standard*, non-equilibrium conditions. It is thus a derived, not a primary, relationship.

Equation **7.2** states that at equilibrium the concentrations of all participating substances can take any individual values so long as the concentration quotient equals a constant K known as the equilibrium constant. This behaviour is confirmed by experiment, and is known as the equilibrium law. The law is obeyed more precisely at low concentrations. The equilibrium constant for a reaction is unchanged by catalysts, or changes in pressure or volume; but it is dependent upon temperature, just as $\Delta G^{\ominus}$ is.

For the general reaction:

$$a\text{A} + b\text{B} + \cdots \longrightarrow x\text{X} + y\text{Y} + \cdots$$

$$K_{\text{c}} = \frac{[\text{X}]_{\text{eq}}^{x}[\text{Y}]_{\text{eq}}^{y} \cdots}{[\text{A}]_{\text{eq}}^{a}[\text{B}]_{\text{eq}}^{b} \cdots}$$

where square brackets denote molar concentrations. Since K_{c} is merely the quotient Q_{c} but for equilibrium concentrations, the remarks made in §7.2 still apply. For example, undissolved substances do not appear, as their concentrations are considered to be standard and constant. For example,

$$2\text{Fe}^{3+}(\text{aq}) + \text{Zn (s)} \longrightarrow 2\text{Fe}^{2+}(\text{aq}) + \text{Zn}^{2+}(\text{aq});$$

$$K_{\text{c}} = \frac{[\text{Fe}^{2+}]^{2}[\text{Zn}^{2+}]}{[\text{Fe}^{3+}]^{2}}$$

For a gas reaction it may be more convenient to express concentration as partial pressures measured in atmospheres, and the equilibrium constant is then symbolized K_p. For ideal gases the van't Hoff isotherm holds precisely: $\Delta G^{\ominus} = -RT \ln K_p$. For real gases the relationship is still close. The connection between K_p and K_c is $K_p = (RT)^{\Delta n} K_c$ where Δn = no. moles products − no. moles reactant (gases only).

It is important to understand how widely the *individual* concentrations can vary, while still being in accordance with the equilibrium constant.

ILLUSTRATION

If $[C][D]/[A][B] = K_c = 3$ (say), the following are possibilities:

[A]	[B]	[C]	[D]	[C][D]	[A][B]	K
1.0	1.0	1.7	1.7	3	1	3
0.1	0.1	0.17	0.17	0.03	0.01	3
10	0.01	30	0.01	0.3	0.1	3
0.26	0.8	0.8	0.8	0.64	0.21	3

The number of possible combinations is infinite. It is clear, then, that while the equilibrium constant can be calculated from a given set of equilibrium concentrations, it is impossible to calculate the concentrations from the constant without further information, and such calculations are not often simple. This does not detract from the usefulness of K as an indication of the 'position of equilibrium'.

The equilibrium constant can be used as a measure of a reaction's feasibility, i.e. its 'tendency to go', as follows:

If $\log K > 4$ $(K > 10^4)$ the reaction tends to go almost to completion; the *rate* of reaction is not determined by K, however, and may be any value, down to zero.

If $\log K$ is between 2 and -2 the reaction reaches equilibrium with comparable concentrations of all the substances.

If $\log K < -4$ there is virtually no reaction.

Equilibrium constants are found up to 10^{50}, and it is rare to find one in the narrow range, say 10^{-2} to 10^2, in which both reactants and products are present in easily measurable quantities. Most equilibria lie well to one side. At constant temperature, then, such reactions can only be made reversible by providing a large excess of reactants and by arranging for the products to be removed from the region of reaction.

An example of this behaviour, drawn from geology, is:

$$CaCO_3 \text{ (s)} + H_2O \text{ (1)} + CO_2 \text{ (aq)} \rightleftharpoons 2CaHCO_3 \text{ (aq)}$$

since this formation and decomposition of the bicarbonate has produced stalactites even in the constant temperature conditions of underground caves.

Even so, comparatively few reactions can be reversed in this way at the same temperature. More commonly reversible reactions are sent in one direction or the other by varying the temperature, and so changing the value of the equilibrium constant.

7.5 Le Chatelier's Principle

The result of altering any of the factors which control an equilibrium can usually be predicted by means of a generalization known as Le

Chatelier's Principle: *When a system at equilibrium is subjected to a constraint, the equilibrium shifts in the direction which tends to reduce that constraint to a minimum.*

If this were not so, and the shift tended to augment the constraint, the system would change with ever-increasing speed (like a branching chain reaction) and equilibrium would not be restored.

The 'constraint' may be a change in temperature, pressure, volume, or concentrations of substances. The principle is a useful short-cut for predicting the direction of change, but cannot be used to estimate the extent. In each case a more fundamental approach to the problem, through free-energy or the equilibrium constant, will give a better understanding of the change of equilibrium, and will allow quantitative calculations of it.

The addition of a reagent or removal of a product

Le Chatelier's principle predicts that equilibrium will 'move to the right', that is, that reaction will proceed so as to consume the added reagents or replace the missing product. This follows from the nature of the equilibrium constant:

$$K_{eq} = \frac{\prod [\text{products}]_{eq}}{\prod [\text{reactants}]_{eq}}$$ 7.2

K_{eq} must not change (at constant temperature), so any change in the concentration of one participant substance must result in an adjustment of the others. If a reactant concentration is momentarily made larger, the ensuing reaction will increase [products] and decrease [reactants].

Changes in pressure or volume

If a mixture of gases is at equilibrium, and the volume of the vessel is decreased (and the pressure increased), Le Chatelier's Principle predicts that reaction will occur so as to decrease the total number of gas molecules. This can only occur if the numbers of reactant and product molecules in the equation are unequal.

(a) For the gas reaction:

$$A\,(g) \longrightarrow B\,(g) + C\,(g) \quad (\Delta n = +1)$$

$$K_p = \frac{p_B \cdot p_C}{p_A}$$

If the volume of the vessel is decreased from V to V/x, the partial pressure of each gas will momentarily increase by a factor x, so the new quotient of pressures will be:

$$Q_p = \frac{x p_B \cdot x p_C}{x p_A} = x \left(\frac{p_B \cdot p_C}{p_A} \right) = x\,K_p$$

Since this is greater than K_p, reaction must occur to reduce the quantities of B and C relative to A.

(b)

$$A\,(g) + B\,(g) \longrightarrow 2C\,(g) \quad (\Delta n = 0)$$

$$K_p = \frac{p_C^2}{p_A \cdot p_B}$$

If the volume is decreased from V to V/x, the momentary quotient of partial pressures becomes

$$Q_p = \frac{(xp_C)^2}{xp_A \cdot xp_B} = \frac{p_C^2}{p_A p_B} = K_p$$

Despite the volume change, the partial pressures are still in accordance with the equilibrium constant, and no adjustment will occur.

Change in temperature

Le Chatelier's principle predicts that the reaction will move in the direction which minimizes the temperature change. Thus an increase in temperature will favour the endothermic direction, as this will absorb heat and lower the temperature.

It was shown in §7.1 that since ΔH and $\Delta S^\ominus$ are usually of the same sign, the ΔH and $T\Delta S$ terms act in opposition in the free-energy equation. For example, the decomposition of ammonia is endothermic, with a positive entropy change because of the increase in gas molecules:

$$2NH_3 \rightleftharpoons N_2 + 3H_2; \quad \Delta H = +, \quad \Delta S^\ominus = +$$

Therefore $\Delta G^\ominus$ changes from being positive at low temperatures, through zero (actually at 850 K) to an increasingly negative value at high temperatures. Since $\log K_{eq} = -\Delta G^\ominus/(2.3\,RT)$, at low temperatures $\log K_{eq}$ is negative, and K_{eq} is less than one; at 850 K $\log K_{eq} = 0$, and $K_{eq} = 1$; at higher temperatures $\log K_{eq} =$ positive and $K_{eq} > 1$. Increased temperature favours the reaction as written, which is the endothermic direction.

An interesting situation arises when ΔH and $\Delta S^\ominus$ are of opposite signs. This is not common, but it is the case with the following examples:

$$2N_2 + O_2 \longrightarrow 2N_2O; \quad \begin{cases} \Delta H_r = +163 \text{ kJ} \\ \Delta S_r^\ominus = -155 \text{ J K}^{-1} \end{cases}$$

and the decomposition of HCl, HBr, and HI into the gaseous elements, e.g.

$$2HI\,(g) \rightleftharpoons H_2\,(g) + I_2\,(g); \quad \Delta H_r = +10 \text{ kJ}$$
$$\Delta S_r^\ominus = -21 \text{ J K}^{-1}$$

The last example is a well-known gas-phase equilibrium but it is not always realized that it is exceptional in that $K_p < 1$ at all temperatures.

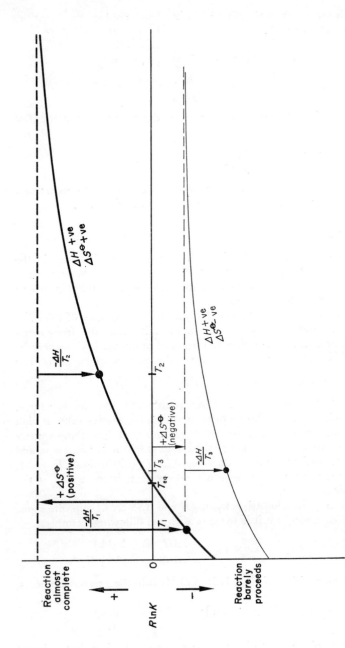

Fig. 7.2 Graphs of $R \ln K$ vs. T for two endothermic reactions. The upper (bold) line shows the usual case, with ΔH and $\Delta S^{\ominus}$ of the same sign. K_{eq} changes from <1 at low temperatures, through 0 at T_{eq}, to >1 at high temperatures; the limit is $R \ln K \rightarrow \Delta S^{\ominus}$. A knowledge of the sign of ΔH gives a prediction of the direction of change of K, but an estimate of $\Delta S^{\ominus}$ gives the high-temperature equilibrium position. The lower line is discussed in the text (§7.5)

The equilibrium position never moves over to the right, but merely approaches the central position as the temperature rises (until atomization of the I_2 interferes). The reason for this is as follows:

> ΔH is positive but $\Delta S^\ominus$ is negative, therefore
> $\Delta G^\ominus$ is positive at all temperatures.
> As T increases, $\Delta G^\ominus$ becomes *more* positive.

This appears to give the wrong prediction, and to be contrary to Le Chatelier's Principle. However, as was shown in §5.10, the driving-force of a reaction is $\Delta G/T$, not ΔG alone. This must be so since the equilibrium constant is a function of $\Delta G^\ominus/T$, not merely $\Delta G^\ominus$.

$$R \ln K = -\frac{\Delta G^\ominus}{T} = -\frac{\Delta H}{T} + \Delta S^\ominus \qquad 7.4$$

Therefore, if $\Delta S^\ominus$ is negative and ΔH is positive, log K is negative at all temperatures, and $K < 1$. But as T increases, the $\Delta H/T$ term becomes less important, and log K_{eq} becomes less negative; that is, K increases. This is illustrated in Fig. 7.2.

Therefore even though the change in $\Delta G^\ominus$ with T does not always predict the direction of change of equilibrium, the change in $\Delta G^\ominus/T$ is invariably reliable.

7.6 Well-known examples of equilibria

Ethyl acetate

One of the best-known of liquid phase equilibria is the esterification of ethanol and acetic acid. If one mole each of these reagents are mixed and kept at 50°C† they react until equilibrium is reached, and it can be shown (by titrating against standard alkali) that 0.33 mole of acid remains. Therefore, from the stoichiometry, 0.33 mole ethanol must also remain, and 0.67 mole each of water and ethyl acetate must have been produced. If V is the total volume of the mixture,

$$K_c = \frac{[CH_3COOC_2H_5][H_2O]}{[CH_3COOH][C_2H_5OH]} = \frac{\dfrac{0.67}{V} \times \dfrac{0.67}{V}}{\dfrac{0.33}{V} \times \dfrac{0.33}{V}} = 4$$

Hydrogen iodide

One of the first reactions for which the equilibrium law was established was:

$$H_2\,(g) + I_2\,(g) \rightleftharpoons 2HI\,(g); \qquad \Delta H = -10\,kJ$$

† As ΔH is almost zero, K_{eq} varies very little, and good temperature control is unnecessary.

studied, at 723 K (450°C), by Bodenstein, who found that for various mixtures of H_2, I_2 and HI:

$$\frac{p_{HI}^2}{p_{H_2} \cdot p_{I_2}} = K_p$$

where p_{HI} = partial pressure of HI, etc.

K_p is dependent only upon temperature, being 46.0 at 763 K and 55.3 at 700 K. So the exothermic reaction proceeds further at lower temperatures, which is in accordance with Le Chatelier's Principle (§7.5).

Because there are equal numbers of gas molecules for reactants and products, the equilibrium position is unaffected by total pressure.

Nitrogen dioxide

A sealed flask of the brown gas nitrogen dioxide is often available for demonstration purposes. If the temperature is reduced by cooling the flask in ice, the colour fades, due to dimerization to colourless N_2O_4. Warming the gas intensifies the colour. Therefore at room temperature the equilibrium must be in a fairly central position, with K_p not far from unity. In fact at 298 K $K_p = 0.14$.

$$N_2O_4 \rightleftharpoons 2NO_2 ; \qquad \Delta H = +58 \text{ kJ}$$
$$\text{colourless} \qquad \text{brown} \qquad \Delta G_{298}^0 = +6 \text{ kJ}$$

As ΔH is quite large and positive, increase in temperature rapidly moves the equilibrium towards dissociation.

If the gas is held in a closed syringe, and is suddenly expanded, the colour fades immediately, but steadily grows darker over the next few seconds. The initial fading is merely due to the reduction in concentration of the coloured gas before equilibrium is re-established. If the volume is increased from V to xV, the colour will initially fade from intensity I to I/x.

However, since $K_p = p_{NO_2}/p_{N_2O_4}$, when the partial pressures are decreased, the quotient becomes

$$\left(\frac{p_{NO_2}}{x}\right)^2 \div \frac{p_{N_2O_4}}{x} = \frac{K_p}{x}$$

So reaction occurs in the direction of $N_2O_4 \rightarrow 2NO_2$. A quantitative treatment is to be found in *University Chemistry* by B. H. Mahan.

Ammonia synthesis (Haber process)

$$N_2 + 3H_2 \rightleftharpoons 2NH_3 \text{ (g)}; \qquad \Delta H = -92 \text{ kJ}$$
$$\Delta G^{\ominus} = -33 \text{ kJ}$$

According to the theory in §7.5, the proportion of ammonia in the equilibrium mixture should be increased by total pressure, and by decrease in temperature. Haber's observations, summarized in Fig. 7.3 bear this out.

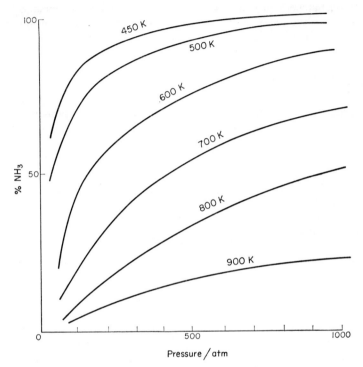

Fig. 7.3   The proportion of ammonia in the equilibrium mixture obtained from a 3:1 hydrogen + nitrogen mixture, at various temperatures. (Adapted from *An Introduction to Physical Chemistry* by G. I. Brown. Longmans, Green & Co., Ltd., London)

In practice a pressure of 300 to 400 atm is used, and a temperature of 720 K (447°C) to 770 K. Lower temperatures would give much better yields, but the reaction would be inconveniently slow. Even at 720 K a good catalyst of iron (with promoters) is essential for a reasonable rate of reaction. About 30% ammonia is formed, and is removed by solution in water before re-circulation of the N_2/H_2 mixture.

Ozone

When a slow stream of oxygen gas is subjected to a silent electric discharge in an ozonizer, a small proportion of ozone is formed:

$$3O_2 \rightleftharpoons 2O_3; \qquad \Delta H = +284 \text{ kJ}$$

The ozone can be detected by its oxidizing action on potassium iodide, mercury, and other substances. When the O_2/O_3 mixture is passed through a hot tube, the ozone concentration is reduced so much that this oxidizing action is lost.

If Le Chatelier's principle is applied to this change there seems to be a paradox, for the increased temperature has caused the reaction to occur in the *exothermic* direction $O_3 \to O_2$. Why is this? (see Question 6 below).

7.7 Exercises

1. Write the equilibrium constants for the following reactions in terms of concentrations of participants. Also estimate the size of each constant (very high, $> 10^5$; small, around 10 to 0.1; very small, $< 10^{-5}$) at about 298 K.

(a) $3Fe^{3+} (aq) + Al (s) \rightleftharpoons 3Fe^{2+} (aq) + Al^{3+} (aq)$

(b) $2H_2 (g) + O_2 (g) \rightleftharpoons 2H_2O (g)$

(c) $NaHCO_3 (s) + H_2S (g) \rightleftharpoons NaHS (s) + H_2O (g) + CO_2 (g)$

(d) $2FeSO_4 (s) \rightleftharpoons Fe_2O_3 (s) + SO_3 (g) + SO_2 (g)$

2. When air (21% O_2, 78% N_2 by volume) is heated to 2300 K until the equilibrium: $N_2 + O_2 \rightleftharpoons 2NO$ is established, and then cooled rapidly, it is found to contain 1.1% nitric oxide by volume. Calculate the equilibrium constant (K_p) and also $\Delta G^\ominus$ for the reaction at 2300 K.

3. (a) Use data from Appendix A and Table 5.1 to calculate $\Delta G_r^\ominus$ for the reaction $N_2 + O_2 \to 2NO$ at 2670 K (2397°C), and so, via K_p, find the approximate percentage of NO in the equilibrium mixture of air at that temperature. (Ignore the change in N_2 and O_2 concentrations.)

(b) Compare your answer with the figure from the previous question, and note the effect of temperature on the extent of the reaction, which is endothermic.

4. The selenate ion can oxidize bromide, in acid solution giving bromine and selenious acid:

$$SeO_4^{2-} (aq) + 2Br^- (aq) + 4H^+ (aq) \longrightarrow H_2SeO_3 (aq) + Br_2 (aq) + H_2O (l)$$

In a mixture which had come to equilibrium at 298 K, the following concentrations were found:

$$[H^+] = [Br^-] = 1.0 \text{ M}; \qquad [Br_2] = 0.52 \text{ M}$$
$$[SeO_4^{2-}] = 0.0050 \text{ M}; \qquad [H_2SeO_3] = 0.995 \text{ M}$$

(a) Calculate the concentration equilibrium constant, and the standard free-energy of reaction.

(b) In another mixture at the same temperature the concentrations were:

$$[H^+] = [Br^-] = 0.80 \text{ M}; \quad [Br_2] = 0.52 \text{ M};$$
$$[SeO_4^{2-}] = 0.10 \text{ M}; \quad [H_2SeO_3] = 0.990 \text{ M}$$

Calculate Q_c and ΔG for the system, and predict the direction of spontaneous change (if it is not at equilibrium).

5.* In an investigation into the reaction:

$$2COCl_2 \text{ (g)} \rightleftharpoons CCl_4 \text{ (g)} + CO_2 \text{ (g)}$$

carbonyl chloride, mixed with a volatile catalyst, was passed through an oven at 800 K (527°C). The gas stream did not necessarily reach equilibrium in the short time available.

The emergent gas was rapidly cooled, and analysed by gas chromatography. Typical results, for three different flow rates, were:

Flow rate	Composition of final gas mixture, by volume			
	$COCl_2$	CO_2	CCl_4	Other gases $(CO + Cl_2)$
1.00 cm³ sec⁻¹	0.10	0.20	0.20	0.50
1.40 ,, ,,	0.13	0.26	0.26	0.35
1.85 ,, ,,	0.18	0.32	0.32	0.18

(a) Calculated the concentration quotient Q_p (in terms of partial pressures) for each flow rate, and interpret the results.

(b) What is the value of the equilibrium constant K_p?

(c) Some CCl_4, together with CO_2 + catalyst, was passed very slowly through the oven at 800 K. The final gas mixture was found to contain 4% CO_2 + 1.6% CCl_4. How much $COCl_2$ would you expect to be present among the other gases?

6.* Explain the 'ozone paradox' in §7.6, p. 104.

7.8* The free-energy of expansion and dilution

In Chapter 3 it was pointed out that while ΔH for a reaction is only slightly dependent upon the concentrations of the participants, this is not at all the case for ΔS and ΔG. So standard conditions are defined (§7.2) and $\Delta S^\ominus$ and $\Delta G^\ominus$ are used whenever exact values are quoted.

The variation of ΔS with concentration is well illustrated by the case of the expansion of a gas into a vacuum. Consider one mole of an ideal gas, at one atmosphere pressure, connected to an evacuated flask of nine times the molal volume. When the tap is opened the gas expands, and its pressure drops to 0.1 atm. No work is done since there was no opposing force, and so both ΔU and ΔH are zero. The temperature does not change.

Nevertheless, the process was spontaneous and irreversible. Each gas molecule now has ten times the original volume to move in, so there has been an increase in randomness: that is, a positive ΔS.

The thermodynamic probability Ω of a system, as introduced in §5.3, is the number of distinguishable ways of arranging the components of the system with regard to location and energy. In the present case Ω for energy distribution is unchanged, but Ω for spatial arrangement is proportional to volume.

For the expansion of an ideal gas into a vacuum from P_1, V_1 to P_2, V_2:

$$\Omega_1/\Omega_2 = V_1/V_2 = P_2/P_1$$

Since $S = R \ln \Omega$,

$$\Delta S = R \ln \Omega_2 - R \ln \Omega_1$$
$$\Delta S = -R \ln (P_2/P_1) \qquad \textbf{7.5}$$

For this process $\Delta H = 0$,

$$\therefore \ \Delta G = 0 - T \Delta S = +RT \ln (P_2/P_1) \qquad \textbf{7.6}$$

For the above example of an expansion from 1 atm to 0.1 atm, at 298 K, $\Delta G = -6 \text{ kJ mol}^{-1}$. The negative ΔG is the reason why the change is spontaneous.

The negative ΔG also suggests that work *could* be obtained from the expansion of a gas under different conditions from those just considered, for example by making the gas flow past a turbine, or push a piston back against a force. Maximum work is obtained under reversible conditions (§5.7) when the pressure against which the gas is expanding is kept only marginally less than the internal pressure. The work is then equal to the integral of $P \, dV$ between the limits V_1 and V_2:

$$\text{work done by system} = -W_{rev} = -\Delta G = \int_{V_1}^{V_2} P \, dV$$

By substituting $P = RT/V$, one obtains:

$$\Delta G = -\int_{V_1}^{V_2} P \, dV = -RT \int_{V_1}^{V_2} \frac{dV}{V}$$
$$= -RT(\ln V_2 - \ln V_1)$$
$$= +RT\left(\ln \frac{RT}{V_2} - \ln \frac{RT}{V_1}\right)$$
$$= RT(\ln P_2 - \ln P_1)$$
$$\Delta G = RT \ln (P_2/P_1) \qquad \textbf{7.6}$$

ΔG for a process is independent of the manner in which the change is brought about, therefore the two derivations, one for zero transfer of work and the other for maximum work, give the same equation **7.6** for the free-energy of expansion.

Similar reasoning can be applied to the dilution of a solution, though real solutions would not be expected to behave in such close accordance with the resulting equations. If Ω for a solute is proportional to the volume of solution occupied, and therefore inversely proportional to concentration, then for the change of one mole of solute from concentration c_1 to c_2:

$$\Delta S = R \ln (\Omega_2/\Omega_1) = -R \ln (c_2/c_1) \qquad \textbf{7.7}$$

For an ideal solution the enthalpy of dilution is zero, so:

$$\Delta G = 0 - T \Delta S = RT \ln (c_2/c_1) \qquad \textbf{7.8}$$

This free-energy change will be negative if $c_1 > c_2$. One way in which the corresponding work of dilution can be harnessed is by osmosis. Solvent will pass through a semi-permeable membrane from the more dilute solution, even against gravity or an applied pressure. It should be possible to demonstrate, with simple apparatus, that a saturated solution of ammonium nitrate can draw water up against gravity, showing that ΔG for the dilution is negative even though ΔH is positive.

An electrochemical method of measuring the free-energy of dilution is described in §8.10. See also Project 5, p. 180.

7.9 ΔG for reaction with non-standard concentrations

In the previous section it was shown that the entropy of dilution of one mole of solute from concentration c_1 to c_2 is:

$$\Delta S = -R \ln (c_2/c_1) \qquad \textbf{7.7}$$

The enthalpy of dilution is small in comparison, and zero for ideal solutions, therefore:

$$\Delta G = RT \ln (c_2/c_1) \qquad \textbf{7.8}$$

The approximation that $\Delta H = 0$ is not really valid for electrolytes except at great dilution, and in a more rigorous treatment, activities would be used in place of concentrations. This refinement will not be pursued in this book.

Equation **7.8** can be used to calculate ΔG_r for a reaction

$$A + B + \cdots \longrightarrow X + Y + \cdots$$

under conditions where reactants are present at concentrations [A], [B], ... and products are present at concentrations [X], [Y], ... The reaction is considered to take place in stages, and the overall ΔG_r is the sum of the ΔG's for the various steps:

(i) Change of concentration of reactant A to standard (i.e. molar or 1 atm):
$$c_1 = [A], \; c_2 = 1. \; \Delta G(i) = RT \ln (1/[A]).$$

(ii) Similar changes for B and other reactants. $\Delta G(ii) = RT \ln (1/[B])$.

(iii) With all reactants now at standard concentration, one g-equation of reaction occurs, forming products at standard concentrations. $\Delta G(iii) = \Delta G_r^{\ominus}$.

(iv) The concentrations of the products are changed from standard to those specified, [X], [Y], etc. $\Delta G(iv) = RT \ln [X] + RT \ln [Y] + \cdots$.

Total free-energy of reaction:

$$\Delta G_r = \Delta G_r^{\ominus} + RT\left(\ln [X] + \ln [Y] \cdots + \ln \frac{1}{[A]} + \ln \frac{1}{[B]} + \cdots\right)$$

$$= \Delta G_r^{\ominus} + RT \ln \frac{[X][Y]\ldots}{[A][B]\ldots}$$

In general,

$$\Delta G_r = \Delta G_r^{\ominus} + RT \ln \frac{\prod [\text{products}]}{\prod [\text{reactants}]} \qquad \textbf{7.1d}$$

or

$$\Delta G_r = \Delta G_r^{\ominus} + RT \ln Q \qquad \textbf{7.1}$$

This is the equation used in §7.2 to give the variation of ΔG with concentration. The further derivation of the isotherm and the equilibrium constant was shown in §7.4.

7.10 The use of the reaction isotherm

$$\Delta G^{\ominus} = -2.303 \; RT \log K_{eq} \qquad \textbf{7.3a}$$

If $\Delta G^{\ominus}$ is in kJ mol^{-1}, R is 8.314×10^{-3} kJ mol^{-1} K^{-1}.

Then, at 298 K:

$$\Delta G^{\ominus} = -5.71 \; (kJ) \log K_{eq}$$

The equation can be used to calculate the equilibrium constant for a reaction which has not been investigated closely, or for which the equilibrium position is too far to the right or the left to be measured. $\Delta G^{\ominus}$ can be calculated from ΔH and ΔS data, or from $\Delta G_f^{\ominus}$ values for all the substances involved, or from electrochemical cell measurements (Chapter 8).

Conversely, if the equilibrium constant can be measured directly, $\Delta G_r^{\ominus}$ can be calculated, and this may give $\Delta G_f^{\ominus}$ data with which to calculate K_{eq} for other reactions.

WORKED EXAMPLES

1. Find K_p at 298 K and 473 K (200°C) for the following reaction:

$$PCl_5 \text{ (g)} \rightleftharpoons PCl_3 \text{ (g)} + Cl_2 \text{ (g)}; \qquad \begin{cases} \Delta H_{298}^{\ominus} = +94 \text{ kJ} \\ \Delta G_{298}^{\ominus} = +38 \text{ kJ} \end{cases}$$

(i) at 298 K:

$$\log K_p = -\frac{38}{2.30 \times 8.31 \times 10^{-3} \times 298}$$

$$= -6.66 = -7 + 0.34$$

$$K_p = 2 \times 10^{-7}$$

(ii) at 473 K: firstly $\Delta G^{\ominus}_{473}$ must be calculated from the data available:

$$\Delta G^{\ominus} = \Delta H^{\ominus} - T \Delta S^{\ominus} \qquad \therefore \Delta S^{\ominus} = \frac{\Delta H^{\ominus} - \Delta G^{\ominus}}{T}$$

$$\Delta S^{\ominus} = \frac{+94 - (+38)}{298} = +185 \text{ J K}^{-1} \text{ mol}^{-1}$$

Assuming $\Delta H^{\ominus}$ and $\Delta S^{\ominus}$ to be constant:

$$\Delta G^{\ominus}_{473} = +94 - 473 \times (+185 \times 10^{-3}) = +6 \text{ kJ}$$
$$\log K_p(473) = -6/(2.30 \times 8.31 \times 10^{-3} \times 473) = -0.66$$
$$K_p(473) = 0.2 \quad (\text{See also } \S 7.11)$$

2. Nitrosyl bromide decomposes thus:

$$2\text{NOBr (g)} \rightleftharpoons 2\text{NO (g)} + \text{Br}_2 \text{ (g)}$$

In an experiment at 350 K, the partial pressures of a mixture at equilibrium were: NOBr 0.50 atm, NO 0.15 atm, Br_2 0.25 atm. Calculate $\Delta G^{\ominus}_{350}$.

$$K_p = \frac{p^2_{\text{NO}} \times p_{\text{Br}_2}}{p^2_{\text{NOBr}}} = \frac{0.15^2 \times 0.25}{0.50^2} = 2.25 \times 10^{-2}$$

$$\log K_p = \overline{2}.35 = -1.65$$
$$\Delta G^{\ominus}_{350} = -2.30RT \log K_p = +2.30 \times 8.31 \times 10^{-3} \times 350 \times 1.65 \text{ kJ}$$
$$= +11 \text{ kJ g-eqn}^{-1}$$

3. Calculate the equilibrium temperature for the following reaction (a) with oxygen at 1 atm pressure, (b) in air, with $p_{O_2} = 0.20$ atm.

$$\text{BaO (s)} + \tfrac{1}{2}\text{O}_2 \text{ (g)} \rightleftharpoons \text{BaO}_2 \text{ (s)}; \qquad \Delta H = -72 \text{ kJ}$$
$$\Delta S^{\ominus} = -105 \text{ J K}^{-1}$$

(a) $$\Delta G^{\ominus} = (-72 + 105 \times 10^{-3} \times T) \text{ kJ}$$

At the temperature at which BaO and BaO_2 are in equilibrium with 1 atm O_2, $\Delta G^{\ominus} = 0$

$$\therefore T_{eq} = 72/(105 \times 10^{-3}) = 680 \text{ K } (407^{\circ}\text{C})$$

(b) If BaO_2 is in equilibrium with 0.2 atm O_2, $K_p = 1/0.2 = 5.0$

$$\Delta G^{\ominus} = \Delta H^{\ominus} - T\Delta S^{\ominus} = -2.30RT \log K$$

Inserting values in joules:

$$-72\,000 + 105T = -2.30 \times 8.31 \times T \times \log 5.0$$
$$105T + 13T = 72\,000$$
$$T = 610 \text{ K (2 sig. figs.)}$$

7.11 Equilibrium constants and enthalpy

The isotherm (equation **7.1**) can be rearranged thus:

$$\ln K = -\frac{\Delta G^{\ominus}}{RT} = \frac{\Delta S^{\ominus}}{R} - \frac{\Delta H}{RT} \qquad \textbf{7.4a}$$

The variation of $\ln K$ with T is then obtained by differentiation:

$$\frac{d(\ln K)}{dT} = +\frac{\Delta H}{RT^2} \qquad \textbf{7.9}$$

Note that the $\Delta S^{\ominus}$ term has disappeared, and the direction of change of K with increasing temperature is determined solely by the sign of ΔH. $\ln K$ (and therefore K) increases with increasing T if ΔH is positive, the conclusion reached at the end of §7.5 (see also Fig. 7.2).

If K_1 and K_2 are the equilibrium constants for a reaction at T_1 and T_2 respectively, substitution into equation **7.4a** (above) gives:

$$\ln K_1 - \ln K_2 = \frac{-\Delta H}{R}\left(\frac{1}{T_1} - \frac{1}{T_2}\right) \qquad \textbf{7.10}$$

Equation **7.10** provides a straightforward way of calculating K for any temperature if K (or $\Delta G^{\ominus}$) is known for 298 K. In §7.10 a specimen calculation was shown, based on the calculation of $\Delta G^{\ominus}$ for the non-standard temperature, followed by conversion to K_p. The same problem will now be solved by means of equation **7.10**.

WORKED EXAMPLE

Calculate K_p at 298 K and 473 K for the reaction:

$$PCl_5 \text{ (g)} \rightleftharpoons PCl_3 \text{ (g)} + Cl_2 \text{ (g)}$$

From tabulated data,

$$\Delta H = +94 \text{ kJ}, \quad \Delta G^{\ominus} = +38 \text{ kJ}; \quad R = 8.31 \times 10^{-3} \text{ kJ K}^{-1} \text{ mol}^{-1}$$

$$\log K_p(298) = -\frac{38}{2.30 \times 8.31 \times 10^{-3} \times 298} = -6.66$$

$$K_p(298) = 2 \times 10^{-7}$$

Using equation **7.10**:

$$\log K_p(473) - \log K_p(298) = -\frac{94}{2.30 \times 8.31 \times 10^{-3}}\left(\frac{1}{473} - \frac{1}{298}\right)$$

$$= -4.9 \times 10^3 \left(\frac{298 - 473}{473 \times 298}\right)$$

$$= 6.1$$

$$\log K_p(473) = 6.1 + (-6.7) = -0.6$$

$$K_p(473) = 0.2$$

7.12 A physical interpretation of the van't Hoff isotherm

$$\varDelta G^{\ominus} = \varDelta H - T\varDelta S^{\ominus} = -RT \ln K \qquad\qquad \textbf{7.3}$$

$$\ln K = +\frac{\varDelta S^{\ominus}}{R} - \frac{\varDelta H}{RT} \qquad\qquad \textbf{7.4a}$$

The equilibrium constant, representing the extent of reaction at equilibrium, depends upon a constant entropy term minus an enthalpy term which becomes less important as temperature rises. This situation can be illustrated by a simple model.

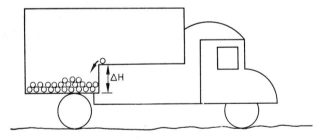

Fig. 7.4   At rest

A closed lorry has a floor with two levels, the half nearer the driver's cabin being about $\frac{1}{2}$ metre higher than the back half. At the start of the journey a few thousand table-tennis balls are thrown in, and naturally they all come to rest in the rear (lower) section.

The lorry moves off along a bumpy track, and the balls are shaken about. Soon the movement is so great that some of them find their way into the higher, forward section. As the violence of the agitation is increased, the number of balls in the higher part increases. The limit would be reached when there were approximately equal concentrations of balls in each half of the lorry.

The height of the step represents $\varDelta H$ in the 'reaction'. The degree of bumping about represents the temperature. When T is small, the equilibrium constant $K = $ (no. in front)/(no. in back) is almost zero. The tendency for balls to spread into the whole of the available space represents ΔS, and this is proportional to

$$\log \frac{\text{total available space}}{\text{available space in rear section}}$$

As T increases, the $\Delta H/T$ term becomes less important, and at the limit, when the agitation is very violent, the height of the step becomes a negligible barrier to equal distribution: the ΔS term prevails (Fig. 7.5).

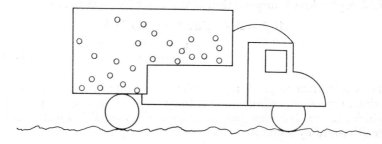

Fig. 7.5   Moving—balls at equilibrium

As an extension of the model, imagine now that a small gate has been fixed at the edge of the upper section in an attempt to keep the balls out (Fig. 7.6). Now the enthalpy of activation (§6.11) of the forward reaction is represented by the difference in floor levels *plus* the height of the gate. The enthalpy of activation of the reverse ('exothermic') change is the height of the gate alone.

Also, the area of the hole separating the two sections has been restricted, so that a ball finding its way from one section to the other suffers a temporary restriction of movement during the change-over.

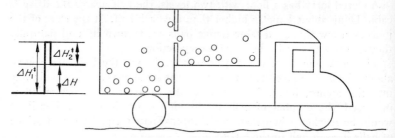

Fig. 7.6   Moving less rapidly—balls not at equilibrium yet

Now the rate of movement forwards is equal to:

$$\text{a constant} \times \begin{bmatrix} \text{Activation} \\ \text{energy} \\ \text{term} \end{bmatrix} \times \begin{bmatrix} \text{'Restricted} \\ \text{movement during} \\ \text{transition' term} \end{bmatrix} \times \begin{bmatrix} \text{Concentration} \\ \text{of balls in} \\ \text{back section} \end{bmatrix}$$

In thermodynamic symbols:

$$\text{Rate (forward)} = k_1 \times \exp\left(-\Delta H_1^{\ddagger}/RT\right) \times \Delta\Omega_1^{\ddagger}$$
$$\times \text{concentration of balls in back}$$

$$\text{Rate (backward)} = k_2 \times \exp\left(-\Delta H_2^{\ddagger}/RT\right) \times \Delta\Omega_2^{\ddagger}$$
$$\times \text{concentration of balls in front}$$

where $\Delta H^{\ddagger}$ = enthalpy of activation, and $\Delta\Omega^{\ddagger}$ = reduction of thermodynamic probability (§5.3) in transition state.

When T is low the equilibrium is not easily reached: balls put in the forward section tend to be kept there by the gate even though they would drop back if the gate were removed (see Fig. 7.5).

As agitation increases, the balls bounce high enough to clear the gate, and many move to the rear. In time, the correct equilibrium distribution is reached. The equilibrium constant at any one temperature is given by:

$$K = \frac{\text{concentration in front}}{\text{concentration in back}}$$

and since equilibrium is established when the forward micro-rate equals the reverse micro-rate (§6.13):

$$K = \frac{k(\text{rev})}{k(\text{forw})} = \frac{\text{const} \times \exp\left(-\Delta H_2^{\ddagger}/RT\right) \times \Delta\Omega_2^{\ddagger}}{\text{const} \times \exp\left(-\Delta H_1^{\ddagger}/RT\right) \times \Delta\Omega_1^{\ddagger}}$$

$$\ln K = \frac{-\Delta H_2^{\ddagger}}{RT} + \ln \Delta\Omega_2^{\ddagger} + \frac{\Delta H_1^{\ddagger}}{RT} - \ln \Delta\Omega_1^{\ddagger}$$

The difference between the enthalpies of activation is the enthalpy of reaction:

$$\Delta H_2^{\ddagger} - \Delta H_1^{\ddagger} = \Delta H_r$$

Similarly,

$$\ln \Delta\Omega_2^{\ddagger} - \Delta\Omega_1^{\ddagger} = \frac{\Delta S_2^{\ddagger} - \Delta S_1^{\ddagger}}{R} = \frac{\Delta S^{\ominus}}{R}$$

Therefore

$$\ln K = \frac{\Delta S^{\ominus}}{R} - \frac{\Delta H}{RT} = \frac{-\Delta G^{\ominus}}{RT} \qquad \text{(Q.E.D.)}$$

It may be that this illustrative model will help the student to grasp the principles of dynamic equilibrium, and the energy and entropy of activation. A formal treatment can be found in advanced texts of physical chemistry.

7.13 Exercises

1. ΔG for non-standard concentrations

(a) Gypsum and Plaster of Paris are in equilibrium with 1 atm steam at 100°C:

$$CaSO_4 2H_2O \text{ (s)} \longrightarrow CaSO_4 . \tfrac{1}{2}H_2O \text{ (s)} + \tfrac{3}{2}H_2O \text{ (g)}; \qquad \Delta G_{373} \approx 0$$

What is ΔG_{373} if $p_{H_2O} = 0.1$ atm?

(b)

$$3Fe \text{ (s)} + 4H_2O \text{ (g)} \longrightarrow Fe_3O_4 \text{ (s)} + 4H_2 \text{ (g)}; \qquad \Delta G_{298}^{\ominus} = -100 \text{ kJ}$$

Calculate ΔG for the following partial pressures (atm).

(i) H_2O 1.0 H_2 0.01
(ii) H_2O 0.5 H_2 0.5
(iii) H_2O 10^{-5} H_2 1.0

(c) $Sn^{4+} \text{ (aq)} + H_2S \text{ (aq)} \longrightarrow Sn^{2+} \text{ (aq)} + S \text{ (s)} + 2H^+ \text{ (aq)};$
$$\Delta G_{298}^{\ominus} = -2 \text{ kJ}$$

What is ΔG if $[Sn^{4+}] = [Sn^{2+}] = 1$ M, $[H_2S] = 0.1$ M, and $[H^+] = $ (i) 1 M, (ii) 0.01 M?

2. Reaction isotherm

(a)

$$2CaO \text{ (s)} + 2Cl_2 \text{ (g)} \longrightarrow 2CaCl_2 \text{ (s)} + O_2 \text{ (g)}; \qquad \Delta G_{298}^{\ominus} = -292 \text{ kJ}$$

Calculate the pressure of oxygen which is in equilibrium with CaO, $CaCl_2$ and 5 atm chlorine at 298 K.

(b) Use data from Appendix A to calculate $\Delta G_{298}^{\ominus}$, and hence K (the 'solubility product', see §7.17) for:

$$Ca(OH)_2 \text{ (s)} \longrightarrow Ca^{2+} \text{ (aq)} + 2OH^- \text{ (aq)}$$

(Do not expect great accuracy in calculations of this kind.)

(c) $HNO_2 \text{ (aq)} + 2Fe^{3+} \text{ (aq)} + H_2O \text{ (l)} \longrightarrow$
$$NO_3^- \text{ (aq)} + 2Fe^{2+} \text{ (aq)} + 3H^+ \text{ (aq)}; \qquad \Delta G^{\ominus} = +32.6 \text{ kJ}$$

Calculate K, and find the maximum $[H^+]$ at which the reaction *will* go, with all other substances in standard concentrations.

3. Calculation of $\Delta G^{\ominus}$

When dry HBr gas (1 atm) was passed through a tube at 623 K (350°C) the maximum partial pressure of Br_2 vapour observed was 1.35×10^{-5} atm.

(a) Calculate K_p and $\Delta G^{\ominus}_{623}$ for the reaction:

$$2HBr\ (g) \longrightarrow Br_2\ (g) + H_2\ (g)$$

(b) Calculate $\Delta G^{\ominus}$, $\Delta H^{\ominus}$ and K_p at 298 K (25°C) for the same reaction, using energies of formation.

Then use equation **7.10** (§7.11) to calculate K_p at 623 K. What fraction of the total bromine is present as the element at this temperature? (Ignore dissociation into Br atoms.)

7.14 Equilibria in solution: dissociation constants

Equilibria in solution are usually established very rapidly, so the chemistry of such reactions depends greatly upon the equilibrium constants. Two types of reaction in particular will be considered: the dissociation of electrolytes (especially acids and bases), and the solubility of ionic salts.

Acids in aqueous solution are always present as an equilibrium mixture of the undissociated molecules, hydrated hydrogen ions, and the anions; e.g.

$$HNO_2 + H_2O \rightleftharpoons H_3O^+ + NO_2^-$$

The water is omitted from the equilibrium constant, because it is in large excess, and virtually of constant and standard concentration. This gives the 'dissociation constant of the acid', K_a, the form:

$$K_a = \frac{[H_3O^+][NO_2^-]}{[HNO_2]}$$

The value of K_a can vary from over 100 for a strong acid such as hydrochloric to 10^{-10} or less for a very weak acid such as phenol. K_a for nitrous acid is 5×10^{-4}.

For convenience these constants are often used in the form of pK values, where p$K = -\log_{10} K$ (cf. pH $= -\log_{10} [H_3O^+]$). E.g., if $K_a = 5 \times 10^{-4}$, p$K = 3.3$, since $\log_{10} 5 = 0.7$, and so $\log (5 \times 10^{-4}) = 0.7 - 4 = -3.3$.

7.15 Entropy of dissociation of acids and bases

Let us consider in more detail the best-known weak acid, acetic acid. At 298 K,

$$K_a = \frac{[CH_3COO^-][H_3O^+]}{[CH_3COOH]} = 1.8 \times 10^{-5}; \qquad pK_a = 4.75$$

The pH of a solution of acetic acid, e.g. 0.1 M, may be calculated as follows:

Since K_a is small, almost all the acid is undissociated,

$$[CH_3COOH] = 0.1$$

From the equation it follows that $[CH_3COO^-] = [H_3O^+]$ since there is no other appreciable source of acetate or hydrogen ions. (H_3O^+ from the dissociation of water is negligible in this case.)

$$\therefore [H_3O^+]^2 = 1.8 \times 10^{-5} \times 0.1$$
$$[H_3O^+] = 1.34 \times 10^{-3}$$
$$pH = 2.87$$

$\Delta G^\ominus$ for the dissociation of acetic acid is easily calculated from K_a:

$$\Delta G^\ominus = -2.3RT \log K_a$$
$$= +2.30 \times 8.31 \times 298 \times 4.75 \text{ J mol}^{-1}$$
$$= +27 \text{ kJ mol}^{-1}$$

ΔH is known from the enthalpy of neutralization at 1 M concentration (§2.6):

$CH_3COOH + Na^+OH^- \longrightarrow CH_3COO^-Na^+ + H_2O$; $\quad \Delta H = -56.2 \text{ kJ}$
$H_3O^+ + Na^+OH^- \longrightarrow Na^+ + 2H_2O$; $\quad\quad\quad \Delta H = -57.6 \text{ kJ}$

$\overline{CH_3COOH + H_2O \rightleftharpoons CH_3COO^- + H_3O^+}$; $\quad \Delta H = +1.4 \text{ kJ}$

It is sometimes erroneously stated that acetic acid is weak because of the high energy needed to break the O—H bond; and that in the chloro-acetic acids the withdrawal of electrons by the chlorine atoms weakens the bond and causes an increase in the dissociation constant. This cannot be the true explanation, because $+1.4$ kJ mol^{-1} is a very small enthalpy—no more than the strength of van der Waals forces. The fairly large positive value of $\Delta G^\ominus$ must be due to a large and *negative* $\Delta S^\ominus$. This is surprising, if the ionization is thought of as the traditional

$$CH_3COOH \rightleftharpoons CH_3COO^- + H^+,$$

as this would be expected to have a positive entropy. Hydration must cause more order in the water molecules than the disorder caused by the dissociation of the acid. Although the one acid molecule becomes two particles, the charges on the ions hold some of the polar water molecules by electrostatic forces, and restrict their movement. Entropy is a decisive factor in the strengths of most acids and bases.

The interplay of ΔH and $\Delta S^\ominus$ is well illustrated by the three successive ionizations of phosphoric acid.

	ΔH	$T\Delta S^\ominus$	$\Delta G^\ominus$
	(in kJ at 298 K)		
$H_3PO_4 \text{ (aq)} + H_2O \rightleftharpoons H_2PO_4^- \text{ (aq)} + H_3O^+ \text{ (aq)}$	-13	-26	$+13$
$H_2PO_4^- + H_2O \rightleftharpoons HPO_4^{2-} + H_3O^+$	$+4$	-38	$+42$
$HPO_4^{2-} + H_2O \rightleftharpoons PO_4^{3-} + H_3O^+$	$+15$	-54	$+69$

7.16 Exercises

1. 0.1 M and 0.5 M H_2S solutions have hydrogen ion concentrations equal to 1.0×10^{-4} and 0.7×10^{-4} mole H^+ per litre respectively. Calculate the dissociation constants of H_2S as if it were (a) a dibasic acid, (b) a monobasic acid, and so deduce the actual behaviour.

2. The enthalpy of dissociation of acetic acid is $+1.4$ kJ mol^{-1}. How much would you expect the $[H^+]$ of a given solution of acetic acid to change with temperature?

3*. The pH of a 0.1 M solution of a certain monobasic acid is 2.878 at 298 K and 2.861 at 348 K. Calculate (a) K_a at the two temperatures, (b) ΔH of dissociation.

4. Account for the following: the dissociation of aqueous hydrofluoric acid is exothermic ($\Delta H = -12.5$ kJ mol^{-1}) yet the acid is quite weak ($K_a = 7 \times 10^{-4}$ at 298 K).

7.17 Solubility

An important class of ionic equilibrium is the dissolution of electrolytes. A general equation can be written thus:

$$A_xB_y\,(s) + aq \rightleftharpoons xA^{m+}\,(aq) + yB^{n-}\,(aq)$$

The equilibrium constant for the reaction is known as the solubility product:

$$K_{s.p.} = [A^{m+}]^x[B^{n-}]^y$$

The concentrations of the solid is standard by definition, and does not appear in the equilibrium constant. The constancy of the solubility product leaves much to be desired except for very sparingly soluble salts. The true equilibrium constant is the product of activities rather than concentrations.

Despite this reservation, solubility products can give useful information about the maximum ionic concentrations possible under various circumstances. For example, $[Ag^+][Cl^-] = 2 \times 10^{-10}$, and if pure water is saturated with silver chloride the equilibrium is reached when both ionic concentrations are $\sqrt{2} \times 10^{-5}$ M. But if the equilibrium has resulted from the mixing of ions and the precipitation of silver chloride, the final ionic concentrations need not be equal. If one drop of silver nitrate solution is added to a large volume of 2 M sodium chloride, reaction will occur until $[Ag^+]$ is reduced to 10^{-10} M.

Solubility curves

Figure 7.7 shows some common solubility curves. These are graphs of specific solubility (measured as grams solute per 100 g water) versus temperature. Most solubility curves have a positive gradient, corresponding to an increase in solubility product with rising temperature, and this indicates a positive enthalpy of solution (§7.11). For such electrolytes the enthalpy of hydration must have a slightly smaller magnitude than the crystal lattice enthalpy. If, despite this positive ΔH, a molar solution can be obtained, it follows that for $\Delta G^\ominus$ to be zero or negative, the standard entropy of solution must be positive. This is not surprising, since the disintegration of a regular crystal into freely-moving ions would seem to be an increase in disorder. If the enthalpy of dissolution is too positive, $T \Delta S^\ominus$ cannot equal it, and the substance will be only sparingly soluble.

Some substances (for example sodium chloride) have enthalpies of dissolution which are almost zero.

Some exceptional crystals evolve heat on dissolution, and their solubility curves slope downwards. Examples are calcium hydroxide and citrate, and anhydrous sodium sulphate (above 305 K, see Fig. 7.7).

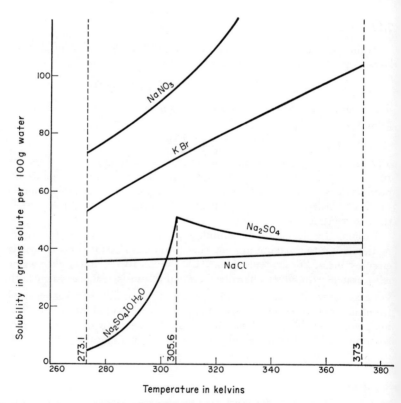

Fig. 7.7   Solubility curves for some salts

In such cases equilibrium (saturation) must result from the opposing of the negative enthalpy by a negative entropy change.

A negative entropy of solution can only be interpreted as an entropy of hydration. The crystal disintegrates, increasing their disorder; but the ions bond with water molecules, restricting their movement, and creating a more orderly arrangement.

Such an increase in hydration cannot occur if the crystal is rich in water of crystallization, for the ions are then already hydrated, and dissolution can only increase disorder. So the sodium sulphate decahydrate has a positive gradient on the solubility graph, even though that for the anhydrous salt is negative.

7.18 Exercises

These exercises are all of substantial length.

1. The solubility of $KClO_4$ is given below. Calculate the solubility product at two temperatures and the corresponding values of $\Delta G^{\ominus}$. From these obtain $\Delta S^{\ominus}$ and ΔH of dissolution. (For these dilute solutions,

$$\frac{\text{concentration}}{\text{mol litre}^{-1}} \approx \text{molality.})$$

Also plot a graph of log solubility vs. temperature, and interpret the slope.

Temperature/(°C)	0	10	20	30
Solubility, $\left(\dfrac{\text{mass solute}}{\text{mass water}} \times 100\right)$	0.75	1.05	1.80	2.6

2. The solubility product for $CH_3COO^-Ag^+$ is 3×10^{-3} $(mol^2$ litre$^{-2})$. Calculate the solubility of the salt in grams per litre, and explain why it dissolves readily in dilute nitric acid.

What is the lowest pH at which some of 1 mole of silver acetate can remain undissolved in one litre of solutions? (Use data from §7.15.)

3. *Simple solubilities*. Use Appendix A to calculate the free-energies and enthalpies of solution of the following substances, and hence the solubility products, approximate specific solubilities and change of solubility with temperature: (a) $PbBr_2$, (b) Br_2

4.*

$$Fe\ (s) + Ni^{2+}\ (aq) \longrightarrow Fe^{2+}\ (aq) + Ni\ (s); \qquad \Delta G^{\ominus} = -38.6\ kJ$$

It is observed that although the above reaction is able to proceed when all participants are in standard concentrations (both ions 1 M), the addition of ammonia hinders the reaction, and tends to reverse it when

5—c.e.

[NH$_3$ (aq)] exceeds 0.4 M. This is attributed to the formation of the Ni(NH$_3$)$_6^{2+}$ complex, reaction between NH$_3$ and Fe^{2+} being negligible in comparison. Calculate the value to which [Ni^{2+}] must be lowered by the ammonia, and hence the equilibrium constant for the reaction:

$$Ni(NH_3)_6^{2+} \rightleftharpoons Ni^{2+} + 6NH_3 \text{ (aq)}$$

8 Electrochemical potentials

8.1 Electron transfer reactions

A large number of reactions come into the category of oxidations and reductions. Elementary definitions of these processes (e.g. 'oxidation = loss of hydrogen') are limited in scope. They can be replaced by the comprehensive definition:

Oxidation is the complete loss of one or more electrons by an elementary particle.†

Reduction is, conversely, the complete gain of electrons. (The word 'complete' excludes the partial gain or loss of a pair of electrons by co-ordinate bond formation.)

The substance which loses electrons, and is oxidized, is known as the reductant, or reducing agent. The substance which gains electrons, and is reduced, is called the oxidant. Any momentary doubt about this can always be dispelled by the consideration of some straightforward example such as the burning of magnesium in oxygen.

Oxidation of one substance cannot proceed without the reduction of another substance, so the whole process is a reduction-oxidation, or *redox* reaction.

Half-equations

The stoichiometric equation for any redox reaction can be split into two half-equations, one showing the reduction, the other showing the oxidation. They must be balanced with respect both to atoms and charges.

ILLUSTRATIONS

1. $2KI + Cl_2 \longrightarrow 2KCl + I_2$ $\begin{cases} 2I^- \longrightarrow I_2 + 2e^- \text{ (ox)} \\ Cl_2 + 2e^- \longrightarrow 2Cl^- \text{ (red)} \end{cases}$

2. $Zn + Br_2 \longrightarrow ZnBr_2$ $\begin{cases} Zn \longrightarrow Zn^{2+} + 2e^- \text{ (ox)} \\ Br_2 + 2e^- \longrightarrow 2Br^- \text{ (red)} \end{cases}$

3. $\left. \begin{array}{l} FeCl_2 + HCl + HNO_3 \longrightarrow \\ \quad FeCl_3 + NO_2 + H_2O \end{array} \right\}$ $\begin{array}{l} Fe^{2+} \longrightarrow Fe^{3+} + e^- \text{ (ox)} \\ NO_3^- + 2H^+ + e^- \longrightarrow NO_2 + H_2O \text{(red)} \end{array}$

† D. R. Pelmore Esq once asked a class (which had just been learning electrostatics) 'Does this mean that an ebonite rod is oxidized when it is rubbed with fur?'

It will be noticed that each pair of half-equations adds up to the whole equation (in some cases the unchanged 'spectator ions' have to be included on both sides) and so the number of electrons in each half-equation must be equal. It is not possible to combine two oxidation or two reduction half-equations, because the electrons do not then cancel out.

Another point to notice is that where complex oxy-ions are involved (e.g. NO_3^- in Illustration 3) there may be the participation of H^+, OH^- or H_2O. A useful rule for balancing of such half-equations is that a redundant oxygen atom can be removed, in acid solution, by the addition of $2H^+$ and enough electrons to balance the charges. In basic solution the trick is to add H_2O to the side with redundant oxygen, and $2OH^-$ to the other side.

WORKED EXAMPLE

Construct half equations to show the oxidation of (a) sulphite to sulphate, and (b) V^{2+} to VO_2^+, in both acid and basic solution. Also (c) construct an equation for the hypothetical reduction of sulphuric acid by V^{2+}.

(a)
$$SO_3^{2-} \longrightarrow SO_4^{2-}$$

Add $2H^+$ to the right, which has redundant O, and H_2O to the left:

$$SO_3^{2-} + H_2O \longrightarrow SO_4^{2-} + 2H^+$$

Add electrons to balance charges:

$$SO_3^{2-} + H_2O \longrightarrow SO_4^{2-} + 2H^+ + 2e^- \quad \text{(acid solution)}$$

Alternatively, add $2OH^-$ to the left, which is deficient in O:

$$SO_3^{2-} + 2OH^- \longrightarrow SO_4^{2-} + H_2O + 2e^- \quad \text{(basic solution)}$$

(b)
$$V^{2+} \longrightarrow VO_2^+$$

In acid solution, add $4H^+$ to the right:

$$V^{2+} + 2H_2O \longrightarrow VO_2^+ + 4H^+$$

The total charge on the right now exceeds that on the left by $3+$, so $3e^-$ must be added to the right:

$$V^{2+} + 2H_2O \longrightarrow VO_2^+ + 4H^+ + 3e^-$$

As a check, notice that the number of electrons in the half-equation will always equal the algebraic difference in oxidation states of the atoms involved. In this illustration the oxidation state of vanadium changes from $+2$ to $+5$.

In basic solution the procedure gives:

$$V^{2+} + 4OH^- \longrightarrow VO_2^+ + 2H_2O + 3e^-$$

But this is not very meaningful since neither species V^{2+} nor VO_2^+ exists in basic solution. The more realistic half-equation is obtained by including the two *non-redox* processes:

$$V^{2+}+2OH^- \longrightarrow V(OH)_2 \text{ (s)} \quad \text{and} \quad VO_2^+ +2OH^- \longrightarrow VO_3^- +H_2O$$

to give:

$$V(OH)_2 \text{ (s)}+4OH^- \longrightarrow VO_3^- +3H_2O+3e^-$$

(c) The hypothetical reduction of H_2SO_4 (aq) by V^{2+} would consist of the combination of the two half-equations:

$$SO_4^{2-} +2H^+ +2e^- \longrightarrow SO_3^{2-} +H_2O \qquad \text{(red)}$$
$$V^{2+} +2H_2O \longrightarrow VO_2^+ +4H^+ +3e^- \quad \text{(ox)}$$

As they stand, the two half-equations contain different numbers of electrons. In order that they add up to a whole equation, the first must be multiplied through by 3, and the second by 2. Then the electrons cancel out.

$$3SO_4^{2-} +6H^+ +6e^- \longrightarrow 3SO_3^{2-} +3H_2O \qquad \text{(red)}$$
$$2V^{2+} +4H_2O \longrightarrow 2VO_2^+ +8H^+ +6e^- \qquad \text{(ox)}$$
$$\text{Sum: } 2V^{2+} +3SO_4^{2-} +H_2O \longrightarrow 2VO_2^+ +3SO_3^{2-} +2H^+ \quad \text{(redox)}$$

The device of combining half-equations has here been put to use in balancing a redox equation that would have been almost impossible to balance simply 'by inspection'.

8.2 Exercises

Practice in devising and combining half-equations.

1. Analyse the following reactions into pairs of redox half-equations, omitting the ions which remain unchanged throughout the reaction. Show which half is oxidation and which reduction, and name the oxidant and reductant.

(a) $SnCl_2$ (aq)$+Cl_2$ (g)$\longrightarrow SnCl_4$ (aq)
(b) $CuCl_2$ (aq)$+Cu$ (s)$\longrightarrow 2CuCl$ (s)
(c) $H_2SO_3+H_2O+I_2 \longrightarrow H_2SO_4+2HI$

2. The half-equation for the action of permanganate as an oxidant in acid solution is:

$$MnO_4^- +8H^+\text{(aq)}+5e^- \longrightarrow Mn^{2+} +8H_2O$$

Combine this with the following oxidations to give complete ionic equations.

(a) $Fe^{2+} \longrightarrow Fe^{3+} +e^-$
(b) $C_2O_4^{2-}$ (oxalate) $\longrightarrow 2CO_2+2e^-$
(c) $I^- \longrightarrow \frac{1}{2}I_2+e^-$

3. The VO_2^+ ion can react, under different conditions, to form either VO^{2+} or VO^{3+}. Write balanced equations for these changes and state whether each is an oxidation or a reduction or neither.

4. Hydrogen peroxide can transfer electrons in two different ways:

$$H_2O_2 \longrightarrow 2H^+ + O_2\,(g) + 2e^- \quad \text{and} \quad H_2O_2 + 2e^- \longrightarrow 2OH^-$$

Write equations for reactions which might occur between H_2O_2 and (a) ozone O_3; (b) alkaline sodium sulphite.

(Note: $O_3 + 2H^+ + 2e^- \rightarrow O_2 + H_2O$.)

8.3 Reaction at a distance

The analysis of redox reactions into electron gain and loss is more than a hypothetical device for balancing equations. Its reality is convincingly demonstrated by the reaction of an oxidant with a reductant when the two are in separate vessels, connected only by a wire to carry the electrons which are being transferred.

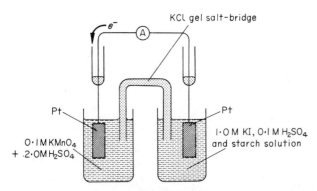

Fig. 8.1

Set up the apparatus in Fig. 8.1. The KCl salt-bridge† is approximately 1% KCl plus 4% gelatin, which sets to a firm jelly; this allows migration of ions to maintain electrical balance between the two solutions, but avoids random diffusion of the electrolytes.

At the platinum electrode in the permanganate solution, electrons are being taken from the platinum by the half-reaction:

$$MnO_4^- + 8H^+ + 5e^- \longrightarrow Mn^{2+} + 8H_2O$$

At the same time, the platinum electrode in the potassium iodide solution is receiving electrons from the half-reaction:

$$5I^- \longrightarrow \tfrac{5}{2}I_2 + 5e^-$$

† See §3.13.

The milliammeter in series with the two electrodes will show a small deflection, and will indicate the direction of flow of electrons.

After this the ammeter should be short-circuited, to allow the reaction to run for some hours. The blue starch-iodine complex should appear around the electrode in the iodide solution.

A control may be run if desired, with identical apparatus but without electrical contact.

8.4 Cell potentials

When a chemical reaction is carried out in an electrochemical cell, some of the chemical energy is converted into electrical energy. In the demonstration described above, the reaction between permanganate and iodide was driving a small electric current through the external circuit. This harnessed reaction therefore gave out less heat per gram-equation than it would have done if the reagents had been stirred together in a single beaker. ΔH is constant for the reaction, however it is carried out; but $\Delta H = $ heat + work, not heat alone. This has been discussed in §§3.12 and 2.11.

$$\begin{array}{ccccc} \text{electrical work} & = & \text{quantity of} & \times & \text{electric potential} \\ \text{obtained} & & \text{electricity} & & \text{difference} \\ -W & = & nF & \times & E \end{array} \qquad \textbf{8.1}$$

If the equation for the reaction can be split into a pair of half-equations each containing n electrons, then one gram-equation of reaction results in the transfer of quantity nF of electricity (where $F = $ the Faraday constant, or the quantity of electricity carried by one mole of electrons). E is the cell potential, and by convention E is positive for a reaction which can proceed spontaneously. As F is 96 500 C mol^{-1} (of electrons) the work W is in units of volts × coulombs, that is, joules. (To convert J to kJ, divide by 10^3.)

The *maximum* work which can be obtained is equal to ΔG; or, if conditions are standard, to $\Delta G^{\ominus}$. This maximum is only obtainable when almost no current is being drawn from the cell, so that the reaction is under reversible conditions (§3.13). The p.d. is then a maximum, and if concentrations are standard this p.d. is the *standard reversible cell potential*, $E^{\ominus}$.

$$-W_{\max} = -\Delta G^{\ominus} = nFE^{\ominus} \qquad \textbf{8.2}$$

with commonly-used units:

$$-\Delta G^{\ominus}/\text{kJ} = \frac{n(F/\text{C})\,(E^{\ominus}/\text{V})}{10^3\ \text{J}/(\text{kJ})} = 96.5nE^{\ominus}/\text{V} \qquad \textbf{8.2a}$$

Under non-reversible conditions the e.m.f. of the cell will be lower than the maximum E, but comparisons of different reactions will give e.m.f.'s which are roughly the same proportion of the E. The experiments in §8.5 are rough comparisons of e.m.f.'s of various cells in which the reductant is a metal and the oxidant is, mainly, the H^+ ion. The metals can be placed approximately in order of $E^\ominus$ for the cells driven by the half-reactions:

$$M \longrightarrow M^{n+}(aq) + ne^- \quad \text{(ox)}$$
$$2H^+(aq) + 2e^- \longrightarrow H_2(g) \qquad \text{(red)}$$

This order is the familiar electro-chemical series.

8.5 Practical work

A rough comparison of the electrode potentials of some metals

Materials and apparatus: Voltmeter, to read 2 V. Connecting wires. Crocodile clips. Small solid samples of Zn, Pb, Cu, Mg, Fe, Na,† Ca. M/2 sulphuric acid.

Measure the voltage between the following pairs of metals when they are dipped in the same solution of sulphuric acid. Do not let the crocodile clips touch the liquid. Note which metal is the negative electrode, and is sending electrons out to the external circuit.

(a) Copper foil as one electrode, against all the others in turn.
(b) Zn+Pb; Fe+Pb; Mg+Pb.
(c) Zn+Fe; Mg+Fe.

Arrange the metals in order so that a higher one is always the negative electrode compared to a lower one, and the voltage increases as pairs are chosen from further apart in the list.

It must be emphasized that no *quantitative* results can be obtained from this experiment, for at least three reasons: (i) the cell is not in equilibrium, and is not functioning reversibly; (ii) concentrations (especially of products) are uncertain, and far from 'standard'; (iii) there is uncertainty about the nature of the electron-absorbing (reduction) half-reaction.

8.6 Reduction potentials

In §§8.3 and 8.4 it was shown that the cell potential for a reaction can be measured by arranging for the two half-reactions (oxidation and reduction) to occur at separate electrodes. It is found that any cell potential is the sum of the two half-cell potentials, which are constant (for given temperatures and concentration) regardless of the other half-reactions with which they are paired. The terms *reduction potential* and *oxidation potential* are used to distinguish the two half-cell potentials, and either may be called, indiscriminately, a *redox potential*.

† The experiment with sodium must be performed under supervision.

Since no redox potential can be measured in isolation, it is necessary to define an arbitrary zero, that is, a chosen half-reaction to which the oxidizing or reducing power of any other half-reaction can be compared. The standard electrode must be accurately reproducible, and metal electrodes are found to be unsuitable because their exact potential varies with their history of physical treatment, annealing, and surface condition. Therefore the zero redox potential was allotted to the *hydrogen electrode* (Fig. 8.2):

$$2H^+ \text{ (aq, 1 molal)} + 2e^- \rightleftharpoons H_2 \text{ (g, 1 atm);} \qquad E^\ominus = 0.00 \text{ V}$$

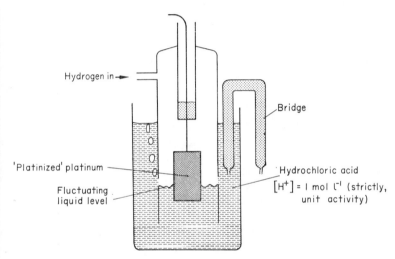

Fig. 8.2   The standard hydrogen electrode ($E^\ominus = 0.00$ V)

If concentration conditions are standard (1 mole solute per kg water or 1 atm partial pressure) for the reactants and products of the half-reaction, the redox potential is denoted $E^\ominus$. Temperature is 298 K unless otherwise stated.

The sign convention is that if a half-reaction tends to occur as a reduction, compared to H^+ (aq, 1 m) $+ e^- \rightarrow \frac{1}{2}H_2$ (g), it is given a positive reduction potential, because the electrode in the solution will become positive relative to the hydrogen electrode.

For example:

$$H_2 \text{ (g)} + Cl_2 \text{ (g)} \longrightarrow 2H^+ \text{ (aq)} + 2Cl^- \text{ (aq);} \quad E^\ominus = +1.36 \text{ V}$$

The reduction half-reaction is:

$$Cl_2 \text{ (g)} + 2e^- \longrightarrow 2Cl^- \text{ (aq)}$$

and since this occurs in preference to the reduction of H^+ (aq), the reduction potential for it is positive ($E^\ominus_{\text{red}} = +1.36$ V).

Conversely, zinc metal is oxidized by H^+ aqueous ions, so the half-reaction:

$$Zn^{2+}(aq) + 2e^- \longrightarrow Zn\,(s)$$

is not spontaneous in conjunction with the H_2/H^+ half-cell, so the reduction potential of Zn^{2+}/Zn is negative at -0.76 V.

8.7 Addition of redox potentials

If a half-equation is reversed, the sign of the redox potential must be change, e.g.:

$$Cl_2\,(aq) + 2e^- \longrightarrow 2Cl^-\,; \qquad E^{\ominus}_{red} = +1.36 \text{ V}$$
$$2Cl^- \longrightarrow Cl_2 + 2e^-\,; \qquad E^{\ominus}_{ox} = -1.36 \text{ V}$$

(The subscripts 'red', 'ox' and 'cell' will be used to indicate reduction, oxidation and cell potentials.)

If a half-equation is multiplied through, however, the redox potential must *not* be altered; e.g.

$$\tfrac{1}{2}Cl_2 + e^- \longrightarrow Cl^-\,; \qquad E^{\ominus}_{red} = +1.36 \text{ V}$$

The reason is that although the ΔG for the half-reaction would be multiplied, so would n, the number of electrons; therefore $E^{\ominus}$, which equals $-\Delta G^{\ominus}/nF$, is unchanged.

The addition of any half-equation for a reduction with the reversed form (oxidation) of any other half-equation can give a complete reaction, if the numbers of electrons are equal (see §8.1); then the cell potential for the complete reaction† is the algebraic sum of $E^{\ominus}_{red}$ and $E^{\ominus}_{ox}$, the two redox potentials. This is the most common and valuable use of redox potentials, since the sign and size of the cell potential enables predictions to be made regarding the feasibility of reaction: as will be described in the next section §8.8). E.g.

$$2Fe^{3+} + 2e^- \longrightarrow 2Fe^{2+}\,; \qquad\qquad E^{\ominus}_{red} = +0.77$$
$$H_2SO_3 + H_2O \longrightarrow SO_4^{2-} + 4H^+ + 2e^-\,; \qquad E^{\ominus}_{ox} = -0.17$$

$$2Fe^{3+} + H_2SO_3 + H_2O \longrightarrow 2Fe^{2+} + SO_4^{2-} + 4H^+\,; \qquad E^{\ominus}_{cell} = +0.60 \text{ V}$$

If the numbers of electrons are *not* equal and opposite, however, the addition of two half-equations gives a third half-equation, and then the third redox potential is *not* the sum of the first two. E.g.

$$Fe \longrightarrow Fe^{2+} + 2e^-\,; \qquad E^{\ominus}_{ox} = +0.44$$
$$Fe^{2+} \longrightarrow Fe^{3+} + e^-\,; \qquad E^{\ominus}_{ox} = -0.77$$
$$Fe \longrightarrow Fe^{3+} + 3e^-\,; \qquad E^{\ominus}_{ox} \neq -0.33$$

† Strictly, only *cells* have cell potentials, and to give a *reaction* a potential is to imply a cell in which it could take place and, in particular, a value for n, the number of electrons transferred. If n is ambiguous, as it is in disproportionation reactions for example, a definite value for E_{cell} must be linked with an explicitly stated value for n. ΔG is of course unambiguous.

The free-energies are additive, however, and $\Delta G^{\ominus} = -nFE^{\ominus}$. Since $-F$ is constant, $nE^{\ominus}$ can be added:

	$E^{\ominus}$	$nE^{\ominus}$
$Fe \longrightarrow Fe^{2+} + 2e^-$;	$+0.44$	$+0.88$
$Fe^{2+} \longrightarrow Fe^{3+} + e^-$;	-0.77	-0.77
$Fe \longrightarrow Fe^{3+} + 3e^-$;		$+0.11$

$$\therefore E^{\ominus} = +0.11/3 = +0.04 \text{ V}$$

8.8 Application of redox potentials to inorganic chemistry

When redox potentials are combined as described above, the redox potential (cell potential) for a complete reaction is obtained. If this is negative the reaction is most unlikely to go, and in any case will stop at an equilibrium before the half-way point. If $E^{\ominus}$ is positive (corresponding to a negative $\Delta G^{\ominus}$) the reaction is exergonic, and can proceed unless the energy of activation is too high. It is found that simple electron-transfer reactions between ions have very low E_a, and will go quite rapidly and completely if $E^{\ominus} > +0.3$ V or so.

BEWARE of predicting the feasibility of a reaction from the sign of a reduction or oxidation potential alone. The signs of cell potentials for *whole* reactions are meaningful, but the signs of redox potentials of half-reactions are arbitrary, and relative to the hydrogen electrode.

Reactions in which covalent bonds have to be broken, or those in which gases are formed, may have large E_a, which differs according to the nature of the electrodes. The additional voltage required to make the reaction proceed in such cases is known as the 'over-voltage'.

Examples are:

$$S_2O_8^{2-} + 2I^- \longrightarrow 2SO_4^{2-} + I_2;$$
$$\text{reaction slow even though } E^{\ominus} = +1.47 \text{ V}$$

$$2H_2O_2 \longrightarrow 2H_2O + O_2;$$
reaction slow in acid solution, unless catalysed, though $E^{\ominus} > 1$ V

$$(COOH)_2 \text{ (aq)} + SO_4^{2-} + 2H^+ \longrightarrow H_2SO_3 + 2CO_2 \text{ (g)};$$
$E^{\ominus} = +0.32$, but this reaction does not proceed at all.

Further illustrations will be taken from the reactions of permanganate and the halide ions:

$MnO_4^- + 8H^+ + 5e^- \longrightarrow Mn^{2+} + 4H_2O$;	$E^{\ominus}_{red} = +1.51$
$5Br^- \longrightarrow \frac{5}{2}Br_2 \text{ (aq)} + 5e^-$;	$E^{\ominus}_{ox} = -1.06$
$MnO_4^- + 5Br^- + 8H^+ \longrightarrow Mn^{2+} + 4H_2O + \frac{5}{2}Br_2$;	$E^{\ominus}_{cell} = +0.45$ V

The above reaction is in fact complete and rapid. But the reaction between permanganate and dilute (1 M) hydrochloric acid at 298 K is less straightforward, and a brown precipitate of hydrated MnO_2 may be formed. This is because the cell potential for the reaction to form Cl_2 (aq) $+ Mn^{2+}$, though positive, is small ($+1.51 - 1.36 = +0.15$ V). Some of the permanganate is reduced according to another half-equation, which has a more positive reduction potential:

$$MnO_4^- + 4H^+ + 3e^- \longrightarrow MnO_2 \text{ (s)} + 2H_2O; \qquad E_{red}^{\ominus} = +1.70 \text{ V}$$

The cell potential for the reaction which produces $Cl_2 + MnO_2$ is $+1.70 - 1.36 = +0.34$ V, so this reaction predominates.

Since $E^{\ominus}$ for $Br^- + MnO_4^- \to Br_2 + MnO_2$ ($+0.64$) is larger than that for reaction to Mn^{2+} ($+0.54$ V) why does bromide not also produce MnO_2? There are two answers: possibly the reaction to Mn^{2+}, which has an adequately large $E^{\ominus}$, is faster than that to solid MnO_2; but furthermore, any MnO_2 produced would itself be reduced by more Br^-, since:

$$MnO_2 + 4H^+ + 2e^- \longrightarrow Mn^{2+} + 2H_2O; \qquad\qquad E_{red}^{\ominus} = +1.23$$

hence

$$MnO_2 + 4H^+ + 2Br^- \longrightarrow Mn^{2+} + 2H_2O + Br_2 \text{ (aq)}; \quad E^{\ominus} = +0.17$$

whereas

$$MnO_2 + 4H^+ + 2Cl^- \longrightarrow Mn^{2+} + 2H_2O + Cl_2 \text{ (aq)}; \quad E^{\ominus} = -0.13$$

Potential diagrams

The chemistry of elements with three or more oxidation states is greatly clarified by the use of potential diagrams, and the standard work by W. M. Latimer† lists these for most elements. They are also used in several textbooks of inorganic chemistry.

The diagrams show the oxidation states of the element, and the redox potential for the half-reaction from one to the next. Two diagrams are necessary, one for acid solution, $[H^+] = 1$, and one for alkaline, $[OH^-] = 1$.

If the steps are written as reductions, and the potential $E^{\ominus}$ for any pair A → B is large and positive, A is a good oxidant; if it is negative or small and positive, B is a good reductant. If the potential for the two-stage process A → C is larger than A → B, this will be shown, since A will then normally react straight to C. (Remember that $nE^{\ominus}$, not $E^{\ominus}$ alone, is additive). Figure 8.3 gives simplified potential diagrams for Mn, Cl, Br and I.

† W. M. Latimer, *Oxidation Potentials*, Prentice-Hall, 2nd ed., 1952.

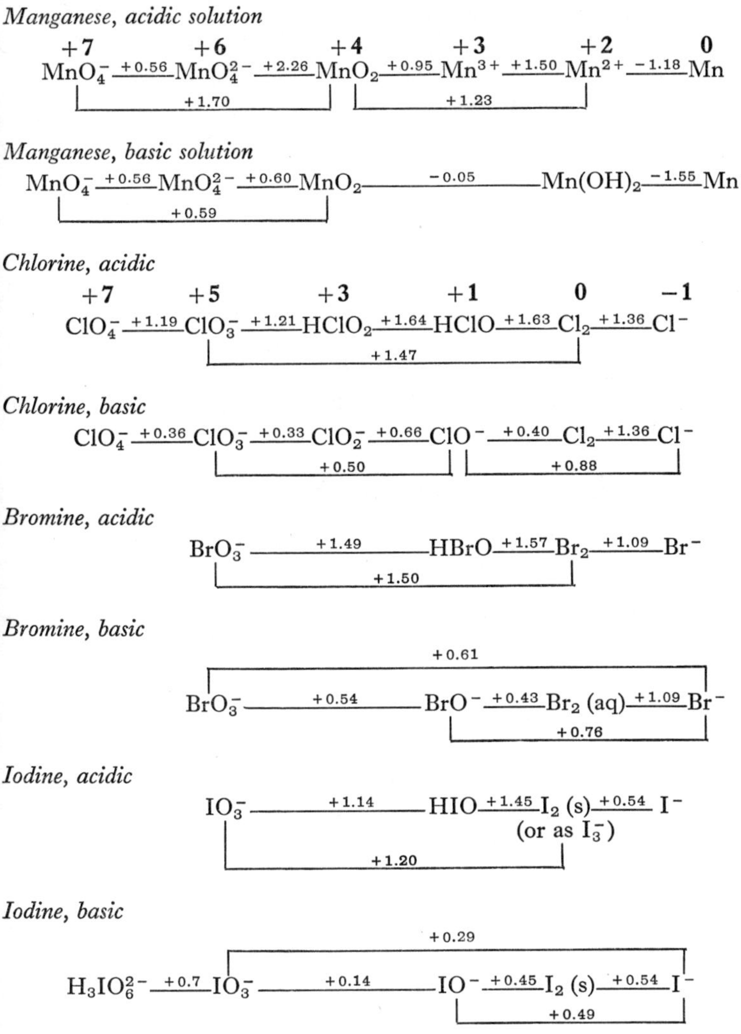

Manganese, acidic solution

$$\underset{}{\overset{+7}{MnO_4^-}}\xrightarrow{+0.56}\overset{+6}{MnO_4^{2-}}\xrightarrow{+2.26}\overset{+4}{MnO_2}\xrightarrow{+0.95}\overset{+3}{Mn^{3+}}\xrightarrow{+1.50}\overset{+2}{Mn^{2+}}\xrightarrow{-1.18}\overset{0}{Mn}$$

$$\underset{+1.70}{\rule{4cm}{0.4pt}}\qquad\underset{+1.23}{\rule{4cm}{0.4pt}}$$

Manganese, basic solution

$$MnO_4^-\xrightarrow{+0.56}MnO_4^{2-}\xrightarrow{+0.60}MnO_2\xrightarrow{\quad-0.05\quad}Mn(OH)_2\xrightarrow{-1.55}Mn$$

$$\underset{+0.59}{\rule{3cm}{0.4pt}}$$

Chlorine, acidic

$$\overset{+7}{ClO_4^-}\xrightarrow{+1.19}\overset{+5}{ClO_3^-}\xrightarrow{+1.21}\overset{+3}{HClO_2}\xrightarrow{+1.64}\overset{+1}{HClO}\xrightarrow{+1.63}\overset{0}{Cl_2}\xrightarrow{+1.36}\overset{-1}{Cl^-}$$

$$\underset{+1.47}{\rule{5cm}{0.4pt}}$$

Chlorine, basic

$$ClO_4^-\xrightarrow{+0.36}ClO_3^-\xrightarrow{+0.33}ClO_2^-\xrightarrow{+0.66}ClO^-\xrightarrow{+0.40}Cl_2\xrightarrow{+1.36}Cl^-$$

$$\underset{+0.50}{\rule{4cm}{0.4pt}}\qquad\underset{+0.88}{\rule{4cm}{0.4pt}}$$

Bromine, acidic

$$BrO_3^-\xrightarrow{\quad+1.49\quad}HBrO\xrightarrow{+1.57}Br_2\xrightarrow{+1.09}Br^-$$

$$\underset{+1.50}{\rule{5cm}{0.4pt}}$$

Bromine, basic

$$\overset{+0.61}{\rule{5cm}{0.4pt}}$$

$$BrO_3^-\xrightarrow{\quad+0.54\quad}BrO^-\xrightarrow{+0.43}Br_2\,(aq)\xrightarrow{+1.09}Br^-$$

$$\underset{+0.76}{\rule{4cm}{0.4pt}}$$

Iodine, acidic

$$IO_3^-\xrightarrow{\quad+1.14\quad}HIO\xrightarrow{+1.45}\underset{\text{(or as }I_3^-)}{I_2\,(s)}\xrightarrow{+0.54}I^-$$

$$\underset{+1.20}{\rule{5cm}{0.4pt}}$$

Iodine, basic

$$\overset{+0.29}{\rule{5cm}{0.4pt}}$$

$$H_3IO_6^{2-}\xrightarrow{+0.7}IO_3^-\xrightarrow{\quad+0.14\quad}IO^-\xrightarrow{+0.45}I_2\,(s)\xrightarrow{+0.54}I^-$$

$$\underset{+0.49}{\rule{4cm}{0.4pt}}$$

Fig. 8.3 Potential diagrams for Mn, Cl, Br, and I, showing reduction potentials in volts. Oxidation states are shown in bold figures.

Many points of interest appear in these diagrams. Mn (metal) is of course a good reductant; $Mn(OH)_2$ is quite easily oxidized to MnO_2 and even MnO_4^{2-} (manganate) in basic solution. (However, the significance of the values differs between acid and basic solutions: $+0.5$ V for $A \rightarrow B$ in acid means B is quite a good reductant; in alkali it means A is a good oxidant.)

The halogens are all good oxidants, as $X_2 \rightarrow X^-$ is positive, but decreasing in order Cl_2, Br_2, I_2. ClO_3^- and BrO_3^- are among the best oxidants on the diagrams (for acid solutions), but IO_3^- is less powerful. So chlorate can oxidize iodine thus:

$$2ClO_3^- + I_2 \longrightarrow 2IO_3^- + Cl_2; \qquad E^\ominus = +1.47 - (+1.20) = +0.27 \text{ V}$$

Disproportionation

Whenever the pattern $A \xrightarrow{E_1^\ominus} B \xrightarrow{E_2^\ominus} C$ appears with $E_2^\ominus$ more positive than $E_1^\ominus$, substance B is unstable with respect to disproportionation, since the reaction $B \rightarrow C$ can drive the reaction $B \rightarrow A$, so $2B \rightarrow A + C$ will have a positive cell potential. Examples are provided by all the halogens in basic solution; $X_2 \rightarrow X^-$ is more positive than $XO^- \rightarrow X_2$, and the reactions $X_2 + 2OH^- \rightarrow X^- + XO^- + H_2O$ all occur readily, e.g.

$$Cl_2 + 2OH^- \longrightarrow Cl^- + ClO^- + H_2O; \qquad E^\ominus = +0.94 \text{ V}$$

The manganate ion, MnO_4^{2-}, which is stable in concentrated alkali, disproportionates in acid, or even on dilution:

$$3MnO_4^{2-} + 4H^+ \longrightarrow 2MnO_4^- + MnO_2 + 2H_2O; \qquad E^\ominus = +1.7 \text{ V}$$

A complicated potential diagram can be made easier to read if it is set out in two dimensions, like a graph. The horizontal axis shows oxidation numbers, while the vertical scale is free-energy, or $E^\ominus \times n$. As the lines may be rather crowded, they can be spread out by exaggerating the differences in slope. This is illustrated in Fig. **8.4**.

The *slope* of any line measures the reduction potential for the step. The greatest positive slopes

show the best oxidants (A), while the steepest downward slopes

show the best reductants (D). 'By-pass' lines

show that two or more reaction steps normally occur at once: $E \rightleftarrows G$.
Points where the gradient increases,

$$
\begin{array}{ccc}
H & & J \\
\backslash & \text{or} & / \\
I\!-\!J & & H\!-\!I
\end{array}
$$

show states which disproportionate (I).

8.9 Exercises

Use the redox potentials listed in Appendix B, p. 196.

1. Write down, from memory, half-equations involving the following
substances, and give reasonable guesses for the signs and values of the
reduction potentials: F_2, I_2, $KMnO_4$ (acid), Mg, HNO_3.

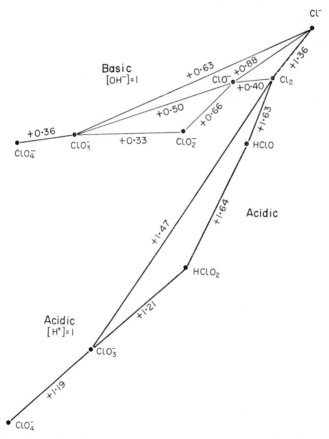

Fig. 8.4   Two-dimensional redox potential diagrams for chlorine

2. Write the following overall equations as pairs of redox half-equations, and calculate $E^\ominus$ for the reaction. Reactions have been chosen in which the energy of activation (overvoltage) is small, so the results should be consistent with your previous knowledge of the direction and vigour of the reactions.

(a) H_2SO_3 (aq) $+I_2$ (aq) $+H_2O \longrightarrow SO_4^{2-} +2I^- +4H^+$
(b) $2Fe^{2+}$ (aq) $+I_2$ (aq) $\longrightarrow 2Fe^{3+} +2I^-$
(c) $Fe^{3+} +Ag \longrightarrow Fe^{2+} +Ag^+$
(d) MnO_2 (s) $+4HCl$ (aq) $\longrightarrow MnCl_2$ (aq) $+2H_2O + Cl_2$ (aq)

If you doubt the prediction from this last calculation, try the action of 1 M hydrochloric acid on manganese dioxide. See also §8.10.

3. Calculate $E^\ominus$ for the oxidation by persulphate ions of (a) H_2S to S and H^+; (b) H_2O to O_2 and H^+. In fact potassium persulphate solution does not evolve oxygen: suggest a reason for the high energy of activation.

4. The electrode potential of Ca^{2+}/Ca is more negative than that of Na^+/Na, yet calcium is generally placed below sodium in the activity series. On what reactions is this decision made? What might be the reason for the interchanging of positions? Is there necessarily any connection between relative electrode potential and reactivity?

5. Warm potassium permanganate in 1 M sulphuric acid will oxidize oxalate ions to carbon dioxide. If it were suggested that the acid is not

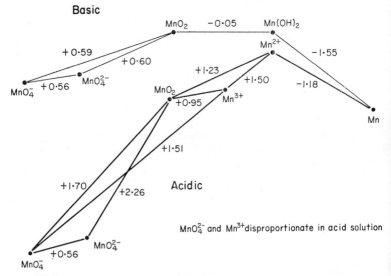

Fig. 8.5

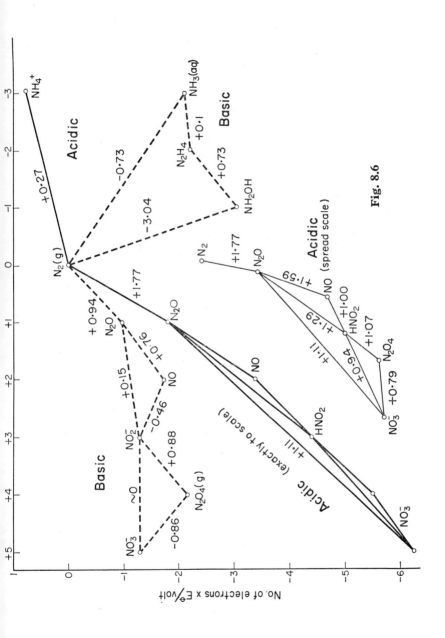

Fig. 8.6

required only by the permanganate, but also by the oxalate ions (to produce oxalic acid as a first step), what experiment could be set up to test the suggestion?

6. Use the information in the electrode potential diagrams (Figs. 8.3–8.6) for this question.

(a) From each of the following groups select (i) the most powerful oxidant, and (ii) the oxidant which will bring about the greatest amount of oxidation of excess reductant:

$$\begin{array}{lllll}
\text{(acidic)} & Cl_2\,(aq) & ClO_3^- & HClO & Cl^- \\
\text{(basic)} & Br_2\,(aq) & I_2\,(aq) & BrO_3^- & IO^- \\
\text{(acidic)} & MnO_4^- & MnO_4^{2-} & MnO_2 & Mn\,(s)
\end{array}$$

(b) Which of the following are susceptible to disproportionation? Write equations for the most likely reactions, and indicate those which you know to occur:

$$\begin{array}{llllll}
\text{(acidic)} & N_2\,(g) & N_2O_4\,(aq) & Mn^{2+} & MnO_4^{2-} & I_2\,(aq\ or\ s) \\
\text{(basic)} & MnO_4^- & I_2\,(aq) & N_2O_4 & ClO^- & Mn(OH)_2
\end{array}$$

(c) In alkaline solution nitrates and nitrites can be reduced beyond N_2 to a -1, -2 or -3 oxidation state. On the basis of $E^{\ominus}$, which compound is the most likely product?

(d) Calculate $E^{\ominus}$ for the following, and predict the likelihood of reaction:

(i) $2NO_2^- + H_2O \longrightarrow \tfrac{1}{2}N_2O_4\,(aq) + 2OH^- + NO\,(g)$ (basic)
(ii) $2HNO_2 \longrightarrow \tfrac{1}{2}N_2O_4\,(aq) + 2NO\,(g) + H_2O$ (acidic)
(iii) $2NH_3\,(aq) + 3ClO^- \longrightarrow N_2 + 3Cl^- + 3H_2O$ (basic)
(iv) $2NH_4^+ + 3HClO \longrightarrow N_2 + 3Cl^- + 3H_2O + 5H^+$ (acidic)

7.*

$$\begin{array}{lll}
Cu^{2+}\,(aq) + e^- \longrightarrow Cu^+\,(aq); & E^{\ominus} = +0.16\ \text{V} \\
Cu^{2+}\,(aq) + Cl^-\,(aq) + e^- \longrightarrow CuCl\,(s); & E^{\ominus} = +0.54\ \text{V} \\
Cu^{2+}\,(aq) + 2e^- \longrightarrow Cu\,(s); & E^{\ominus} = +0.46\ \text{V}
\end{array}$$

Suggest a reason why the second of the above reactions has a more positive reduction potential than the first Cu. Is the Cu(II) ion a better, although both are for the change Cu(II) to Cu(I), or a worse oxidant in the presence of chloride ions?

From the above data (only), calculate standard potentials for the following†; interpret the results for (b) and (c):

(a) $Cu^+\,(aq) + e^- \longrightarrow Cu\,(s)$
(b) $CuSO_4\,(aq) + Cu\,(s) \longrightarrow Cu_2SO_4\,(aq)$
(c) $CuCl_2\,(aq) + Cu\,(s) \longrightarrow 2CuCl\,(s) + aq$

† See footnote, p. 128.

8.10 Concentration cells

In §3.13 a simple experiment with a concentration cell was described. Two identical copper electrodes were placed in solutions of copper sulphate at different concentrations, linked by a salt-bridge. When the external circuit was closed a current was observed, with the electrons leaving the electrode in the more dilute solution. The electrode reactions were:

$$Cu \ (s) \longrightarrow Cu^{2+} \ (aq, \ dilute) + 2e^-$$
$$Cu^{2+} \ (aq, \ concentrated) + 2e^- \longrightarrow Cu \ (s)$$

The reactions are those which tend to bring about an equalization of the concentrations, and the spontaneous net reaction is the transfer of Cu^{2+} ions from the concentrated solution (c_1) to the dilute (c_2). The salt-bridge allows ions to migrate, to maintain electrical neutrality in the solutions, and it also avoids the transport-number effects which would occur at a direct liquid junction.

It has been shown (§7.8) that the free-energy of dilution is $RT \ln (c_2/c_1)$, which is negative if $c_1 > c_2$.

Substituting this into $\Delta G = -nFE$ gives:

$$E = -\frac{RT}{nF} \ln \frac{c_2}{c_1}$$

for the feasible process $M^{n+} \ (aq, \ c_1) \rightarrow M^{n+} \ (aq, \ c_2)$. This process occurs in the cell:

$$M \mid M^{n+} \ (aq, \ c_2) \mathbin{\vdots} M^{n+} \ (aq, \ c_1) \mid M$$

The right-hand electrode, in the more concentrated solution, is positive.

The experiment in §3.13 was only qualitative, to demonstrate the polarity, and to provide evidence for free-energy of dilution. If quantitative results are to be obtained, some care is required. The circuit in Fig. 3.2 may be used (with a sensitive millivoltmeter) or the potentiometer circuit in Fig. 3.3. The copper electrodes must first be treated so that there is no p.d. between them when they are in the *same* solution.

Table 8.1   Potentials of concentration cells
Cell: $Cu \mid Cu^{2+} (c_2) \mathbin{\vdots} Cu^{2+} (c_1) \mid Cu$

$\dfrac{c_1}{\text{mol litre}^{-1}}$	$\dfrac{c_2}{\text{mol litre}^{-1}}$	ratio $\dfrac{c_1}{c_2}$	$\dfrac{E_{cell}}{V}$	$\dfrac{\Delta G_{dil}}{\text{kJ mol}^{-1}}$
1.0	1.0	1	0.000	0.0
1.0	0.5	2	+0.009	−1.8
1.0	0.25	4	+0.019	−3.7
1.0	0.10	10	+0.03	−5.7
2.0	0.05	40	+0.05	−9.6

This is not necessarily found to be so, if the metal is under any stress. Annealing may help, or electro-deposition of copper on carbon rods may be resorted to. A good leak-proof salt-bridge is also essential (see footnote on p. 37).

It is found that the concentration cell potential is proportional to the logarithm of the ratio of the concentrations (see Table 8.1).

8.11 Non-standard redox potentials: the Nernst equation

If a concentration cell has one metal electrode in a standard solution of its ions, while the other solution is $[M^{n+}]$, the cell potential will be $+RT/nF \ln [M^{n+}]$. Therefore the electrode potential (IUPAC) of a metal electrode in a non-standard solution of its ions is given by equation 8.4.

$$E_{red} = E_{red}^{\ominus} + \frac{RT}{nF} \ln [M^{n+}] \qquad \textbf{8.4}\dagger$$

Substitution of the numerical values $R = 8.31 \text{ J mol}^{-1} \text{ K}^{-1}$, $T = 298$ K, and $F = 96\,500$ C mol^{-1}, and conversion to base-ten logarithms gives equation 8.5

$$E_{red} = E_{red}^{\ominus} + \frac{0.058V \log [M^{n+}]}{n} \qquad \textbf{8.5}\dagger$$

Note that as most metal electrode potentials are negative, they tend to become less negative with increase in concentration of the metal ion. The effect is slight unless the ion concentration is very large (which is impossible in practice) or very small.

The relationship in equation **8.5** provides a method of measuring accurately small concentrations of ions. For instance, the electrode potential of a silver electrode can be used to indicate $[Ag^+]$ in an investigation into the solubilities of silver halides, or the instability constants of complex ions. Another example of the practical use of this relationship is the pH meter.

Non-standard redox potentials depend upon the concentrations of substances on *both* sides of the half-equation. The convention is to write the half-equations as reductions, thus:

$$\text{oxidized form} + \text{electrons} \longrightarrow \text{reduced form}$$

Then the reduction potential will become more positive if the concentration of 'reactants' (i.e. oxidants) is increased, but more negative if the

---

† In equations **8.4** to **8.7** the square brackets should, strictly, denote *activities*. All the concentrations, including those which define the standard state, should be multiplied by an *activity coefficient* which allows for the effect of inter-ionic interference.

concentration of 'products' (i.e. reductants) is increased. Equation **8.6**, which expresses this dependence, is known as the **Nernst equation**.

$$E_{red} = E_{red}^{\ominus} + \frac{RT}{nF} \ln \frac{\prod [ox]}{\prod [red]} \qquad \textbf{8.6}$$

where $\prod [ox]$ denotes the product of the concentrations† of all the substances on the oxidized (left) side of the half-equation, and [red] refers similarly to the reduced side.

WORKED EXAMPLE

To show the pH dependence of the reduction potential of permanganate.

$$MnO_4^- + 8H^+ + 5e^- \rightleftharpoons Mn^{2+} + H_2O; \qquad E^{\ominus} = +1.50 \text{ V}$$

Substituting as for equation **8.5** gives, for 298 K,

$$E/V = +1.5 + \frac{0.058}{5} \log \frac{[MnO_4^-][H^+]^8}{[Mn^{2+}]}$$

Within reasonable limits, the concentrations of MnO_4^- and Mn^{2+} are unimportant, and the equation may be simplified to

$$E/V \approx 1.5 + \frac{1}{10} \log [H^+] = 1.5 - \frac{pH}{10}$$

It is interesting to note that if $[H^+]$ is less than about 10^{-3} M, permanganate becomes incapable of oxidizing chloride ions to chlorine by this reaction.

The concentration correction can also be applied to the cell potential for a complete redox reaction (see §8.13):

$$E = E^{\ominus} - \frac{RT}{nF} \ln \frac{\prod [products]}{\prod [reactants]} \qquad \textbf{8.7}$$

The student is advised not to rely on memory alone when quoting this equation, but rather to reconstruct it logically as follows:

(i) $E = E^{\ominus} \pm$ 'concentration correction',
(ii) 'concentration correction' $= k \log Q_c$,
(iii) a positive E corresponds to a feasible reaction,
(iv) E becomes more negative with increase in [products] (which hinder reaction), therefore $k \log Q_c$, which is positive when [products] is large, must be *subtracted*.

8.12 Exercises

1. Calculate the maximum reversible cell potential for the following concentration cells at 298 K:

† See footnote, p. 138.

(a) zinc electrodes in 0.5 M and 0.01 M $ZnCl_2$ solution;

(b) clean aluminium electrodes in 0.5 M and 0.01 M $AlCl_3$ solution.

2. An iron electrode in a standard solution of Fe^{2+} ions is positive with respect to a cadmium electrode in a certain concentration of Cd^{2+} ions. What can you deduce about this concentration? (See Appendix 8.)

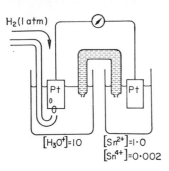

H_2(1 atm)

Pt

$[H_3O^+]=10$ $[Sn^{2+}]=1\cdot0$
                $[Sn^{4+}]=0\cdot002$

Fig. 8.7

3. What is the free-energy change for the dilution of one mole of sodium chloride from 200 cm³ solution to 10 litres (at 298 K)? (Assume ideal behaviour.) How could some of the available work be harnessed?

4. Which way will the electrons flow in the external circuit of the cell shown in Fig. 8.7? (See Appendix B.)

8.13 The Ag/Ag⁺ : Fe²⁺/Fe³⁺ equilibrium

In *Chemical Systems*, the CBA textbook, this electrochemical equilibrium is studied in some detail as an introduction to the equilibrium

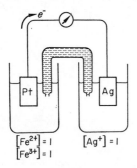

Pt   Ag

$[Fe^{2+}] = 1$ $[Ag^+] = 1$
$[Fe^{3+}] = 1$

Fig. 8.8

constant. In this course it could serve as a useful revision of that concept and its connection with free-energy.

Two half-cells are set up (Fig. 8.8) and connected by an ammonium nitrate salt-bridge. One is a silver electrode in a solution of silver ions (e.g. silver nitrate); the other is a platinum electrode in a solution containing both iron(II) and iron(III) ions (e.g. the chlorides).

When both half-cells are standard, with the ionic concentrations equal to 1 mol litre⁻¹, the cell potential is 0.03 V (the difference between the standard redox potentials, $+0.80$ and $+0.77$ V) with the silver electrode as the more positive. The spontaneous reaction is:

$$Ag^+ + e^- \longrightarrow Ag\,(s); \qquad E^\ominus_{red} = +0.80\ V$$
$$Fe^{2+} \longrightarrow Fe^{3+} + e^-; \qquad E^\ominus_{ox} = -0.77\ V$$

$$Ag^+ + Fe^{2+} \longrightarrow Ag + Fe^{3+}; \qquad E^\ominus_{cell} = +0.03\ V$$

The maximum reversible cell potential is measured by a potentiometer (or, less accurately, by a high-resistance millivoltmeter) as described in §3.13.

The concentrations of Fe^{2+} and Fe^{3+} are then varied. It is found that an increase in [Fe^{2+}] or a decrease in [Fe^{3+}] leads to a higher cell potential; while changes in the opposite direction, increasing the Fe^{3+} : Fe^{2+} ratio, at first decreases the cell potential, which becomes zero when this ratio is about 3 to 1. Beyond this point the cell potential rises again, but with reversed polarity (the silver half-cell now being negative), showing that the feasible reaction is now:

$$Fe^{3+} + Ag \longrightarrow Fe^{2+} + Ag^+$$

These variations are shown in Fig. 8.9

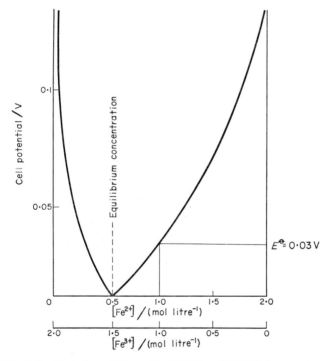

Fig. 8.9   Variation of E_{cell} with [Fe^{2+}] and [Fe^{3+}] (see text)

The Nernst equation gives the variation of cell potential with concentration:

$$E = E^\ominus - \frac{RT}{nF} \ln \frac{\prod [\text{products}]}{\prod [\text{reactants}]} \qquad \textbf{8.7}$$

which gives:

$$E = +0.03 - 0.058 \log \frac{[Fe^{2+}][Ag^+]}{[Fe^{3+}]}$$

So the cell potential will become zero when the log concentration quotient equals $0.030/0.058 = 0.52$. If $[Ag^+] = 1$ this comes about when the ratio $Fe^{3+} : Fe^{2+}$ is about 3, in accordance with experiment. Changing the silver ion concentration upsets this equilibrium position, but changing the mass or shape of the silver metal electrode has no effect.

Thus the experimental results confirm the general law that when equilibrium is established, with $E_{cell} = 0$,

$$E^\ominus = +\frac{RT}{nF} \ln \frac{\prod [products]}{\prod [reactants]} = \frac{RT}{nF} \ln K_{eq}$$

where K_{eq} is the equilibrium constant.

And since $\Delta G^\ominus = -nFE^\ominus$ (equation 8.2) it follows that:

$$\Delta G^\ominus = -RT \ln K_{eq}$$

This relationship is the van't Hoff isotherm, which has been introduced and used in Chapter 7.

8.14 Restricted ion concentration

Sometimes the concentration of one of the ions in a reaction cannot be increased above a certain value because that ion is involved simultaneously in some other equilibrium. This will clearly have an important effect on the redox potential.

Perhaps the simplest case is that in which the ion is in equilibrium with one of its sparingly soluble compounds. The standard reduction potential of silver metal in a solution of Ag^+ ions is $+0.80$ V. But if chloride ions are present the Ag^+ concentration is restricted by the limitation that the product $[Ag^+][Cl^-]$ must not exceed 2×10^{-10}. In a suspension of washed silver chloride $[Ag^+]$ will be about 10^{-5}, so the non-standard electrode potential of Ag^+/Ag in saturated AgCl is given by:

$$\begin{aligned} E_{red} &= +0.80 + 0.06 \log 10^{-5} \\ &= +0.80 - 0.3 \\ &= +0.5 \text{ V (at 298 K)} \end{aligned}$$

If chloride ion concentration is high, the silver ion concentration will be even lower; e.g. if $[Cl^-] = 1$, then $[Ag^+] = 2 \times 10^{-10}$, and so

$$\begin{aligned} E(\text{Ag in 1 M Cl}^-) &= +0.80 + 0.06 \log (2 \times 10^{-10}) \\ &= +0.80 - 0.58 \\ &= +0.22 \text{ V} \end{aligned}$$

This could be said to be the standard reduction potential of:

$$AgCl\ (s)+e^- \longrightarrow Ag\ (s)+Cl^-\ (aq)$$

In other cases the reduction potential may be remote from the standard because the concentration of an ion is controlled by its being in equlibrium with some other species. The standard electrode potential of S/S^{2-} is -0.51 V, but it would be wrong to use this value in a calculation involving H_2S as a reductant in acid solution, because:

$$H_2S\ (aq)+2H_2O \rightleftharpoons 2H_3O^+ +S^{2-}; \qquad K = 10^{-20}$$

If $[H_2S, aq]$ and $[H_3O^+]$ both equal 1, then $[S^{2-}] = 10^{-20}$, and from **8.6**:

$$E = -0.51+\frac{0.06}{2}\log\frac{1}{10^{-20}}$$
$$= -0.51+0.6$$
$$= +0.1\ V$$

The accepted value is:

$$S+2H_3O^+ +2e^- \rightleftharpoons H_2S+2H_2O; \qquad E^{\ominus} = +0.14\ V$$

Similarly the redox potential for the oxidation of water to oxygen in neutral or acid solution is very different from the standard O_2/OH^- potential, because $[OH^-]$ is restricted by the equilibrium constant $[OH^-][H_3O^+] = 10^{-14}$ at 298 K.

8.15 Exercises

(Standard reduction potentials are listed in Appendix B.)

1. The standard reduction potential of lead (Pb^{2+}/Pb) is -0.126 V. Calculate the non-standard reduction potential of lead in a saturated solution of lead sulphate (which has a solubility product of 2×10^{-8}), in 2 M H_2SO_4 as in a car battery.

2. Draw a graph showing the variation of redox potential of molar dichromate (plus molar Cr^{3+}) with pH. Over what pH range can the solution oxidize bromide ions to bromine?

3. (a) What is the ratio of concentrations of Fe^{2+} to Fe^{3+} ions if these are in equilibrium with silver metal and 0.1 M Ag^+ ions?
   (b)* Excess silver powder is stirred with a quantity of 1.0 M iron(III) nitrate solution; reaction occurs until equilibrium is reached. What concentration of silver ions would you expect to find? How could you test your prediction experimentally?

4. (a) The instability constant of the tetrammino-zinc ion is:

$$Zn(NH_3)_4^{2+} \rightleftharpoons Zn^{2+} +4NH_3\ (aq); \qquad K = 10^{-9}$$

What is the electrode potential of Zn^{2+}/Zn in the presence of 1 M ammonia solution? (This is relevant to the Leclanché cell.)

(b) From the standard reduction potential for zinc in alkaline solution, calculate the instability constant for the zincate ion, i.e. K for:

$$Zn(OH)_4^{2-} \rightleftharpoons Zn^{2+} + 4OH^-$$

5. Calculate the reduction potential for $O_2(g)$ at 298 K at pH = 1, 3, 7 and 14. Draw a sketch graph to show the variation of oxidizing power with pH. What are the optimum conditions for O_2 to oxidize I^- to I_2? Test this experimentally.

6.* In an investigation into the nature of the mercury(I) ion, the following concentration cell was set up:

$$Hg \begin{vmatrix} Hg^I \text{ nitrate} \\ (20 \text{ g/l}) \\ \text{in dil } HNO_3 \end{vmatrix} \begin{matrix} Hg^I \text{ nitrate} \\ (2.0 \text{ g/l}) \\ \text{in dil } HNO_3 \end{matrix} \begin{vmatrix} \\ Hg \\ \end{vmatrix}$$

The cell potential at 25°C was found† to be 0.028 V. Show how this result enables a decision to be made between the two possiblities, Hg^+ and $(Hg_2)^{2+}$.

8.16 Fuel cells

No course on energetics would be complete without a mention of fuel cells, which have been hailed as the major future development in electricity generation.

Present-day methods of generating electricity from the chemical energy of fuels consist of burning the fuel, either in an internal combustion engine to give mechanical energy direct, or in a boiler to give high-pressure, high-temperature steam, which then drives a turbine. Then the mechanical energy drives the electrical generator. Either way, the process is very inefficient, and only 25–35% of the enthalpy of combustion is converted to electricity. The inefficiency is largely intrinsic and irremovable: even if all friction and mechanical loss were eliminated, the maximum efficiency would be less than 50%, because the conversion of heat to work (5.6) is limited by the Carnot factor $(T_1 - T_2)/T_1$ where T_1 is the temperature of the heat source, say 600 K, and T_2 is the low-temperature 'sink', say 300 K.

Electrochemical cells are not subject to this restriction, because they convert the free-energy of reaction ('work') directly to electricity. Cells have been designed which consume oxygen at one electrode and a fuel such as hydrogen or methanol at the other, and produce small currents at almost 100% efficiency.

† Data from p. 316 of *Modern Approach to Inorganic Chemistry*, by C. F. Bell & K. A. K. Lott, Butterworths.

A simple fuel cell for use in schools is available†, and consists essentially of two nickel gauze electrodes. The one which is to act as the oxygen (air) electrode is immersed in 5% $AgNO_3$ (aq), and the other is put in 1% chloroplatinic acid; after an hour both are rinsed, and put into a beaker of aqueous methanol. When air is bubbled past, the one electrode becomes positive:

$$O_2 \text{ (g)} + 4H^+ \text{ (aq)} + 4e^- \longrightarrow 2H_2O \text{ (l)}$$

while the other becomes negative:

$$CH_3OH + H_2O \longrightarrow HCOOH + 4H^+ \text{ (aq)} + 4e^-$$

Sufficient current can be drawn to operate a transistor radio.

The difficulties in designing an *economic* full-scale fuel cell have yet to be overcome; much research has been done, but some early reports were over-optimistic. There are two categories:

(1) Fuel cells which run on specially prepared fuels at comparatively high cost, used for transport (ships, buses) or emergency electricity supplies. An example is the Union Carbide cell which runs off hydrogen and oxygen, with porous carbon electrodes and hot aqueous potassium hydroxide electrolyte.

(2) Fuel cells to produce electric power at low cost, which must consume hydrocarbons (natural gas or oil) and so far these have only functioned at high temperatures (> 1000 K), where corrosion problems are serious.

† Write to Esso Petroleum Co. Ltd., Victoria St., London S.W.1.

9 Energetics and the extraction of metals[†]

9.1 Introduction

The sequence of operations for the extraction of any metal from its ore usually conforms to the pattern:

- (i) concentration of the ore by physical treatment;
- (ii) conversion to a compound (often the oxide) suitable for reduction;
- (iii) chemical reduction, at elevated temperature, to give the crude metal;
- (iv) final purification.

This chapter will be concerned with step (iii), the heart of the process, because the choice of materials and conditions is determined largely by thermodynamic considerations. The problem is to find a reaction by which the free metal might be produced, for which ΔG is negative at some industrially attainable temperature. The objection that an exergonic reaction still might not proceed, for kinetic reasons (i.e. high energy of activation), is not likely to apply at the high temperatures used.

9.2 The calculation of $\Delta G_r^{\ominus}$ for metallurgical reactions

The standard free-energy of reaction $\Delta G_r^{\ominus}$ can always be calculated from $\Delta G_f^{\ominus}$ data (by the method shown for ΔH_r in §2.15): e.g.

$$ZnO + H_2 \text{ (g)} \longrightarrow Zn \text{ (s)} + H_2O \text{ (g)}$$

$$\Delta G_f^{\ominus}/(\text{kJ mol}^{-1}) \quad -318 \quad 0 \quad\quad 0 \quad\quad -229$$

$$\Delta G_r^{\ominus}(298) = -229 - (-318) = +89 \text{ kJ}$$

Since $\Delta G_f^{\ominus}$ is zero for the elements, $\Delta G_r^{\ominus}$ is just the algebraic difference between $\Delta G_f^{\ominus}$ for the two compounds.

In other cases the calculation is a little more complicated, and the answer is not visible at a glance: e.g.

$$2Al_2O_3 + 6H_2 \longrightarrow 4Al + 6H_2O \text{ (g)}$$

$$\Delta G_r^{\ominus} = 6 \times (-229) - 2 \times (-1576) = +1780 \text{ kJ}$$

[†] This chapter can be studied profitably at any point after Chapter 3.

However, such a calculation would regain the simplicity of the first example if free-energies of formation were listed for the masses of compound which contain one mole of oxygen atoms. For Al_2O_3 this would be one-third of the usual $\Delta G_f^\ominus$; for TiO_2 it would be one-half, and so on. A few such quantities are listed in Table 9.1.

Table 9.1   Standard free-energies of formation (298 K) in kilojoule, of selected oxides in amounts containing one mole of oxygen atoms

$\frac{1}{3}Al_2O_3$	-525	FeO	-240	PbO	-189
ZnO	-318	H_2O (g)	-229	CuO	-127
$\frac{1}{4}Fe_3O_4$	-253	$\frac{1}{2}CO_2$	-197	Ag_2O	-11
$\frac{1}{3}Fe_2O_3$	-247				

Table 9.1 shows immediately that any element can potentially reduce any oxide lower in the list, which is similar to the familiar 'activity series' or electrochemical series. For example, the reaction between aluminium and iron oxide is thermodynamically favoured (at 298 K), and the exact value of $\Delta G^\ominus$ is readily calculated:

$$\tfrac{2}{3}Al + \tfrac{1}{4}Fe_3O_4 \longrightarrow \tfrac{1}{3}Al_2O_3 + \tfrac{3}{4}Fe; \quad \Delta G^\ominus = -272 \text{ kJ.}$$

(This 'thermite' reaction can be demonstrated, by mixing the powdered reagents and initiating with a magnesium-ribbon fuse. It is very violent and the iron is formed in the molten state.)

In general it is necessary to know $\Delta G_r^\ominus$ for higher temperatures than 298 K, and it would be useful to have data such as that in Table 9.1 available for all temperatures up to, say, 2500 K. The next two sections follow up this point.

9.3 Exercises (in preparation for §§9.4 and 9.5)

1. From $\Delta H_r^\ominus$ and $\Delta G_f^\ominus$ data for ZnO calculate:

    (i) $T\Delta S_f^\ominus$ at 298 K,
    (ii) $T\Delta S_f^\ominus$ at 600 K and 1200 K,
    (iii) $\Delta G_f^\ominus$ at 600 K, 900 K and 1200 K.

Use these results in Exercise 3 below.

2. From the general equation for the formation of a divalent metal oxide:

$$M \text{ (s)} + \tfrac{1}{2}O_2 \text{ (g)} \longrightarrow MO \text{ (s)}$$

predict the sign of $\Delta S^\ominus$, and draw conclusions about the variation of $\Delta G^\ominus$ with temperature.

3. (a) Plot a graph of the following data, together with the answers to

Exercise 1. Let the T scale (horizontal) extend to 1800 K. Graphs of this kind are known as Ellingham diagrams.

$\Delta G_f^{\ominus}$ in kJ per mole of O atoms, at various temperatures

	300 K	600 K	900 K	1200 K
CuO	−127	−101	−76	−50
FeO	−240	−222	−203	−184
$\frac{1}{3}Al_2O_3$	−525	−495	−464	−433
$\frac{1}{2}TiO_2$	−439	−407	−372	−335
MnO	−360	−341	−322	−302

(b) What can you deduce about the variation of $\Delta G_r^{\ominus}$ with T for a reaction between one metal and the oxide of another?

(c) Read off $\Delta G_r^{\ominus}$ for the following:

(i) $\frac{2}{3}Al + FeO \longrightarrow Fe + \frac{1}{3}Al_2O_3$ (at 900 K)
(ii) $Zn + CuO \longrightarrow Cu + ZnO$ (at 700 K)

4. All the lines on the graph in Exercise 3 can be extended at least to 1800 K by linear extrapolation, with the exception of the ZnO line. This changes direction sharply at the boiling point of zinc (1180 K; $\Delta G_f^{\ominus} = -230$ kJ) and passes through -104 kJ at 1800 K.

(a) Make these additions to your graph.

(b) Write equations for the formation of ZnO (s) above and below 1200 K, and compare the signs and sizes of $\Delta S_f^{\ominus}$ which would be predicted from them. Explain the change in slope of the $\Delta G_f^{\ominus}/T$ line at the boiling-point of any metal.

(c) Is the line continuous at the boiling-point, or is there a small but definite break?

9.4 Reduction of oxides by other metals and by hydrogen

From the Exercises above it will have been found that the lines on the Ellingham diagram for the oxides of metals are all roughly parallel, and sloping upwards so that $\Delta G^{\ominus}$ becomes about 8 kJ less negative for every 100 K rise. Since ΔH is approximately independent of temperature, this slope must be attributed to the negative entropy change accompanying the formation of the oxides. In each case this was mainly due to the disappearance of $\frac{1}{2}$ mole O_2 (g) with $\Delta S^{\ominus} \approx -100$ J K^{-1}.

Table 9.1 was a list showing a decreasing order of thermodynamic stability of metal oxides, which is, more loosely, the order of decreasing reactivity of the metals. Any metal higher in the list could potentially displace any lower metal from its oxide, because $\Delta G_r^{\ominus}$ for such a reaction is necessarily negative. Now since the lines on the $\Delta G_f^{\ominus}/T$ graph are roughly parallel for the metal oxides, the order of metals remains the same for higher temperatures, at least up to the boiling-points.

Hydrogen can reduce some metal oxides. $\Delta G_f^{\ominus}$ for H_2O (g) is -229 kJ mol^{-1}, so hydrogen comes rather low in Table 9.1. Furthermore, the hydrogen/steam line is parallel to the metal oxide lines on the Ellingham diagram, since the reaction H_2 (g)$+\frac{1}{2}O_2$ (g) $\rightarrow H_2O$ (g) involves the loss of $\frac{1}{2}$ mole of gas, and $\Delta S^{\ominus}$ is again $c.\ -100$ J K^{-1}.

Higher temperature does not improve the performance of hydrogen as a reducing agent.

9.5 Exercise

The free-energy of formation of any metal oxide becomes less negative with increasing temperature. Therefore the reduction to the metal should become easier at higher temperatures, if only all the reducing agents were not affected in the same way. Is it possible to find a substance which has a free-energy of oxidation which stays the same (or, better still, becomes more negative) with rise in temperature?

Before reading on, write down the requirements of such a reductant, with examples. It may help to consider the general equations:

$$X\ ((s),\ (l)\ \text{or}\ (g))+O_2\ (g) \longrightarrow XO_2\ ((s),\ (l)\ \text{or}\ (g))$$
$$2X\ ((s),\ (l)\ \text{or}\ (g))+O_2\ (g) \longrightarrow 2XO\ ((s),\ (l)\ \text{or}\ (g)),\ \text{etc.}$$

The variables are the physical states of the reductant and the oxidation product. What entropy change is required? How must these variables be arranged to provide it? Does the requirement rule out all the metals?

9.6 The oxides of carbon

The problem posed in §9.5 contained some stringent restrictions. In order for $\Delta G_f^{\ominus}$ to stay the same or become more negative with increasing temperature, $\Delta S_f^{\ominus}$ has to be zero or positive. Since oxygen gas disappears in the reaction, it follows that the oxide product must be a gas, in order that there shall not be a net decrease in the number of gas molecules. This virtually rules out all the metals, since they have solid oxides (but see §9.7, 7.). The same reason eliminates almost all the gaseous candidates, because if such elements form stable oxides at all, it is with negative $\Delta S^{\ominus}$. (Some gaseous *compounds* such as ammonia and hydrocarbons have a positive entropy of combustion.)

The search, then, is for solid or liquid element which burns to a gaseous oxide. As an academic exercise it has three solutions†; as an industrial problem it has only one: *carbon*.

The relevant thermodynamic data are:

$$C\ (s)+O_2\ (g) \longrightarrow CO_2\ (g);\quad \Delta H = -393.5,\quad \Delta G^{\ominus} = -394.5\ \text{kJ}$$
$$2C\ (s)+O_2\ (g) \longrightarrow 2CO\ (g);\quad \Delta H = -221.0,\quad \Delta G^{\ominus} = -274.6\ \text{kJ}.$$

† Besides C, S up to 718 K, Se from 590 K to 958 K, and some metals over small temperature ranges.

When carbon burns to carbon dioxide, there is no overall change in the number of gas molecules, and the entropy change is almost zero. Consequently $\Delta G^{\ominus}$ does not vary with T, and the Ellingham plot is a horizontal straight line. On the 'one mole of O' scale it comes at about -200 kJ.

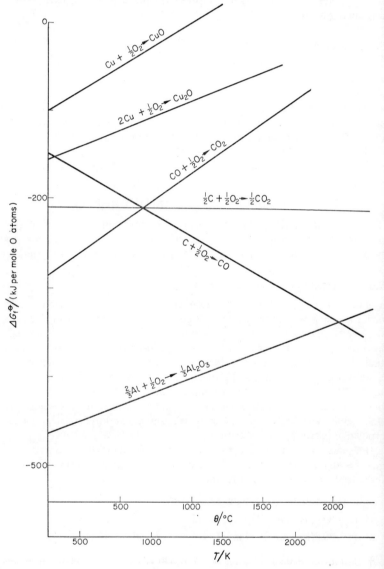

Fig. 9.1   Oxides

The combustion of carbon to its monoxide has a considerably smaller $\Delta G^{\ominus}$ at 298 K, but the reaction is unique in that it produces more gas than the oxygen it consumes and therefore has a positive $\Delta S^{\ominus}$ ($+90$ J K^{-1}). The $C + \frac{1}{2}O_2 \rightarrow CO$ line is the only one which slopes downwards, intersecting many of the metal-oxide lines as T increases. At about 1000 K $\Delta G_f^{\ominus}$ for CO becomes equal to that of $\frac{1}{2}CO_2$, and above this temperature it is more negative, and carbon monoxide is then the main product of the reduction of metal oxides by coke (but see §9.8, 4).

Another line on the graph is that for the reaction:

$$CO + \tfrac{1}{2}O_2 \longrightarrow CO_2$$

$\Delta G^{\ominus}$ is quite large at 298 K at -257 kJ, but since $\Delta S^{\ominus}$ is negative the line slopes upwards, roughly parallel to those for the metal oxides. Carbon monoxide is quite an effective reducing agent at lower temperatures, but above 1500 K it becomes less effective than hydrogen.

The three carbon lines and those of a few metals are shown in Fig. 9.1.

9.7 The Ellingham diagram for oxide formation

Figure 9.2 is a graph of $\Delta G^{\ominus}$ versus T for the formation of the oxides of the common elements. At the cost of some repetition, the principle features are set out in this section.

1. The free-energy which is plotted is in every case that for reaction with the amount of O_2 (g) which contains one mole of oxygen atoms (one mole O_2 molecules is sometimes specified instead); this is not necessarily the same as the standard free-energy of formation of one mole of the *oxide*.

2. The diagram gives immediate information about the free-energy of reaction between any one element and the oxide of any other. A vertical line at any chosen temperature will cut each line once. The favoured direction of reaction (i.e. for which $\Delta G_r^{\ominus}$ is negative) will be the formation of the oxide with the lower intersection and decomposition of the oxide which is uppermost. The vertical distance apart of the two lines gives a direct reading of the free-energy of reaction (for the transfer of one mole O).

For example, at 298 K the Na$_2$O line is below that of MnO, and we see that:

$$2\text{Na (s)} + \text{MnO (s)} \longrightarrow \text{Mn (s)} + \text{Na}_2\text{O (s)}; \qquad \Delta G_r^{\ominus} \approx -8\text{kJ}$$

but at 1000 K the positions are reversed, and:

$$\text{Mn (s)} + \text{Na}_2\text{O (s)} \longrightarrow 2\text{Na (l)} + \text{MnO (s)}; \qquad \Delta G_r^{\ominus} \approx -25 \text{ kJ}$$

So it would not be profitable to try to reduce manganese(II) oxide with sodium metal, despite the well-known reactivity of the latter.

6—C.E.

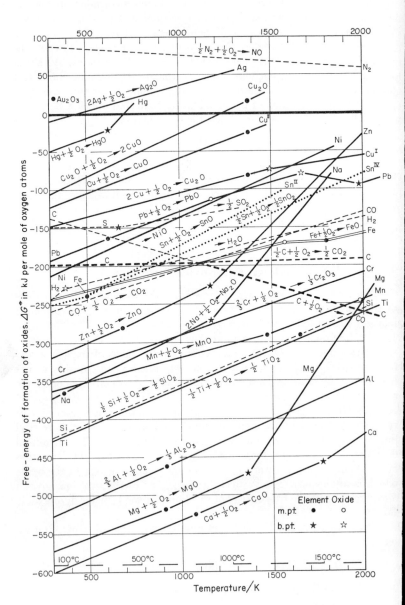

Fig. 9.2   Free-energy of formation of oxides. $\Delta G^{\ominus}$ in kJ per mole of oxygen atoms

3. All the lines are straight (between phase-changes) and almost all have upward (positive) slopes, roughly parallel up to the boiling-point of the element. Since ΔH_f is approximately independent of temperature, this slope must be due to the entropy of formation of the oxide. In fact the slope equals $-\Delta S^{\ominus}$, and $\Delta S^{\ominus}$ is usually negative, the common factor being the disappearance of half a mole of gas.

4. The element carbon shows outstanding individuality, and its line $C + \frac{1}{2}O_2 \rightarrow CO$ slopes downwards, cutting across the others. The more lines there are on the diagram the more spectacular this behaviour appears. At temperatures above about 2200 K, carbon is thermodynamically capable of reducing almost all metal oxides.

5. The intersection of two lines gives the equilibrium temperature, at which the two elements and both the oxides can be present at equilibrium in comparable quantities. E.g. at about 1200 K a mixture of ZnO (s) and carbon will be in equilibrium with one atm. partial pressure of both carbon monoxide and zinc vapour. Above this temperature the reaction goes to produce greater pressures of these two gases, but below 1200 K it tends to reverse, and as the gaseous products are cooled some of the zinc is re-oxidized as a result of $Zn + CO \rightarrow ZnO + C$. For this reason the mixture must be 'flash-cooled' as rapidly as possible.

6. At the boiling-point of the metal, the line for the formation of its oxide makes a sharp upward deflection, the change in slope often being considerable. This is due to the entropy change for

$$M\,(g) + \tfrac{1}{2}O_2\,(g) \longrightarrow MO\,(s)$$

being more negative than that for

$$M\,((s)\ or\ (l)) + \tfrac{1}{2}O_2\,(g) \longrightarrow MO\,(s)$$

The increase in $-\Delta S^{\ominus}$ is equal to the entropy of vaporization of M, which equals the enthalpy of vaporization $\div$ boiling-point.

At the boiling-point of the oxide there is a sharp levelling-off, for a similar reason. Deflections can also occur at the melting-points, but they are usually slight.

The last question in §9.3 was 'Are the lines really continuous at the boiling-points?' The student will probably have come to the conclusion that as $\Delta G^{\ominus}$ for the oxidation of the gaseous element at any given temperature is less than $\Delta G^{\ominus}$ for the oxidation of the solid or liquid by an amount equal to the free-energy of vaporization, and since this latter is zero at the b.pt, the lines are in fact continuous. The sudden drop which would have been caused by ΔH_{vap} is exactly equalled by the rise due to $T_b\,\Delta S^{\ominus}_{vap}$.

7. The lead(II) oxide line is interesting, because the boiling-point of the oxide is about 250 K lower than that of the metal. So for a limited temperature range the reaction is:

$$Pb\,(l) + \tfrac{1}{2}O_2\,(g) \longrightarrow PbO\,(g); \qquad \Delta S^{\ominus} = +ve$$

This exceptional reaction involves an increase in gas molecules, a positive entropy change, and hence a downward-sloping line. At 2000 K the lead boils and the line resumes its upward slope, but with the metal more active than it would otherwise have been.

8. A few lines cross the zero-line and enter the region of positive $\Delta G_f^\ominus$. Au_2O_3 is there even at room temperature, and Ag_2O crosses at about 400 K. Note also the NO line. These compounds are thermodynamically unstable with respect to their elements.

At about 720 K $\Delta G_f^\ominus(HgO) = 0$, so the oxide is in equilibrium with 1 atm each of mercury vapour and oxygen, and unless the total pressure is kept at 2 atm or more the oxide will decompose completely. At a slightly lower temperature (such as the b.pt of mercury) $\Delta G_f^\ominus$ is sufficiently negative for mercury to combine with oxygen from air. Lavoisier was able to exploit these facts, even without a knowledge of thermodynamics.

9.8 The extraction of metals

The Ellingham diagram for oxide formation (Fig. 9.2) enables certain conclusions to be drawn immediately regarding the extraction of metals. These will be compared with actual practice.

1. The metals gold, silver, mercury and copper, which have small negative, or even positive, free-energies of formation of their oxides could possibly occur native, since they would hardly react with atmospheric oxygen. They could, of course, occur as other, more stable compounds, and in fact the sulphides are common ores. A simplified Ellingham diagram for sulphides is given as Fig. 9.3, which shows that Ag_2S is much more stable than Ag_2O.

2. Besides the above four metals, bismuth, lead, nickel, cobalt, cadmium and tungsten oxides can be reduced by hydrogen.

3. Below 1000 K carbon monoxide can reduce all the above oxides plus (with difficulty) those of iron and tin.

4. The oxidation of carbon to carbon monoxide is the reaction which brings about the reduction of the oxides of iron, zinc, tin, manganese, magnesium and even aluminium. The actual mechanism may involve reaction between carbon monoxide and the metal oxide, e.g.:

$$ZnO + CO \rightleftharpoons Zn + CO_2$$

followed by reduction of the carbon dioxide by carbon:

$$CO_2 + C \longrightarrow 2CO$$

This second reaction is highly favoured above 970 K, and keeps the concentration of CO high and that of CO_2 low; so that the actual ΔG of the first reaction is not $\Delta G^\ominus$ (which would be positive at this temperature) but a non-standard ΔG which approaches the $\Delta G^\ominus$ for:

$$ZnO + C \longrightarrow Zn + CO$$

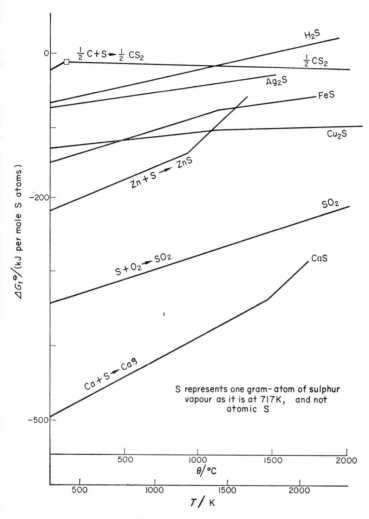

Fig. 9.3 Sulphides

5. Aluminium can be produced by carbon reduction of bauxite at extremely high temperatures, but the method has not been widely used in the past because the product contains carbon impurity. A recently developed purification process, based on the reversible formation of the monochloride:

$$AlCl_3 \, (g) + 2Al \, (s) \rightleftharpoons 3AlCl \, (g)$$

may have solved this problem.

6. Electrons at a potential of > 3 V are a more powerful reductant

than any element, and cathodic reduction provides an effective, though expensive, method of metal extraction.

Aluminium is usually obtained by the electrolysis of a solution of aluminium oxide in molten cryolite ($AlF_3 + NaF$). Calcium, magnesium, sodium, potassium and other Group IA and IIA metals are also obtained by electrolysis, usually of their molten chlorides.

7. Titanium dioxide can be reduced by carbon, but the metal then reacts to from the extremely stable and intractable TiC. The metal must therefore be made by an alternative method, such as the reduction of $TiCl_4$ by magnesium or sodium. Zirconium is also made in this way.

8. As the demand for magnesium increased, an alternative to the expensive electrolytic method was sought. Although MgO can be reduced by C above 1830 K (see Fig. 9.2) the problem of back-reaction during cooling is severe:

$$Mg\ (g) + CO\ (g) \longrightarrow MgO\ (s) + C\ (s)$$

The Mg and CO vapours cannot be separated, and flash-cooling produces a dangerously pyrophoric magnesium powder.

The ingenious Pidgeon process, which avoids these difficulties, is based on the reduction of MgO by silicon. Cheap ferro-silicon is used and the magnesium ore is dolomite, $MgCO_3 + CaCO_3$. The CaO which is produced along with the MgO when the dolomite is calcined is beneficial, as it reacts with the SiO_2 product, and makes ΔG for the reduction more negative than $\Delta G^{\ominus}$. The magnesium is distilled off at low pressure which also favours the reaction.

9.9 Exercises

1. From Fig. 9.2 estimate $\Delta G^{\ominus}$ for the following reactions at 300 K 800 K and 1300 K:

   (i) $FeO + CO \longrightarrow Fe + CO_2$
   (ii) $FeO + C \longrightarrow Fe + CO$
   (iii) $FeO + \frac{1}{2}C \longrightarrow Fe + \frac{1}{2}CO_2$

Comment on the likelihood of each reaction at 300 K.

2. Estimate $\Delta G^{\ominus}$ at 773 K and 1473 K for:

$$Na_2O + C \longrightarrow 2Na\ (g) + CO$$

Suggest a reason why the reaction is not used for the manufacture of sodium.

3. At what temperatures, if any, are the following reactions feasible?

   (i) $Si + 2MnO \longrightarrow SiO_2 + 2Mn$
   (ii) $Pb + NiO \longrightarrow PbO + Ni$
   (iii) $S + 2H_2O \longrightarrow SO_2 + 2H_2$ (standard concentrations).

4. Using Fig. 9.2 discuss the temperature requirements for the 'water–gas reaction':

   (i) $C + H_2O$ (g) $\longrightarrow CO + H_2$

Is the reaction (ii) $C + 2H_2O$ (g) $\rightarrow CO_2 + 2H_2$ feasible in one stage? If so, find out whether it is used for the manufacture of hydrogen.
   What would be a suitable temperature for:

   (iii) $CO + H_2O$ (g) $\longrightarrow CO_2 + H_2$
   (iv) $CO_2 + H_2 \longrightarrow CO + H_2O$ (g)?

5. Find three or four A-level questions which could be answered more neatly with the aid of a simple Ellingham diagram, and sketch (from memory) the diagrams which would be required.

6. Could the following reactions occur *at all* at 1800 K? How could the products, if any, be obtained from the reaction mixtures?

   (i) $S + 2H_2O \longrightarrow SO_2 + H_2$
   (ii) $\frac{1}{2}N_2 + \frac{1}{2}O_2 \longrightarrow NO$
   (iii) $4Cr + 3TiO_2 \longrightarrow 2Cr_2O_3 + 3Ti$

7. (In preparation for §9.10)
   From ΔH and $\Delta G^{\ominus}$ (298 K) data, calculate $\Delta G^{\ominus}$ at 298 K and 1200 K for the following reactions:

   (i) $2Cu + \frac{1}{2}O_2 \longrightarrow Cu_2O$
   (ii) $Cu + \frac{1}{2}O_2 \longrightarrow CuO$

Assuming straight lines, plot a graph of free-energy versus temperature, and show how these lines can be used to find $\Delta G^{\ominus}$ for:

$$Cu_2O + \frac{1}{2}O_2 \longrightarrow 2CuO$$

Over what temperature range is this $\Delta G^{\ominus}$ positive, and how is this to be interpreted?

9.10 Multiple oxidation states: disproportionation

If an element forms more than one oxide there can be an Ellingham line for the oxidation of a lower oxide to a higher. For example, copper forms CuO and Cu_2O, so there is the possibility of the reaction:

$$Cu_2O + \frac{1}{2}O_2 \longrightarrow 2CuO$$

If $\Delta G^{\ominus}$ for this is calculated for various temperatures, it could give an Ellingham line along with the two for the direct formation of Cu_2O and CuO. In fact, if these two are already known, the line for the reaction under consideration can readily be obtained, since at any given temperature the free-energy equals $2\Delta G_f^{\ominus}(\text{CuO}) - \Delta G_f^{\ominus}(\text{Cu}_2\text{O})$, and these can be read from the graph.

The three lines for copper are to be found on Fig. 9.2. Taking 900 K (627°C) for instance, $\Delta G_f^{\ominus}$ for CuO is -76 kJ (per mole of O), while that for Cu_2O is -99. Therefore $\Delta G_r^{\ominus}$ for the oxidation of Cu_2O is

$$[2 \times (-76) - (-99)] = -46 \text{ kJ}$$

per mole of oxygen atoms transferred.

The Cu_2O line is below the CuO line at all temperatures, so in one sense, i.e. for a limited quantity of oxygen, copper(I) oxide is the more stable; $CuO + Cu \rightarrow Cu_2O$ will always tend to go.

In the other sense, though, CuO is the more stable at lower temperatures, since $Cu_2O + \frac{1}{2}O_2 \rightarrow 2CuO$ tends to go. The line for this reaction is in the negative $\Delta G^{\ominus}$ region up to about 1300 K, but then crosses into the positive. Then Cu_2O is the more stable oxide in both senses, and, even in the presence of oxygen, copper(II) oxide will decompose:

$$2CuO \longrightarrow Cu_2O + \frac{1}{2}O_2$$

The lines for tin differ in several respects from those for copper. Up to 505 K (232°C) the lines for SnO and $\frac{1}{2}SnO_2$ are almost identical in position, which means that $\Delta G_r^{\ominus}$ for $SnO + \frac{1}{2}O_2 \rightarrow SnO_2$ is, by coincidence, equal to the free-energies of formation of SnO and $\frac{1}{2}SnO_2$, and is again the same line. As this is quite a large negative value, tin(II) oxide tends to be oxidized to tin(IV) oxide. However, the reaction: $SnO_2 + Sn \text{ (s)} \rightleftharpoons 2SnO$ is not favoured in either direction, as $\Delta G^{\ominus} \approx 0$.

Above 505 K SnO becomes the less stable on both counts, and not only takes up oxygen if it is available $(SnO + \frac{1}{2}O_2 \rightarrow SnO_2)$ but also *disproportionates* into the higher oxide plus the free element

$$2SnO \text{ (s)} \longrightarrow SnO_2 \text{ (s)} + Sn \text{ (l)}$$

The term disproportionation is used when a compound reacts alone to form products in both higher and lower valency states than itself. (In the example just discussed, $2Sn^{II} \rightarrow Sn^{IV} + Sn^0$.) It will tend to occur whenever the Ellingham line for the higher valency state is below that for the lower state. This was not so for the oxides of copper. Disproportionation in aqueous solution was discussed in §8.8.

9.11 Exercises

1. At what temperatures, if any, are the following reactions thermodynamically feasible?

  (i) $Hg + NO \longrightarrow HgO + \frac{1}{2}N_2$
  (ii) $2Cu_2O + O_2 \longrightarrow 4CuO$
  (iii) $2Cu_2O \longrightarrow 4Cu + O_2$
  (iv) $4Cu + SnO_2 \longrightarrow 2Cu_2O + Sn$
  (v) $Sn + \text{limited } O_2 \longrightarrow SnO$

2. An often-performed school experiment is the reduction of copper(II) oxide by hydrogen. Would it be possible, by using a restricted quantity of hydrogen, to stop the reaction half-way?

$$2CuO + H_2 \longrightarrow Cu_2O + H_2O$$

(Compare $\Delta G^\ominus$ for this reaction with that for the full reduction to Cu at, say, 800 K.)

3. Plot lines for the three oxides of iron, calculated from the data below. Then plot the line for

$$3FeO + \tfrac{1}{2}O_2 \longrightarrow Fe_3O_4.$$

  (i) Can FeO reduce SnO_2 to Sn? Write the equation and calculate $\Delta G^\ominus$ at 973 K.

 (ii) Can FeO reduce FeO to iron? Write the equation and calculate $\Delta G^\ominus$ at 973 K.

(iii) Could FeO ever be oxidized to Fe_2O_3 rather than to Fe_3O_4?

	$\Delta G^\ominus$ (298 K)	$\Delta G^\ominus$ (900 K)
FeO	−240 kJ	−203 kJ
Fe_2O_3	−741 kJ	−526 kJ
Fe_3O_4	−1014 kJ	−743 kJ

4. At what temperature can MgO be reduced by C? Describe some of the practical difficulties. It is found that even if the Mg vapour (and other gases) are led away from the carbon before condensing the metal, it contains carbon impurity. Explain why this is so.

Also outline the more usual manufacture of magnesium.

5. Give two examples of *disproportionation*, either in the solid state or in aqueous solution.

From the standard free energies of formation listed in Appendix A, find whether mercury(I) oxide or chloride are susceptible to disproportionation at 298 K.

10 Energy considerations in biochemistry

10.1 Introduction

The energetics of life processes are most extraordinary. In a universe where spontaneous changes invariably result in a net increase in entropy and disorder (§5.10), living things manage to bring about local decreases in entropy. They grow into complex but specific shapes. They raise themselves up against gravity, they create low-salt solutions in an environment of sea-water, they synthesize amazingly elaborate molecules from simple components, and they manufacture fuels from the products of combustion. These are all changes towards increased order, which cannot occur spontaneously in inanimate systems.

This is not to say that life processes defy the Second Law of Thermo-dynamics, since the decrease in entropy which they are able to achieve is possible only because the organisms interact with the sun's radiation, and hold back (for a time) part of the enormous *increase* in entropy which would normally result from the absorption of this radiation by matter. What is remarkable about living organisms is that some are able to use radiation to synthesize compounds with a large positive free-energy of formation, and that all are able to use the energy of such compounds in bringing about work-absorbing, entropy-decreasing changes such as the ones mentioned above.

10.2 The steps of metabolic processes

Recently biochemists have been paying great attention to the energetics of metabolic processes, and great advances have been made in working out how the living cell is able to build up energy-rich compounds, and to re-distribute that energy efficiently. One of the most surprising discoveries has been that the same few reaction steps can be found underlying almost all cellular life, whether in single-celled organisms such as bacteria, or in complex multi-cellular organisms such as man and other mammals.

For example, certain bacteria in milk obtain their energy from the conversion of glucose to lactic acid, by a series of steps (Fig. 10.1):

$$C_6H_{12}O_6 \longrightarrow 2CH_3CH(OH)COOH; \qquad \Delta G^\ominus = -150 \text{ kJ} \, (-36 \text{ kcal})$$

(This is the process which causes untreated milk to go sour on standing.)

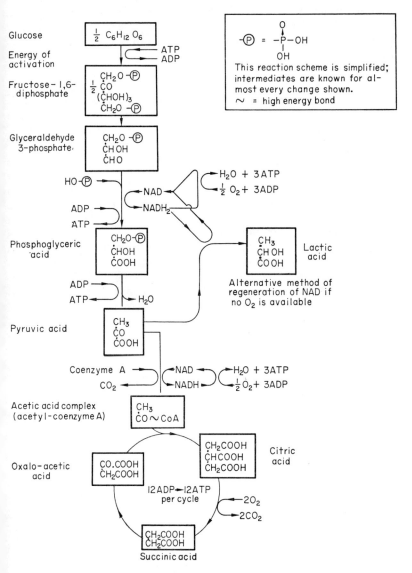

Fig. 10.1   Biochemical pathways for the reactions:

$$\tfrac{1}{2}C_6H_{12}O_6 \longrightarrow CH_3CH(OH)COOH$$
$$\tfrac{1}{2}C_6H_{12}O_6 + 3O_2 \longrightarrow 3CO_2 + 3H_2O$$

In animal muscle the source of energy is normally a sequence of reactions which has the overall effect of combining glucose (produced from stored-up glycogen) with oxygen (carried there in the bloodstream, loosely combined with the haemoglobin) to produce carbon dioxide and water:

$$C_6H_{12}O_6 + 6O_2 \longrightarrow 6CO_2 + 6H_2O \text{ (l)}; \quad \varDelta G^\ominus = -2892 \text{ kJ} (-690 \text{ kcal})$$

But if the oxygen supply becomes insufficient, as it does during prolonged violent exercise, the muscle tissue can resort to using just the first few steps in the chain, i.e. the less rewarding anaerobic catabolism of glucose to lactic acid. This is the same reaction as occurs in milk, and although the free-energy available is only one-nineteenth of that from complete oxidation, it is available instantly.

It is interesting that the energy-transfer chain is being studied in connection with cancer research, since the discovery (Warburg, 1926) that neoplastic (cancer) cells produce excessive lactic acid, perhaps because energy release is blocked in some way.

Yeast cells also obtain energy from the anaerobic breakdown of glucose. The first steps, to pyruvic acid, are the same (see Fig. 10.1) but then the yeast takes the process beyond lactic acid, to ethanol, by a decarboxylation step. This is the familiar fermentation of sugars to alcohol and carbon dioxide, as occurs in the making of wines and beer.

The breakdown (catabolism) of glucose to lactic acid yields only 150 kJ mole^{-1} of free-energy, out of a total of 2892 kJ. The remainder is obtained when the pyruvic acid is oxidized, by oxygen from air, to carbon dioxide and water. It is not intended to give here the details of the many steps, but they are to be found in any textbook of biochemistry. (See also §10.6 and Fig. 10.1.)

10.3 Enzymes

The chemical reactions in living cells differ in several important respects from those normally found in non-living systems. For one thing, the overall reaction is usually one which has a large energy of activation, and would not normally take place at an appreciable rate in the 0–40°C range. Secondly, the living organism is able to make a substance react in a specific way, even when there is the possibility of another reaction for which $\varDelta G$ is more negative. Thirdly, a cell can often bring about a reaction for which $\varDelta G$ is positive, without any immediate external supply of work. It manages such an endergonic process by 'coupling' the reaction to an exergonic reaction (for which $\varDelta G$ is negative) so that the overall result is a release of free-energy.

These remarkable chemical achievements are brought about by enzymes, which are large protein molecules, coiled and folded, and held in place by hydrogen bonds. Their elaborate shape and constitution gives them very specific catalytic powers, for they have evolved in such a way as to have 'active spots' which are capable of taking up particular molecules in a particular way, holding them by weak bonds until a particular reaction has taken place, and releasing the products.

In most respects enzymes behave in an exactly similar way to catalysts from non-living sources. They are not restricted to operating within the cell, but can be extracted, purified (and often crystallized), and made to exhibit their catalytic powers under test-tube conditions. This can easily be demonstrated in the case of catalase, an enzyme which very effectively decomposes hydrogen peroxide to water and oxygen. (H_2O_2 is a product of certain cell reactions, and could cause serious interference if allowed to accumulate.) Details of simple experiments with catalase and diastase can be found in many biology textbooks. They will doubt-less include the effect of heat: enzymes are 'denatured' at temperatures above about 325 K (52°C), and their activity is permanently lost. This is the basis of pasteurization, etc.

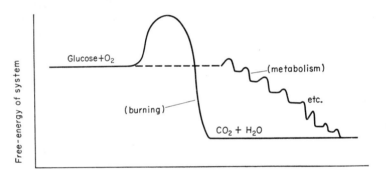

Fig. 10.2 Reaction diagram for the oxidation of glucose

By means of enzymes, the living organism is able to make an energy-rich substance like glucose go through a series of reactions in which the free-energy content is gradually reduced. The enzyme causes the energy of activation of the one specific reaction to be very small in comparison to those of perhaps hundreds of other possible reactions, even those for which ΔG is more negative. This makes it clear why life can only flourish at temperatures well *below* those at which the energy of activation could be obtained from thermal motion: at the higher temperatures there would be no specificity.

Enzymes, like all catalysts, have no power to determine the direction of any reaction step. In fact the same enzymes often appear in an ana-bolic chain (such as photosynthesis) and a catabolic one (aerobic res-piration), catalysing the same step, but in opposite directions. The specific nature of reaction chains arises in some instances (including genetic action and energy release) from a definite spatial arrangement of the enzymes, so that a substance encounters the enzymes one after another, in the right order.

10.4 The re-distribution of energy

$$C_6H_{12}O_6 + 6O_2 \longrightarrow 6CO_2\,(g) + 6H_2O\,(l); \qquad \Delta G^{\ominus} = -2892 \text{ kJ}$$
$$(-690 \text{ kcal})$$
$$\Delta H = -2820 \text{ kJ}$$
$$(-673 \text{ kcal})$$

The complete combustion of one mole of glucose in a calorimeter produces (after adjustment to constant pressure) 2820 kJ of heat. The conversion of one mole of glucose to the same products by respiration could under some circumstances ultimately produce 2820 kJ of heat, but not necessarily so. The First Law (§5.9) decrees that $\Delta H = Q_p + W_{\text{opt}}$, where $-Q_p$ = heat evolved and $-W_{\text{opt}}$ = work done by the reaction; and in the living organism work *can* be harnessed. The Second Law lays down that the *maximum* work obtainable from the reaction is $-\Delta G^{\ominus}$, that is 2892 kJ. Under conditions of maximum work no heat would be evolved at all, and a little would even be absorbed; but in fact no known organism is efficient enough to transform more than, say, three-quarters of the free-energy into work.

In this book (e.g. Chapter 3), 'work of reaction' has most often been in the form of electrical work. In the living organism, work of reaction is not usually electrical (though this is possible) but other kinds which can be summarized as (1) mechanical work such as acceleration, (2) chemical work such as the production of food reserves from substances of lower potential energy, (3) physical work such as transport of solutes from dilute to concentrated solution (§7.8), (4) 'informational work' such as the synthesis of a meaningful rather than a random sequence of amino-acids.

These work-absorbing processes take up some fraction of the 2892 kJ available from the one mole of glucose, and so reduce the amount of heat evolved; though some or all of the processes may later be reversed, and the final total of heat evolved may not be far off 2820 kJ. Nevertheless, for the study of any given metabolic reaction it is important to remember that the available work is *not* connected with the calorimetric heat of reaction ΔH except very loosely, as a consequence of the fact that at the temperatures of living cells $\Delta G^{\ominus}$ is often not very far removed from ΔH. Since $\Delta G^{\ominus}$ is frequently the more difficult quantity to measure, biochemists have sometimes been driven to substitute a known value of ΔH instead; but regrettably they have not always stated explicitly that they were making the approximation.

The work-absorbing processes do not, of course, all occur at the same time or at the same place as the oxidation of glucose. Therefore the harnessing of the work of reaction must involve some kind of energy-transfer intermediates. These will be reversible reactions which can go in the endergonic direction when free-energy is available (as during the catabolic breakdown of glucose), then later reverse, and release the energy 'on demand'.

This redistribution of energy is of supreme importance for the survival and operation of every cell. Remarkably, it has been found that just one type of substance is employed for this purpose in virtually all metabolic systems. The substance is *adenosine monophosphate* (*AMP*), and it is capable of taking up a phosphoryl or a pyrophosphoryl group by endergonic esterification, to form respectively *adenosine diphosphate* (*ADP*) or *adenosine triphosphate* (*ATP*) (see Fig. 10.3):
Using the abbreviation AdOH for adenosine,

$$C_5N_5H_4 . C_4H_6O_3CH_2OH$$

AMP may be given the formula $AdOPO(OH)_2$. The energy-transfer reactions are then as follows.

$$\underset{\text{AMP}}{AdOPO(OH)_2} + \underset{\substack{\text{phosphoric} \\ \text{acid}}}{PO(OH)_3} \rightleftharpoons \underset{\text{ADP}}{AdOPO(OH).O.PO(OH)_2} + H_2O$$

$$AdOPO(OH).O.PO(OH)_2 + PO(OH)_3 \rightleftharpoons$$
$$AdOPO(OH).O.PO(OH).O.PO(OH)_2 + H_2O$$

Both of these reactions are endergonic ($\Delta G^{\ominus\prime}$ positive), and take place only when they are coupled to an energy-releasing reaction. Conversely, the reverse reactions, which are the hydrolyses of ester linkages, are exergonic, with a standard free-energy ($\Delta G^{\ominus\prime}$, for pH 7) of about -34 kJ (-8 kcal) for each step. This is a large value for a single-step metabolic reaction, so the ester linkages in ATP and ADP have come to be known as 'high energy bonds'. (This is *not* to say that they have 'high bond energy', which means almost the opposite—see §4.2.)

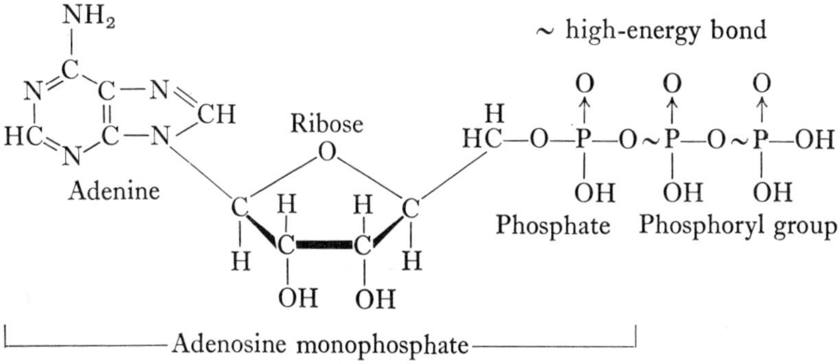

Fig. 10.3 ATP

During many of the steps of the breakdown and oxidation of an energy-rich compound such as a sugar or lipid, ATP molecules are produced, and in such cases the heat evolved is less than the ΔH of the step by about 34 kJ for each phosphate bond formed. This process is remarkably efficient, and often over 40% of the overall free-energy is redistributed via ATP. In the case of glucose the breakdown path is now fairly well known, and it is thought that 38 high-energy phosphate bonds are formed for every one glucose molecule oxidized; at 34 kJ free-energy increase per bond, this represents the storage of at least 1292 kJ out of a possible 2892 kJ, that is, over 44%.

10.5 Photosynthesis

In the discussion so far the emphasis has been on the use and redistribution of the free-energy of breakdown and oxidation of substances such as carbohydrates and lipids (fats). Obviously the reverse reactions must be occurring as well, otherwise life on this planet would have come to an end by exhausting the supply of reduced substances. The only important process which increases chemical potential energy by taking in work from an external source is photosynthesis. The reaction sequence is a complicated one, and this section will only refer to one or two points of interest.

The essential light-absorbing substance is chlorophyll, which is a large molecule containing one atom of magnesium. Part of the incident sunlight is absorbed, in the red and blue regions of the spectrum, and the remainder which is reflected looks green in consequence. The absorption of light raises chlorophyll to an activated state, and enables it to split one molecule of water into oxygen (evolved as $\frac{1}{2}O_2$ gas) and two atoms of hydrogen attached by extremely energy-rich bonds to the co-enzyme NAD (nicotinamide adenine dinucleotide). It has been shown by ^{18}O tracer experiments that all the oxygen evolved during photosynthesis is derived from the water, and none from the carbon dioxide.

It has been reported that in experiments using red light, eight photons absorbed produced, initially, one O_2 molecule and two pairs of active H atoms. But only some of these H atoms become incorporated, along with CO_2, in a glucose molecule; the others are re-oxidized to H_2O via the cytochrome mechanism, and each pair provides the free-energy for the phosphorylation of three ADP molecules to ATP. These in turn provide energy for the various stages of carbohydrate elaboration, which is therefore not *directly* dependent upon light, and can take place in animals as well as plants, as long as the ATP is forthcoming.

It is worth stressing once again the central part played by ATP in life processes. In green plants ATP is built up with energy from light: 'photophosphorylation'; in animals and in fact most organisms ATP can be built up with energy from the oxidation of reduced substances such as sugars: 'oxidative phosphorylation'; and some extraordinary bacteria succeed in building up ATP with energy from the oxidation of inorganic reducing agents, such as sulphur, iron pyrites, and cyanides.

To emphasize the point that the energy from sunlight is stored as work (ΔG) and not as heat (ΔH), consider the phenomenon of bioluminescence. In glow-worms, fireflies and several other animals an enzyme luciferase catalyses an oxidation step in which energy is released as light—a 'high-grade energy' according to the classification in Chapter 5. (See also §10.7, Question 8.)

10.6 Life processes

Some work-absorbing processes essential to life were mentioned in §10.4, and one of these—the synthesis of energy-rich compounds—has been considered in §10.5. Two more of these processes deserve further mention. One is the contraction of protein molecules such as those in muscle tissue, which provides animals with the means of locomotion, breathing, blood circulation, etc. The other is the transportation of materials across biological membranes against a concentration gradient, and this is fundamental to most forms of plant growth and movement, and to many animal functions such as digestion, excretion, and nervous impulses (due in part to electrical imbalances created by the build-up of ionic concentrations). The free-energy for all these processes is obtained from the hydrolysis of the high-energy bond of ATP.

The parts of the cell which specialize in ATP production are called the mitochondria; they have been referred to as the powerhouses of the cell. As was mentioned in §10.2, the first few steps of the respiration chain yield only a few high-energy bonds, but, more important, produce some simple molecules (such as pyruvic and acetic acids) which are much the same whether the original food was carbohydrate, lipid, or protein. The mitochondria take in these molecules and lead them through a specific sequence of electron-transfer reactions, with the accompanying production of large numbers of ATP molecules. Only in the final step is molecular oxygen involved, when the highly active electropositive complex yields up two hydrogen atoms to form water. In mammals this final step is one involving the red pigment cytochrome, and cells, such as muscle, which require large amounts of ATP are rich in mitochondria and cytochrome.

10.7 Exercises

1. $Pb^{2+}(Br^-)_2 \longrightarrow Pb + Br_2; \qquad \Delta G^{\ominus} = +258 \text{ kJ}$

This reaction can be brought about by electrolysis. Devise an alternative method using a sequence of chemical reactions, and make it clear which reactions have been 'coupled' with the decomposition in order to provide the necessary free-energy. (Lead bromide is soluble in hot water.)

2. A typical lipid is stearin, glyceryl tristearate, $C_3H_5(OOC.C_{17}H_{33})_3$ (mol. wt = 891). Write an equation for its complete oxidation. The enthalpy of combustion is $-33\ 700$ kJ mol^{-1}. If 460 molecules of ATP are formed during the oxidation, calculate the efficiency of energy redistribution. (For the ATP bond, $\Delta G^{\ominus\prime} \approx \Delta H \approx +34$ kJ.)

Compare this with the efficiency of the process for the oxidation of glucose, given in the text. Also compare the dieticians' 'calorific value' (kcal per *gram*) of lipid and glucose.

3. Discuss and explain the terms 'strong bond', 'weak bond', 'high energy bond', and 'high bond energy'. Give examples of each of these kinds of bonds from inorganic chemistry, and justify your selection.

4. $$nCO_2 + nH_2O \longrightarrow (CH_2O)_n + nO_2$$
$$\text{starch}$$

The process of photosynthesis, in which water and carbon dioxide are converted into starch, is endothermic but also has a negative entropy change. Examine this in terms of the Second Law of Thermodynamics. Is there likely to be a temperature at which the reaction is spontaneous?

5. Find an example, from simple organic chemistry, of a substance or mixture which can be made to react in two different ways, at the same temperature, by different catalysts. State the analogy with one of the properties of enzymes.

6. Sometimes the value of ΔH for a biochemical reaction is known, but $\Delta G^{\ominus}$ is not. Why might this be so? For what kind of reaction is the difference likely to be small?

Are the values likely to be close for the decarboxylation of lactic acid:

$$CH_3CH(OH)COOH\ (s) \longrightarrow C_2H_5OH\ (l) + CO_2\ (g)$$

7.* (i) Radiation from the sun reaches the earth's surface with an intensity of about 350 J m^{-2} s^{-1}. How long would it take ten leaves, each of area 10 cm^2, to make 1.8 g glucose if 8% of the solar energy is utilized?†

(ii) Suppose that red light of wavelength 6600 Å (1 Å = 10^{-10} m) is absorbed by chlorophyll: what is the energy of one mole of these photons? What is the minimum amount of photons which can provide the energy for the formation of one mole of glucose from $6H_2O\ (l) + 6CO_2\ (g)$, assuming 100% efficiency?†

(Energy of photon = $h\nu = hc/\lambda$, where ν = frequency, λ = wavelength, c = velocity of light = 3.0×10^8 m s^{-1}, and h = the Planck constant = 4.0×10^{-10} J s mol^{-1}.)

† Adapted from an exercise in *Chemistry—an Experimental Science*, the CHEM Study textbook.

(iii) In §10.5 it was stated that 4 photons are absorbed for every two atoms of hydrogen produced in the first stage of photosynthesis. What is the overall efficiency of the conversion of radiation into chemical free-energy in ATP? Compare this answer with the energy efficiency of the aerobic catabolism of glucose (given in the text) and comment.

8.* It has been estimated that mammals generate electricity (in nerves) at an efficiency of 20% conversion of ΔG. Neglecting the difference between $\Delta G^{\ominus}$ and ΔH for the process, investigate the possibility that the mechanism might be that of a heat engine. Calculate the maximum efficiency for the process if the heat of reaction were used to maintain the internal temperature of the cell, while electricity was generated from the transfer of this heat to the exterior at, say, 293 K (see §8.16).

Additional exercises

(*Answers not given*)

Part I Revision questions

1. *Simple calorimetry*

A camper wishes to choose between two fuels, paraffin (kerosene) and Camping-Gaz. Calculate how many pints of water can be brought to the boil from 20°C by one pint of each fuel, assuming 50% heat loss in each case.

[Paraffin 0.75 g cm^{-3}, 10.5 kcal g^{-1}; Camping-Gaz 0.60 g cm^{-3}, 11.8 kcal g^{-1}; 1 kcal = 4.18 kJ.]

2. *Simple latent and specific heats*

A saucepan of water is simmering gently over a constant source of heat, and is losing 3.0 cm^3 water per minute by evaporation. An egg at 20°C is put in the water, and it is exactly 2 minutes before the water comes to the boil again. Calculate the mass of the egg. (Assume specific heat of egg to be the same as for water ($\sim$4.2 J K^{-1} g^{-1}); constant heat supply and loss; and no evaporation when the water is not boiling.) ΔH_{vap} (H$_2$O) $= +41$ kJ mol^{-1} at boiling-point.

3. *Hess's Law*

Calculate the enthalpy of reaction for:

$$C_2H_6 + 3Cl_2 \longrightarrow 2C + 6HCl$$

from the data below. All substances are gases, except carbon, which is the graphite form.

$$
\begin{aligned}
C_2H_2 + 2H_2 &\longrightarrow C_2H_6; & \Delta H &= -311 \text{ kJ} \\
C_2H_2 + Cl_2 &\longrightarrow 2C + 2HCl; & \Delta H &= -411 \text{ kJ} \\
H_2 + Cl_2 &\longrightarrow 2HCl; & \Delta H &= -185 \text{ kJ}
\end{aligned}
$$

4. *Enthalpy of formation*

Use ΔH_f tables to calculate the enthalpies of the reactions:

(a) $2H_2S$ (g) $+ SO_2$ (g) $\longrightarrow 2H_2O$ (l) $+ S$ (s)
(b) CaC_2 (s) $+ 2H_2O$ (l) $\longrightarrow Ca(OH)_2$ (s) $+ C_2H_2$ (g)
(c) CaC_2 (s) $+ 2HCl$ (aq) $\longrightarrow CaCl_2$ (aq) $+ C_2H_2$ (g)

What is the connection between the value of ΔH_f for calcium carbide, and the method used for its manufacture?

5. Hydrazine and hydrogen peroxide have been proposed as rocket fuel. Calculate the total pressure created by the adiabatic reaction of 32 g N_2H_4 with H_2O_2, assuming that the products behave as ideal gases, and no heat is lost.

$$N_2H_4 \text{ (l)} + 2H_2O_2 \text{ (l)} \longrightarrow N_2 \text{ (g)} + 4H_2O \text{ (g)}; \quad \Delta H = -687 \text{ kJ}$$

6. (a) A bomb calorimeter is calibrated as follows. 1.00 g pure benzoic acid is burned in excess oxygen; the temperature rise is 3.82 K after correction for loss. The heat of combustion of solid benzoic acid at constant volume (ΔU) is 3227 kJ mol^{-1}. Calculate the effective heat capacity of the calorimeter.

(b) 0.500 g naphthalene, $C_{10}H_8$, is burned in the same calorimeter, and the temperature rise is 5.77 K. Calculate the heat of combustion of naphthalene at constant volume (ΔU).

(c) Write a balanced equation for the combustion of naphthalene to gaseous carbon dioxide and liquid water. Will the heat of combustion at constant pressure (ΔH) be more or less negative than ΔU?

7. What temperature rise would you expect from the addition of 500cm^3 0.5 M NaOH to the following volumes of 0.5 M HCl, in a container of negligible heat capacity?
(a) 250 cm^3 (b) 500 cm^3 (c) 750 cm^3.

8. Calculate $\Delta G_r^\ominus$ at 298 K, and predict the feasibility of the following reactions:

(a) $Pb(NO_3)_2 \text{ (s)} \longrightarrow PbO \text{ (s)} + 2NO_2 \text{ (g)} + \frac{1}{2}O_2 \text{ (g)}$
(b) $LiH \text{ (s)} + H_2O \text{ (l)} \longrightarrow LiOH \text{ (aq)} + H_2 \text{ (g)}$
(c) $2Fe^{3+} \text{ (aq)} + 2I^- \text{ (aq)} \longrightarrow 2Fe^{2+} \text{ (aq)} + I_2 \text{ (aq, as } KI_3)$

How could the free-energies of (a) and (c) be measured experimentally, at some chosen temperature?

9. Calculate $\Delta G_r^\ominus$ at 298 K for the following reactions, and also predict the sign of ΔS by inspection of the equations. Hence predict the feasibility of reaction at higher temperatures.

(a) $2Au(OH)_3 \text{ (s)} \longrightarrow Au_2O_3 \text{ (s)} + 3H_2O \text{ (g)}$
(b) $N_2 \text{ (g)} + 3H_2 \text{ (g)} \longrightarrow 2NH_3 \text{ (g)}$
(c) $2As \text{ (s)} + 3H_2 \text{ (g)} \longrightarrow 2AsH_2 \text{ (g)}$

In the case of (c), check your prediction by considering Marsh's test for arsenic.

10. Iodine monochloride reacts readily with chlorine at room temperature:

$$ICl \text{ (l)} + Cl_2 \text{ (g)} \longrightarrow ICl_3 \text{ (s)}.$$

(a) By considering bond forming and breaking, and gas production or consumption, estimate the signs of ΔH, $\Delta S^{\ominus}$, $\Delta G^{\ominus}(298)$ and $\Delta G^{\ominus}(900)$.

(b) In fact $\Delta H = \pm 300$ kJ and $\Delta S^{\ominus} = \pm 300$ J K^{-1}. At what temperature can all three components exist together? (Cl_2 at 1 atm.) What will happen above this temperature?

11. The enthalpies of atomization of H_2 (g) and C (graphite) are $+219$ and $+716$ kJ per mole of atoms respectively. The enthalpies of formation of CH_4 (g) and C_2H_6 (g) are -75 and -85 kJ mol^{-1}. Calculate the bond strengths of C—H and C—C in these compounds.

12. *Born–Haber cycle*

Construct a diagram showing the enthalpy changes for the steps in the cycle:

$$Zn \text{ (s)} + CuO \text{ (s)} \longrightarrow Zn \text{ (g)} + CuO \text{ (s)}$$
$$\longrightarrow Zn \text{ (g)} + Cu^{2+} \text{ (g)} + O^{2-} \text{ (g)}$$
$$\longrightarrow Zn^{2+} \text{ (g)} + Cu^{2+} \text{ (g)} + O^{2-} \text{ (g)} + 2e^- \text{ (g)}$$
$$\text{(top of diagram)}$$

$$\longrightarrow Zn^{2+} \text{ (g)} + Cu \text{(g)} + O^{2-} \text{ (g)}$$
$$\longrightarrow ZnO \text{ (s)} + Cu \text{ (g)}$$
$$\longrightarrow ZnO \text{ (s)} + Cu \text{ (s)}$$

Data: Lattice energies: CuO, 4047 kJ; ZnO, 3968 kJ;
Heats of vaporization: Cu 343 kJ; Zn 131 kJ;
Ionization energies: Cu to Cu^{2+} 2714 kJ; Zn to Zn^{2+} 2652 kJ.

Hence obtain a value for the enthalpy of the overall reaction.

13. The heat of combustion of diamond is -396.6 kJ mol^{-1}, while that of graphite is -393.5. Which is the more stable allotrope? Which has the greater enthalpy of sublimation to C (g)? Which solid has more or stronger bonding?

14. How and why would the heats of combustion differ for the isomeric dienes C_5H_8?

$$(CH_2:CH.CH:CH.CH_3 \quad \text{and} \quad CH_2:CH.CH_2.CH:CH_2)$$

15. Plot graphs of the following heats of combustion versus the number of carbon atoms, and extrapolate to C_0. Do the graphs give evidence of the transferability of bond energies? Comment on any anomalies.

ΔH of combustion for gaseous compounds (in kJ mol^{-1})

CH$_3$OH -753	HCHO -561
C$_2$H$_5$OH -1414	CH$_3$CHO -1193
C$_3$H$_7$OH -2043	(CH$_3$)$_2$CO -1815
C$_4$H$_9$OH -2707	(C$_2$H$_5$)$_2$CO -3111

16. The synthesis of hydrogen selenide is strongly endothermic:

$$H_2 \text{ (g)} + Se \text{ (s or l)} \longrightarrow H_2Se \text{ (g)}; \qquad \Delta H \approx +84 \text{ kJ mol}^{-1}$$

Use the rules given in Chapter 2 to predict the sign of ΔS, and hence the position of the high-temperature equilibrium, for the reaction as written.

How would this equilibrium change if the selenium were allowed to boil?

17. *Contact process*

Discuss the importance of the enthalpy and entropy of reaction, and free-energy of activation, in the choice of temperature for the production of sulphur trioxide:

$$2SO_2 \text{ (g)} + O_2 \text{ (g)} \rightleftharpoons 2SO_3 \text{ (g)}$$

Is the catalyst maintained at the optimum temperature by heating or cooling coils? Is there any tendency for the reaction to reverse when the gases have left the catalyst chamber? Use $\Delta H_f^{\ominus}$ and $\Delta G_f^{\ominus}$ data to calculate the equilibrium constants at 600 K and 1200 K.

18. The free-energies of formation of the aqueous ions Mn^{2+} and Ag^{+} are -223 and $+77.1$ kJ respectively. Calculate the standard cell potential for the reaction between manganese metal and silver nitrate solution, and also the non-standard potential for manganese + saturated AgCl, for which $[Ag^{+}] = 1.4 \times 10^{-5}$.

19. The oxidation of Fe^{2+} to Fe^{3+} by acidified dichromate has $E^{\ominus} = +0.57$ V. Fe$^{3+} + e^{-} \rightarrow$ Fe^{2+}; $E^{\ominus} = +0.76$ V. Write the half-equation and redox potential for the reduction of the dichromate. Does dichromate react with 1 M hydrochloric acid? (Cl$_2 + 2e^{-} \rightarrow 2Cl^{-}$; $E^{\ominus} = +1.4$ V.)

Part II Examination questions†

1. What do you understand by the term *free-energy*?

† Reprinted by kind permission from the following sources:
O & C.A. Oxford and Cambridge G.C.E. A-level.
O & C.S. Oxford and Cambridge G.C.E. Special Paper.
C.Schol. Cambridge University Scholarship Examinations.
W.A.A. West African Examinations Council G.C.E. A-level.

What is the relationship between *standard free-energy change* ($\Delta G^\ominus$), the *standard enthalpy change* ($\Delta H^\ominus$), and the *standard entropy change* ($\Delta S^\ominus$) in a chemical reaction?

A fuel cell using concentrated potassium hydroxide as electrolyte and nickel electrodes produces a voltage by converting into electrical energy the chemical free-energy of the reaction:

$$H_2 \text{ (g)} + \tfrac{1}{2}O_2 \text{ (g)} \longrightarrow H_2O \text{ (l)}$$

If such a cell is 80% efficient, calculate the energy (in kcal and also in kWh) produced from one gram mole of hydrogen at 25°C.

How does this value compare with that obtained by burning one gram mole of H_2 (in O_2) and converting the heat evolved (through a steam turbine) into electrical energy with an efficiency of 40%? Give your answer in kcal and kWh.

[For liquid water at 25°C,

$$\Delta H_f^\ominus = -68\ 300 \text{ cal mol}^{-1}; \quad \Delta S_f^\ominus = -39 \text{ cal mol}^{-1} \text{ degree}^{-1};$$

1 calorie = 4.18 joule; 1 watt = 1 joule second^{-1}.]   *O & C.S.*

2. (a) Discuss and explain in terms of the energy factors involved why
   (i) not all exothermic reactions are spontaneous
   (ii) some endothermic reactions are spontaneous.

Illustrate your answer with *one* example in each case.

(b) In the following reactions the amount of heat evolved is different.

At 25°C: $2H_2 \text{ (g)} + O_2 \text{ (g)} \longrightarrow 2H_2O \text{ (l)}$; $\Delta H = -136$ kcal
at 100°C: $2H_2 \text{ (g)} + O_2 \text{ (g)} \longrightarrow 2H_2O \text{ (g)}$; $\Delta H = -115$ kcal

   (i) account for the difference in the amount of heat evolved (ΔH) at the different temperatures.
   (ii) Given that the free-energy change, $\Delta G = -113$ kcal for this reaction at 25°C, calculate the value of the product $T \Delta S$ at this temperature.   *W.A.A.*

3. The standard electrode potentials, $E^\ominus$, between the metals and their unipositive ions are listed below for the elements of groups IA and IB.

Group IA element	$E^\ominus$/V	Group IB element	$E^\ominus$/V
Li	−3.02	Cu	+0.52
Na	−2.71	Ag	+0.80
K	−2.92	Au	+1.42
Rb	−2.99		
Cs	−3.02		

How do you account for:

(a) the large differences in the values of $E^{\ominus}$ between the two groups,
(b) the anomalously large negative value for Li?

Explain briefly how the chemical behaviour of these elements is related to their positions in the electrochemical series. *O & C.S.*

4. What is meant by *electrode potential*? Indicate the way in which an electrode potential can be measured. What is the *electrode potential series* of the elements?

How are the *heats of formation* of the oxides of lead, potassium, silver and zinc related to their position in the electrode potential series?

Explain the difference between heat of formation and free-energy of formation. *O & C.S.*

5. What is meant by heat of combustion, heat of reaction and Hess's Law?

The molar heat of combustion of liquid ethanol is 327 kcal (evolved) and that of liquid acetic acid is 209 kcal (evolved). Calculate the heat of reaction for the oxidation of liquid ethanol to liquid acetic acid. State whether heat is absorbed or evolved. *O & C.A.*

6. Explain the effect of (a) concentration (b) temperature, and (c) catalyst on (i) the rate of a chemical reaction, (ii) the equilibrium state of a chemical reaction. *O & C.A.*

7. Describe how any industrially important ore (*except iron*) is extracted from one of its common ores.

Discuss the reasons why the process which you describe is used for this particular metal in preference to other possible methods of reducing metal ores.

Suggest one method in each case which might be used to obtain (a) calcium from calcium carbonate, (b) mercury from mercuric oxide, giving reasons for your choice. *O & C.A.*

8. The heats absorbed when 1 mole of NO and 1 mole of NO_2 are formed from the elements at 298 K and constant pressure are 90 and 34 kJ respectively. Discuss the effect of temperature and pressure on the chemical equilibrium:

$$2NO_2 \rightleftharpoons 2NO + O_2$$

How will the raising of the temperature change the rate at which equilibrium is attached? If the molar specific heats at constant pressure of NO_2, NO and O_2 between 298 K and 398 K are 36.4, 29.3 and 29.3 J K^{-1} mol^{-1} respectively, calculate the heat of the reaction

$$2NO_2 \longrightarrow 2NO + O_2$$

at 398 K. *C.Schol.* (adapted to SI units)

9. Comment on or suggest explanations for the following observations:

(a) When galvanized iron exposed to moist air is scratched it shows no sign of rust, but when tinplate is scratched in similar circumstances it begins to rust rapidly.

(b) Chlorine reacts with potassium iodide to give potassium chloride, but iodine reacts with potassium chlorate to give potassium iodate.

(c) When added to a solution of copper(II) sulphate, potassium iodide solution precipitates copper(I) iodide and liberates iodine, but potassium chloride solution has no effect on a solution of copper(II) sulphate.

(d) The boiling points of the hydrogen halides are:

HF	HCl	HBr	HI
19°C	−85°C	−67°C	−35°C

O & C.S.

10. What factors determine the stability of a metal ion in the solid state and in aqueous solution?

The first four ionization potentials of aluminium are 5.98, 18.8, 28.4, and 120 eV respectively. Comment upon these values with particular reference to (a) the large difference between the values of the 3rd and 4th ionization potentials, and (b) the non-existence of Al^+ and Al^{++} ions either in the solid state or in aqueous solution.   *C.Schol.*

11. Using the kinetic theory and the concept of reaction velocity, explain the following facts:

(a) When nitric oxide is heated to 1000°C it is almost completely decomposed into nitrogen and oxygen.

(b) When oxygen and nitrogen are heated to 3000°C the mixture of gases is found to contain about 40 per cent. of nitric oxide.

(c) Hydrogen and oxygen combine to form water with the evolution of considerable heat, but the mixture of gases needs heating before combination takes place.   *O & C.S.*

12. (a) Explain how the heat of reaction at constant volume is related to that at constant pressure.

The heat of combustion of gaseous ethylene to form carbon dioxide and liquid water at 300 K and under a constant pressure of one atmosphere is $-1420 \text{ kJ mol}^{-1}$. Calculate the heat of reaction at constant volume at 300 K.

(Assume a value of 8.31 J K^{-1} mol^{-1} for the gas constant R.)

(b) Explain what is meant by the *ionization potential* of an element. How is the standard electrode potential of a metal in an aqueous solution of its ions related to its ionization potential?

O & C.S. (adapted to SI units)

13. Define 'order of reaction' and explain what is meant by 'activation energy'. The reaction velocity constant (k) of the second order reaction $H_2 + I_2 \rightarrow 2HI$ varies with temperature as follows:

T/K	556	700	781
k/(mol^{-1} litre s^{-1})	1.19×10^{-4}	1.72×10^{-1}	3.58

Calculate: (i) the activation energy of the reaction; (ii) the reaction velocity constant of the reaction at 629 K; (iii) the reaction velocity constant of the reverse reaction at 629 K given that the equilibrium constant = 3.73.   *C. Schol.*

14. (a) What is meant by the term 'molar heat of neutralization'? Why is the value of this quantity approximately the same for the neutralization of any strong monobasic acid by a strong base at a given temperature?

Explain why the values of the heat of neutralization of a strong acid by a strong base is *not* the same as the heat of formation of water.

(b) Calculate the molar heat of neutralization from the following data. 100 ml of 0.100 M sodium hydroxide solution is mixed with 100 ml of 0.100 M hydrochloric acid in an insulated container of heat capacity 34.0 cal/°C. The two solutions and the container are all initially at the same temperature; the overall rise in temperature of the system is 0.580°C.

[Assume that the two solutions have a density of 1.00 g/ml and specific heat of 1.00 cal/g°C.]

(c) Use the bond energies given below to calculate the enthalpy change in the following reaction:

$$N_2 \text{ (g)} + 2H_2 \text{ (g)} \longrightarrow \begin{matrix} H & & H \\ \diagdown & & \diagup \\ & N—N & \text{(g)} \\ \diagup & & \diagdown \\ H & & H \end{matrix}$$

Bond	N—N	H—H	N≡N	N—H
Bond energy in (kcal/mole)	38.0	104	225	93.0

W.A.A.

Part III Miscellaneous problems

(*Note:* these may require some ingenuity, and some assumptions may have to be made.)

1. A girl breathes out 100 cm^3 carbon dioxide per second as she walks slowly on a level path. This rate increases to 350 cm^3 s^{-1} as she climbs a

150 ft. hill in 10 minutes. Assuming that the energy for the climb is derived from the oxidation of glucose, calculate the approximate efficiency of conversion of chemical energy to gravitational potential energy. Show clearly what approximations you make.
(9.81 J will raise a mass of 1 kg through 1 m.)

2. The ionization energies of magnesium and lead are almost the same:

$$\left.\begin{array}{l} Mg\ (g) \longrightarrow Mg^{2+}\ (g) + 2e^- \\ Pb\ (g) \longrightarrow Pb^{2+}\ (g) + 2e^- \end{array}\right\} \Delta H = +2145\ kJ$$

The boiling-points are Mg 1383 K, Pb 2017 K. How do the enthalpies of atomization compare? Discuss the factors which make magnesium the more active metal.

3. Deduce the sign and approximate size of ΔH and ΔS, and hence ΔG, for the reactions:

$$H_2 + NO_2\ (g) \longrightarrow NO + H_2O\ (g)$$
$$H_2 + NO\ (g) \longrightarrow \tfrac{1}{2}N_2 + H_2O\ (g)$$

What will be the equilibrium mixture at high temperature?

4. From the principle of micro-reversibility it follows that if k_1 and k_2 are the forward and reverse rate constants at equilibrium, $K_{eq} = k_1/k_2$. k_1 is a function of the forward activation energy $\Delta G_1^{\ddagger}$, and k_2 of the reverse activation energy, $\Delta G_2^{\ddagger}$.

If a catalyst lowers the value of $\Delta G_1^{\ddagger}$ and $\Delta G_2^{\ddagger}$ by x kcal, the *proportional* decrease cannot be the same for both; so how can K_{eq} be unaffected by the catalyst?

5. A student answered the question: 'How does an increase in temperature affect the equilibrium of a mixture of N_2, H_2 and NH_3 in a closed vessel?' as follows:

A rise in temperature increases the total pressure in the vessel, by the gas law $P = (nR/v)T$. By Le Chatelier's Principle the equilibrium will shift to minimize this constraint, that is, in the direction which has less gas molecules, $N_2 + 3H_2 \rightarrow 2NH_3$.

What truth is there in this answer? Would it apply to a hypothetical reaction for which $\Delta H = 0$?

6. The electrochemical series has been used to connect reactivity of metals toward acids, rate of reaction with water or steam, stability of hydroxides and carbonates. Explain these connections, and discuss how closely the different properties do depend on the electrode potentials of the metals in aqueous solutions of their cations.

7. At the boiling point, T_b, of any liquid:

$$T_b \, \Delta S_{vap} = \Delta H_{vap}$$

For most liquids $\Delta S_{vap} \approx 88 \text{ J K}^{-1} \text{ mol}^{-1}$, and so:

$$\Delta H_{vap} \approx 0.088 \text{ T kJ mol}^{-1}$$

Exceptions are H_2O and C_2H_5OH, for which $\Delta S_{vap} = +119$ and $+121$ J K^{-1} and the accepted explanation is that hydrogen-bonding causes an unusual degree of order in the liquid, and so both ΔS and ΔH for the process liquid → gas are greater than normal.

The b.pt of HF is 292 K, and $\Delta H_{vap} = +7.5 \text{ kJ mol}^{-1}$. Calculate ΔS_{vap} and show that HF is an abnormal liquid. Does the explanation given for H_2O and C_2H_5OH explain the facts for HF? If not, suggest an alternative explanation. (Follow this up for NH_3, NF_3, HCl, C_2H_5F, etc.)

Part IV Practical projects

1. *Manometric measurement of K_p and $\Delta G^\ominus$ of decomposition*

Devise and set up an apparatus to measure the pressure of CO_2 in equilibrium with $CuCO_3$ at various temperatures. For the reaction $CuCO_3 \rightleftharpoons CuO + CO_2$, $K_p = p(CO_2)$, so $\Delta G^\ominus$ is readily calculated.

Also measure ΔH_r from the heats of reaction of CuO with acid and $CuCO_3$ with the same acid. Hence obtain $\Delta S^\ominus$.

The dissociation pressure apparatus will probably require an electric furnace (wound with resistance wire and lagged with asbestos tape or plaster of Paris) with one or two thermocouples. The manometer liquid could be silicone oil.

The copper carbonate may have to be prepared specially, since basic copper carbonate should not be used. Other carbonates such as those of cobalt or lead may also be tried.

2. *Electrochemical determination of $\Delta G_r^\ominus$.*

Use a potentiometer to measure $E^\ominus$ for the cell:

$$\text{Pt} \mid \text{Br}_2, \text{Br}^- \parallel \text{I}^-, \text{I}_2 \mid \text{Pt}$$

Carbon electrodes could be substituted for platinum if necessary. It is not possible to obtain 1 M concentrations of the halogens, nor is it desirable. Use more dilute solutions and the Nernst equation. I_2 will be present as I_3^-. Use ice to vary the temperature.

Also measure ΔH calorimetrically. Which is the more accurate determination of ΔH, that from the calorimeter or that from the variation of ΔG with T?

7—C.E.

3. *An investigation of the* $Cu + HCl$ *reaction*

Although $E^{\ominus}$ is negative for the simple reaction

$$Cu + 2H^+ (aq) \longrightarrow Cu^{2+} (aq) + H_2 (g)$$

it may be positive for the reaction of copper with concentrated hydrochloric acid to give $H_2 + CuCl$ or $CuCl_2^-$, or $CuCl_4^{3-}$. Find from the literature the instability constants and hence calculate the cell potentials. If the value of $E^{\ominus}$ is more positive than the overvoltage of hydrogen on copper, set up an experiment to detect the production of hydrogen from copper and $HCl(aq)$ at various temperatures.

Further possibilities are (i) the use of platinum or silver in contact with the copper, to reduce the overvoltage; (ii) the use of concentrated hydriodic acid made by adding KI to $HCl(aq)$.

4. *Measurement of the strength of a hydrogen bond*

Measure the distribution of acetic acid between toluene and water at three temperatures and three or four concentrations. Good thermostatting is essential, and if the acid concentration is to be measured by titration against standard NaOH, CO_2-free water will be required.

At any given temperature the distribution is governed by (i) the partition coefficient of the monomer and (ii) the equilibrium constant for the dimerization in benzene:

$$2CH_3COOH \rightleftharpoons CH_3-C\underset{\displaystyle O-H\ldots O}{\overset{\displaystyle O\ldots H-O}{\diagup\diagdown}}C-CH_3$$

Derive a method of calculating this equilibrium constant from the results for the different concentrations at one temperature. Then from the variation of K_c with T, ΔH for the dimerization is obtained, and this equals twice the bond strength of the hydrogen bond.

5. *An electrochemical measurement of the entropy of mixing*

PRELIMINARY THEORETICAL CALCULATIONS

(i) The thermodynamic probability Ω of N molecules of an ideal gas is given by:

$$\Omega = \frac{N!}{\prod\limits_i N_i!}$$

where N_i identical molecules are all in the ith energy state, and are indistinguishable. Therefore of the $N!$ possible combinations of the N

molecules, $N_i!$ combinations are indistinguishable, and this applies to every energy state. So

$$\Omega = \frac{\text{total combinations}}{\text{indistinguishable combinations}} = \text{distinguishable combinations}$$

Now consider N_i molecules in every ith level being changed, by mixing, to $(N_A)_i$ molecules of A and $(N_B)_i$ molecules of B. What will be the new number of 'indistinguishable combinations'? What will be the new Ω_{AB}?

Take logs, and prove that:

$$\Delta S_{\text{mixing}} = S_{AB} - S_A - S_B = N_A k \ln \frac{N}{N_A} + N_B k \ln \frac{N}{N_B}$$

(where $N_A + N_B = N$, the total number of molecules). Stirling's approximation will be required to eliminate the factorials: $\ln x! \simeq x \ln x - x$.

What is ΔS for the mixing of 1 mole A + 1 mole B?

(ii) In a mixing process at constant total pressure, in which N_A particles in vessel 1 and N_B particles in vessel 2 gradually mix, the extent of the process can be measured by $(N_B)_1$, the number of particles of B which are present in vessel 1. $(N_B)_1 = (N_A)_2$.

Obtain an expression for the change in the entropy of the gas (or solution) in vessel 1 as mixing proceeds, by differentiating the expression ΔS_{mixing} with respect to N_B, and prove that for vessel 1:

$$\frac{d(\Delta S_{\text{mixing}})}{d(N_B)} = Nk \ln \frac{'N_A}{N_B}$$

(iii) Consider the mixing of ions $X^{(n+1)-}$ and X^{n-} in dilute solution. If 1 mole of $X^{(n+1)-}$ is initially in vessel 1, and 1 mole of X^{n-} is in vessel 2, and if the two vessels are linked by a salt-bridge and if inert electrodes in each solution are connected by a conductor, a current will flow and the following electrode reactions will occur:

$$\text{in vessel 1:} \qquad X^{(n+1)-} \longrightarrow X^{n-} + e^-$$
$$\text{in vessel 2:} \qquad X^{n-} + e^- \longrightarrow X^{(n+1)-}$$

If sufficient time were to elapse, both solutions would ultimately contain a mixture of $\frac{1}{2}$ mole each of both ions. In effect, complete mixing would have occurred. The amount of electricity which must pass during this process is one half mole of electrons, that is $\frac{1}{2}F$ coulomb.

There is no net change in the concentration of either ion. The ions are initially separate, and finally mixed, so the entropy of mixing is the only driving-force which can create the cell potential. The cell can also be considered as two concentration cells in series.

The total electrical work would be the integral $\int_0^{1/2F} E\,dc$ where E is the cell potential and c is the amount of electricity. But this work also equals $-\Delta G_{mixing}$ (for the two moles of ions). So the cell potential at any stage of the process is given by:

$$E = -\left(\frac{\partial \Delta G}{\partial c}\right)_T = +T\frac{d(\Delta S)}{dc}$$

Since every electron which flows brings about an increase of one ion of X^{n-} in vessel 1,

$$dc = d(N_B)_1$$

where N_B = number of ions X^{n-}.

Finish the calculation to obtain an expression for E in terms of the ratio of concentrations of the ions in vessel 1. Note that $k(N_A+N_B) = 2R$.

(iv) Use this equation to compute E for cells made up of half-cells with the concentration ratios 99:1, 19:1, 9:1, 4:1, 7:3, 3:2, and 1:1 (representing successive stages in the mixing process).

Plot a graph E (vertical) against c and N_B.

EXPERIMENTAL

Set up a series of cells operating on the free-energy of mixing of $Fe(CN)_6^{4-}$ with $Fe(CN)_6^{3-}$, at the concentration ratios mentioned above, and a total concentration of 0.01 M. Measure the potentials and compare them with those calculated. How 'ideal' is the mixing of the ions?

[As a check, the cell potential of the 9:1 cell is theoretically $+0.114$ V:

$$Pt \mid Fe(CN)_6^{4-}, \ Fe(CN)_6^{3-} \parallel Fe(CN)_6^{4-}, \ Fe(CN)_6^{3-} \mid Pt]$$
$$ 0.009 \text{ M} \qquad 0.001 \text{ M} \qquad 0.001 \text{ M} \qquad 0.009 \text{ M}$$

Plot a graph of E versus $Fe(CN)_6^{3-}/0.01$, which is also a graph of E versus c, the amount of electricity. Therefore the area under the curve represents $\int_0^{F/2} E \, dc = -\Delta G_{mixing}$. Find the area by counting squares or by weighing (the area of one square will be some proportional part of $1 \text{ V} \times (\frac{1}{2}F)C$), and so obtain ΔG of mixing.

Compare this with the theoretical free-energy of mixing one mole A with one mole B, which is $2RT \ln 2$ (if $\Delta H_{mixing} = 0$). Further investigations: find the change in E with temperature, and with dilution, for one chosen concentration ratio.

Answers

1.4

1. (a) C; (b) D; (c) B; (d) A; (e) C; (f) B; (g) F; (h) D, E.
2. Up to a point, all; but (d) is rapid anyway, and (g) hardly goes at all; and (b) and (h) would be hindered by very high temperature.
3. (e), (h).

2.4

1. (i) Al or Na reactions, (ii) $CaCO_3$, (iii) $SrCl_2$.
   (a), (b) and (c) All no, not necessarily.
2. (a) One mole (40 g) of solid MgO, 2 moles of aqueous H^+ ions; (b) 0.02 mole (0.8 g) MgO, 0.04 mole H^+ (aq).
3. (a) $+746$ kJ; (b) -357 kcal.
4. 0.87 g (to provide 20.9 kJ).
5. 17 K rise (1 mole $H_2SO_4 = 98$ g, gives 87 kJ, and 196 g $H_2O = c.$ 11 moles, $\therefore$ absorbs 66 kJ. So $(87 - 66)$ kJ evolved into $c.$ 0.3 kg dilute acid, giving $21/(0.3 \times 4.2) = 17$ K rise. This result suggests a safe way of diluting a large volume of concentrated sulphuric acid quickly).
6. 9 g (300 C $\times$ 10 V $= 3$ kJ, which melts $\frac{3}{6} \times 18$ g ice.)
7. See §2.5.

2.7

1. $\Delta H_r = -147$ kJ.
2. -471 kJ.
3. $FeCl_2$ (s) $+ aq \rightarrow FeCl_2$ (aq); $\Delta H = -81$ kJ.

2.14

1. -3270 kJ mol^{-1}.
2. -235 kJ g-eqn^{-1}.
3. (i) $+35$ kJ, (ii) $+40$ kJ.

2.16

1. (a) -66 kJ (evolved); (b) -368 kJ; (c) -56 kJ; (d) $CaCO_3$ (s) $+ 2H^+$ (aq) $\rightarrow Ca^{2+}$ (aq) $+ H_2O$ (l) $+ CO_2$ (g); $\Delta H = -16$ kJ; (e) ΔH_{sol} $(NaCl + \frac{1}{4}Na_2CO_3.10H_2O) = +4 + 17 = +21$ kJ; (f) -165 kJ, (g) -281 kJ.
2. (a) $+4$ kJ; (b) -11 kJ.
3. For example: $CuO + 2HCl$ (aq) $\rightarrow CuCl_2$ (aq) $+ H_2O$
   $$CuCl_2 \text{ (aq)} + Mg \rightarrow MgCl_2 \text{ (aq)} + Cu$$
   $$MgO + 2HCl \text{ (aq)} \rightarrow MgCl_2 \text{ (aq)} + H_2O$$
4. MgO (s) $+ 2H^+$ (aq) $\rightarrow Mg^{2+}$ (aq) $+ H_2O$ (l); $\Delta H = -147$ kJ g-eqn^{-1}; $-147 - 2(-58) = -31$ kJ g-eqn^{-1}.

3.5

1. (i) −, (ii) +.
2. (i) +, (ii) +, (iii) −, (iv) yes, (v) not necessarily; the rate of reaction cannot be predicted, and may be zero.
3. 960 K (2 sig. fig.).

3.8

1. (a) −ve, reaction reversed at high T; (b) +ve, favoured; (c) −ve, reversed; (d) small and probably negative, little change; (e) +ve; reaction favoured (and since ΔH is −ve, becomes explosive); (f) near to zero; no effect (but see §7.5); (g) +ve, favoured.
2. Negative.
3. Probably negative ΔS, ∴ the synthesis not favoured at any temperature.
4. By measuring ΔH for the reverse reaction, or, better still, by measuring the heats of solution of the anhydrous and the hydrated salts.

3.11

1.

	$\Delta G_r^{\ominus}$/kJ	Feasibility at 298 K	$\Delta S_r^{\ominus}$
(i)	−70	feasible	−ve
(ii)	−193	feasible	−ve
(iii)	+17	unfeasible (equilibrium with reactants in excess)	(?)
(iv)	−105	feasible	−ve
(v)	−5	central equilibrium	+ve
(vi)	+164	unfeasible	+ve

2.

	ΔH/kJ	ΔS/(J K^{-1})	$\Delta G_{400}^{\ominus}$	$\Delta G_{2000}^{\ominus}$
(i)	−112	−140	−56	+170 (2 sig. fig.)
(iv)	+46	+170	−22	−300 (2 sig. fig.)
(vi)	+219	+190	+140	−150 (2 sig. fig.)

3. $\Delta G_{298}^{\ominus} = -76$ kJ; $\Delta S^{\ominus} = -126$ J K^{-1}. Reaction as written is favoured up to 900 K.
4. (i) −301 kJ, (ii) +29 kJ, (iii) −44 kJ; (iv) −144 kJ.

3.14

1. (i) $\Delta G_{323}^{\ominus} = -84.5$ kJ g-eqn^{-1}, $\Delta G_{363}^{\ominus} = -77.5$ kJ g-eqn^{-1}, (ii) opposed, (iii) 'experimental' $\Delta H = +141$ kJ, $\Delta S = -175$ J K^{-1}.
2. (a) −212 kJ; (b) 60 J evolved ($Q_p = \Delta H - W_{opt}$); (c) 590 J evolved.
3. (a) $\Delta G_r^{\ominus} = -9$ kJ, $\Delta H_r^{\ominus} = +10$ kJ; (c) 0.05 V; (d) (i) 10 kJ g-eqn^{-1} absorbed, (ii) 19 kJ g-eqn^{-1} absorbed.
5. ΔG_r more negative.

3.16

1.

	ΔH		ΔG	
	(i)	(ii)	(i)	(ii)
(a)	large −	large −	−	less −
(b)	+	+	+	−
(c)	large −	large −	−	+
(d)	−	−	small −	small −

2. (i) high T, low P (see §7.5), (ii) and (iii) low T, high P.
3. to $H_2 + CO_2$.
4. (a) forward; (b) equilibrium slightly to right; (c) forward.
5. $\Delta G_{298}^{\ominus} = -104$ kJ, $\Delta H = -180$ kJ; $298\Delta S^{\ominus} = -76$ kJ; $\Delta G_{1000}^{\ominus} = +75$ kJ; $\Delta G^{\ominus} = 0$ at 705 K. In air, with partial pressure of $O_2 = \frac{1}{5}$ atm, T_{eq} is lower (for calculation see §7.10).

4.3

1. ΔH_r = (i) -173 kJ, (ii) $+182$ kJ.
2. 366 kJ mol^{-1}.

4.6

1. (b) 327 kJ; (c) -104 kJ.
2. (a) (i) -269 kJ, (ii) -132 kJ, (iii) -7 kJ; (c) -125 kJ mol^{-1}.

4.14

1. See Fig. 4.3 and text. The electron affinity is difficult to measure directly, but once it has been calculated from one salt it can be used for others.
2. CsF -37 kJ, CsCl $+16$ kJ, $\therefore$ CsF probably the more soluble (but see §7.17).

$$\text{CsF (s)} \rightarrow \text{Cs}^+\text{(g)} + \text{F}^-\text{(g)}; \qquad \Delta H = +720 \text{ kJ}$$
$$\text{CsF (aq)} \rightarrow \text{Cs}^+\text{(g)} + \text{F}^-\text{(g)} + \text{aq}; \qquad \Delta H = +757 \text{ kJ}$$

3. (a) $\Delta H_f = -560$ kJ; (b) 683 kJ.

5.11

3. $\Delta S^{\ominus}/\text{JK}^{-1}$ = (i) $+161$, (ii) -120, (iii) -430
   $\Delta G^{\ominus}_{300}/\text{kJ}$ = $\quad +130 \qquad -101 \qquad -500$
   $\Delta G^{\ominus}_{1200}/\text{kJ}$ = $\quad -15 \qquad\quad +7 \qquad -113$

7. (a) The latter; (b) (i) the latter, (ii) both the same; (c) The molecules in the larger volume have greater spatial disorganization; (d) (i) If the 2 litres of gas were suddenly connected to 20.4 litres of vacuum, the expansion would be totally 'irreversible' and would do no work. So $w = 0$, $\Delta u = 0$ and $q = 0$; i.e. no heat change; (ii) Expansion against a loaded piston would transfer work out of the system, so heat would be absorbed since $\Delta u = 0$; (iii) No.

8. Max. work, $-W = \int_{V_1}^{V_2} p\, dV = \int_{V_1}^{V_2} \frac{RT}{V}\, dV = RT \ln \frac{V_2}{V_1} = RT \ln \frac{p_1}{p_2}$
   (see §7.8)

9. On this simple theory,
$$\Delta S_{\text{vap}} = R \ln \left(\frac{22\,400 \times T_b \times \rho}{273 \times M} \right)$$

which gives $\Delta S_{\text{vap}}(\text{CH}_4) = +51.5$ J K^{-1} mol^{-1} and $\Delta H_{\text{vap}} = +5.8$ kJ mol^{-1}. Trouton's Rule (§4.10) shows that empirically $\Delta S_{\text{vap}} =$ approx. 88 J K^{-1} mol^{-1}, so the calculated value is too low, indicating that ΔS_{config} is not the only factor contributing to ΔS_{vap}.

10. $-\Delta H = -\Delta G + T\Delta S$. If ΔS is negative, $(-\Delta G) < (-\Delta H)$, but if ΔS is positive the work done by the system may exceed $(-\Delta H)$ without increasing the orderliness of the universe.

6.4

1. First order; rate $= k\,[(\text{CH}_3\text{CO})_2\text{O}]$; $k = 2.8 \times 10^{-3}$ s^{-1}.

2.

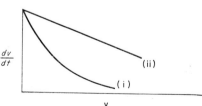

3. First order. Molecularity: not a bimolecular single step. Heterogeneous reaction might occur on the vessel walls; if so, increasing the surface area (e.g. by packing with glass wool) would increase the rate.

6.8

1. Reaction **2** is five times faster.
2. Insufficient information given.
3. 177 kJ.

6.15

1. Shaded area = 4% at T_1, 16% at T_2; $E_a = 8.0$ kJ. At T_2 reaction is four (=16/4) times faster than at T_1; $T_2 = 525$ K.
2. (a) 53 kJ; (b) 1.15 times.
3. At 369 K $\Delta G = 0$, $\therefore$ 369 $\Delta S = \Delta H$; ΔG changes sign at 369 K, becoming negative as T increases, $\therefore \Delta S$ is +ve, and hence ΔH is also +ve.
4.

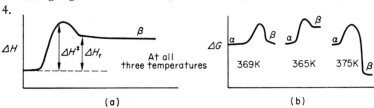

(a)   (b)

5. (a)

	N_2	H_2O	H_2	CO_2	
0°C	0.48	0.61	1.85	0.39	km s^{-1}
−100°C			0.46	0.30	km s^{-1}
1000°C			3.96	0.82	km s^{-1}

(b) None except H_2 leaving the moon at 1000°c; but see §6.9.

7.7

1. (a) $\dfrac{[Fe^{2+}]^3[Al^{3+}]}{[Fe^{3+}]^3}$ (b) $\dfrac{p_{H_2O}^2}{p_{H_2}^2 \cdot p_{O_2}}$ (c) $\dfrac{p_{CO_2} \cdot p_{H_2O}}{p_{H_2S}}$ (d) $p_{SO_3} \cdot p_{SO_2}$

     very large   very large   small   very small

2. $K_p = 6.6 \times 10^{-4}$, $\Delta G^{\ominus}_{2300} = +140$ kJ (2 sig. fig.).
3. (a) $\Delta G^{\ominus}_{2670} = +114$ kJ (using $\Delta S^{\ominus} = +24.7$ J K^{-1}), $K_p = 6 \times 10^{-3}$, $\therefore$ NO = 3.0% v/v. This is a rather extreme extrapolation from 298 K data, and gives an answer higher than the true value of 1.82%.
4. (a) $K_c = 104$, $\Delta G^{\ominus}_{298} = -14.6$ kJ; (b) $Q_c = 19.7$, $\Delta G = \Delta G^{\ominus} + 7.4$ kJ = −7.2 kJ. Reaction will go forward.
5. (a) $Q_p = 4.0$, 4.0 and 3.2 respectively. Since the extra residence time of the 1.00 cm^3 s^{-1} run did *not* cause an increase in Q, equilibrium must have been reached in the two slower runs.
   (b) $\therefore K_p = 4.0$.
   (c) 4.0%. Equilibrium was reached, $\therefore p_{COCl_2} = \sqrt{p_{CO_2} \cdot p_{CCl_4}/K_p}$.
6. The O_2/O_3 mixture was not at equilibrium. The concentration of O_3 was that appropriate to the environment of the high electric field, and was far higher than the normal equilibrium concentration at room temperature. The hot tube increased the *rate of attainment* of true equilibrium.

7.13

1. (a) $\Delta G = -10.7$ kJ.
   (b) (i) −146 kJ, (ii) −100 kJ, (iii) +14 kJ.
   (c) (i) +3.7 kJ, (ii) −19 kJ.

2. (a) 4×10^{52} atm.
(b) $\Delta G^{\ominus} = +30$ kJ; $K = 5 \times 10^{-6}$. The error of ± 1 in $\Delta G^{\ominus}$ will become an error of ± 0.2 in the mantissa of log K, giving a range $(5 \pm 2) \times 10^{-6}$.
(c) $K = 1.9 \times 10^{-6}$, max. $[H^+] = 1.2 \times 10^{-2}$ mol litre^{-1}.
3. (a) $K_p = 1.82 \times 10^{-10}$; $\Delta G^{\ominus}_{623} = +116$ kJ.
(b) $\Delta G^{\ominus} = +109$ kJ, $\Delta H^{\ominus} = +103$ kJ, $K_{298} = 1 \times 10^{-19}$, $K_{625} = 2 \times 10^{-10}$.

7.16

1. (a) As a dibasic acid, K_a is not constant, being 10^{-11} and 0.7×10^{-11}; (b) as a monobasic acid (to $H^+ + HS^-$) K_a is 1×10^{-7} in both cases, so this is the correct description.
2. A very slight increase.
3. (a) $K_{298} = 1.754 \times 10^{-5}$; $K_{348} = 1.897 \times 10^{-5}$;
(b) Using equation **7.10**, $\Delta H = +1.2$ kJ.
4. The weakness of hydrofluoric acid cannot be attributed to bond energy requirements, since ΔH_{diss} is negative. Since $K_a < 1$, $\Delta G^{\ominus}$ must be positive (actually $+18$ kJ), $\Delta S^{\ominus}$ must be large and negative, reminding one that the reaction is not simply HF $\to H^+ + F^-$, but HF (aq) + aq $\to$ H^+ (aq) + F^- (aq), with ordered water molecules around the ions.

7.18

1. (The 'equilibrium constants' will be approximate because of the high ionic concentrations.) K_{sp} (273 K) $= 2.93 \times 10^{-3}$; $\Delta G^{\ominus}_{273} = +13.2$ kJ; $\Delta S^{\ominus} = +550$ J K^{-1}; $\Delta H = +162$ kJ.
2. Solubility $= (5.48 \times 10^{-2}) \times 167 = 9.2$ g litre^{-1}. In acid, $CH_3CO_2^- + H^+$ (aq) $\to CH_3COOH$. At the limit, $[CH_3COO^-Ag^+] = [Ag^+] = 1.0$ and $[CH_3COOH] \approx 1$ M. $\therefore [CH_3COO^-][H^+] = 1.8 \times 10^{-5}$. But from s.p., $[CH_3COO^-] \times 1 = 3 \times 10^{-3}$, $\therefore [H^+]_{max} = 6 \times 10^{-3}$, pH 2.2.
3. (a) $PbBr_2$ (s) $\to Pb^{2+}$ (aq) $+ 2Br^-$ (aq); $\Delta G^{\ominus} = +28$ kJ, $\Delta H = +35$ kJ. From equation **7.1b** with $\Delta G = 0$, $K = 1.2 \times 10^{-5}$. $[Br^-] = 2[Pb^{2+}]$, $\therefore [Pb^{2+}][Br^-]^2 = 4[Pb^{2+}]^3 = 1.2 \times 10^{-5}$. So $[PbBr_2$ (aq)$] = [Pb^{2+}] = 1.4 \times 10^{-2}$ M $= 5.3$ g litre^{-1} at 298 K. Solubility will increase with temperature since ΔH is positive (equation **7.9**). (b) Br_2 (l) + aq $\to$ Br_2 (aq); $\Delta G^{\ominus} = +3.8$ kJ, $\Delta H = -4.6$ kJ. $K = [Br_2$ aq)$] = 0.22$. Solubility $= 35$ g litre^{-1} at 298 K, decreasing slightly with rising temperature.
4. $\Delta G^{\ominus} = -38.6$ kJ, $\therefore$ log $K = +38.6/5.71 = +6.76$. Log $1/K = $ log $([Ni^{2+}]/[Fe^{2+}]) = -6.76 = \bar{7}.24$. So if $[Fe^{2+}] = 1.0$, reaction will reverse when $[Ni^{2+}] < 1.78 \times 10^{-7}$. Initially $[Ni^{2+}] = 1.0$, but this has been reduced almost to zero, $\therefore [Ni(NH_3)_6^{2+}] = 1.0$ and $K = (1.78 \times 10^{-7}) \times 0.4^6 = 7.2 \times 10^{-10}$.

8.9

2. (a) $+0.42$ V; (b) -0.15 V; (c) -0.030 V (see §8.13); (d) -0.13 V.
3. (a) $+1.87$ V; (b) $+1.2$ V at pH 7, $+0.78$ V at pH 0. The evolution of a gas has a high overvoltage unless catalysed; there is also a considerable E_a for the breaking of the O—O covalent bond in $S_2O_8^{2-}$.
4. The connexion between reactivity and $E^{\ominus}$ is a loose one. Electrode potentials measure maximum available work under reversible (static) conditions. 'Reactivity' involves an assessment of rate of reaction, which depends upon E_a, solubility of the products, etc. For example, sodium reacts with water more vigorously than calcium partly because sodium hydroxide is more soluble than calcium hydroxide.

5. Using two adjacent beakers and a salt-bridge, set up the cell:
$$Pt \mid MnO_4^- \,(0.02 \text{ M}), \, H^+ \,(1 \text{ M}) \parallel C_2O_4^{2-} \,(0.5 \text{ M}) \mid Pt$$
Measure the cell potential while the oxalate is neutral, then add some dilute acid to it. If the potential increases, the proposition is proved.

6. (a) (i) $HClO$, Br_2, MnO_4^{2-} (unstable; next is $MnO_4^- \rightarrow MnO_2$), (ii) ClO_3^-, BrO_3^-, MnO_4^- ;

(b) *acidic:*
$$N_2O_4 + H_2O \rightarrow HNO_2 + H^+ (aq) + NO_3^- ; \, E^\ominus = +0.28 \text{ V} \, (n = 1)$$
$$3MnO_4^{2-} + 4H^+ (aq) \rightarrow 2MnO_4^- + MnO_2 \,(s) + 2H_2O; \, E^\ominus = +1.98 \text{ V}$$
$$(n = 2)$$

basic:
$I_2 \,(aq) + OH^- \rightarrow IO^- + I^- ; \, E^\ominus = +0.09 \text{ V} \, (n = 1)$
or $3I_2 \,(aq) + 6OH^- \rightarrow IO_3^- + 5I^- + 3H_2O; \, E^\ominus = +0.34 \text{ V} \, (n = 5)$
N.B. $5 \times E^\ominus \,(IO_3^- - I_2) = 0.45 + 4 \times 0.14.$
$N_2O_4 \,(g) + 2OH^- \rightarrow NO_3^- + NO_2^- + H_2O; \, E^\ominus = +1.74 \text{ V} \, (n = 1)$
$3ClO^- \rightarrow ClO_3^- + 2Cl^- ; \, E^\ominus = -0.06 \text{ V} \, (n = 4)$ according to the data in Fig. 8.3, which means that the equilibrium mixture contains a small excess of ClO^-; but authorities conflict on the ClO^-—Cl^- potential.
(c) Fig. 8.6 shows that although lines from NO_3^- or NO_2^- to NH_2OH, N_2H_4 or NH_3 all have negative slopes, that to NH_3 is the least negative (NO_2^-—NH_3 is actually -0.16 V) so NH_3 is the favoured product.
(d) (i) -1.34 V no reaction.
(ii) -0.07 V meaning that equilibrium is reached with the gases at less than standard concentration. But if the pressure of NO is kept below 1 atm, reaction can proceed.
(iii) $+1.6$ V ($n = 6$) reaction can occur.
(iv) $+1.23$ V ($n = 6$) reaction can occur, but in competition with
$$2NH_4^+ + 6HClO \rightarrow N_2 + 3Cl_2 + 2H^+ + 6H_2O; \, E^\ominus = +1.36 \text{ V} \, (n = 6)$$

7. The standard reduction potential of the second reaction is equivalent to a non-standard E_{red} of the first, with Cu^+ kept low by the need to satisfy the low solubility product of CuCl. Low product concentration favours reaction, and E_{red} is made more positive. The Cu^{2+} ion becomes a *better* oxidant in the presence of Cl^-. (This is developed quantitatively in §§8.11 and 8.14.)
(a) $(2 \times +0.346) - 0.16 = +0.53$ V;
(b)

$Cu^{2+} (aq) + e^- \longrightarrow Cu^+ (aq)$	$E_{red}^\ominus = +0.16$
$Cu \,(s) \longrightarrow Cu^+ (aq) + e^-$	$E_{ox}^\ominus = -0.53$

$$Cu^{2+} (aq) + SO_4^{2-} (aq) + Cu \,(s) \longrightarrow 2Cu^+ (aq) + SO_4^{2-} (aq);$$
$$E_{cell}^\ominus = -0.37 \text{ V} \, (n = 1)$$

(c) Using available data:

$2Cu^{2+} (aq) + 4Cl^- + 2e^- \longrightarrow 2CuCl \,(s) + 2Cl^-$	$E_{red}^\ominus = +0.54$
$Cu \,(s) \longrightarrow Cu^{2+} (aq) + 2e^-$	$E_{ox}^\ominus = -0.35$

$$Cu^{2+} (aq) + 2Cl^- + Cu \,(s) \longrightarrow 2CuCl \,(s)$$
$$E_{cell}^\ominus = +0.19 \text{ V} \, (n = 2)$$

Interpretations: (a) Cu is a better reductant when forming $Cu^{2+} (aq)$ than $Cu^+ (aq)$.
(b) The reaction cannot occur. In fact soluble copper(I) salts disproportionate to Cu(II) and the element Cu(0).

(c) Cu^{2+} (aq) can be reduced by the metal in the presence of Cl^-, to give solid CuCl. The copper(I) state is stable in sparingly soluble salts. (Note: In the usual laboratory preparation of CuCl, the excess concentrated hydrochloric acid gives a complex ion which is an even more stable product. See Additional Exercises, Part IV for a practical Investigation.)

8.12

1. (a) 0.049 V; (b) 0.033 V.
2. $[Cd^{2+}]$ must be less than standard, to make the Cd electrode more negative. Using equation 8.7, for the reaction which must proceed if the iron is positive:

$$Fe^{2+} \text{ (aq, 1 M)} + Cd \text{ (s)} \longrightarrow Fe \text{ (s)} + Cd \text{ (aq, } c_1) \quad E^{\ominus}_{cell} = -0.04 \text{ V}$$
$$(n = 2)$$

$$E_{cell} = \left(-0.04 - \frac{0.058}{2} \log c_1\right) > 0$$

$$\therefore \log c_1 < -0.04 \times 2/0.058$$
$$< -2 + 0.62$$
$$[Cd^{2+}] < 0.042 \text{ M}$$

3. 19.4 kJ (9.7 kJ per mole of particles). Concentration cell or osmosis.

4. $Sn^{4+} + 2e^- \rightarrow Sn^{2+}$; $E_{red} = +0.16 - \frac{0.058}{2} \log \frac{1}{0.002} = +0.16 - 0.08$ V.

This is still positive, so the reaction goes as written, taking electrons from the right-hand Pt, and pulling electrons through the meter from left to right.

8.15

1. -0.358 V.
2. pH $\leqslant 1.8$ if other concentrations are standard. The graph is a straight line from $+1.33$ V at pH 0 to $+0.38$ V at pH 7.
3. (a) 3.0; (b) 0.42 M. Hint: $[Fe^{2+}] = [Ag^+] = x$, $[Fe^{3+}] = 1 - x$. Use the quadratic formula.
4. (a) -1.03 V; (b) 1.6×10^{-16}.
5. $E^{\ominus}_{red} = (1.229 - 0.059 \text{ pH})$ V, $= +1.17, +1.05, +0.82, 0.40$ V. O_2 is most effective in strongly acid solution.
6. The ratio of Hg(I) ion concentrations $= 10$ in either case,

$$\therefore E = \frac{0.058}{n} \log 10$$

Experimentally $E = 0.028$ V, so $n = 2$, corresponding to Hg_2^{2+}.

9.3

1. (i) -30 kJ, (ii) -60 kJ, -120 kJ, (iii) $-288, -258, -228$ kJ.
2. $\Delta S^{\ominus}$ negative; $\Delta G^{\ominus}$ becomes less negative with increasing T.
3. (b) As the lines are roughly parallel, $\Delta G^{\ominus}_r$ will not change much. (c) (i) -261 kJ, (ii) -185 kJ.
4. (b) Above 1200 K: Zn (g) $+ \frac{1}{2}O_2$ (g) $\rightarrow ZnO$ (s); below 1200 K: Zn (l) $+ \frac{1}{2}O_2$ (g) $\rightarrow ZnO$ (s). The former has the larger $\Delta S^{\ominus}$ since $1\frac{1}{2}$ (rather than $\frac{1}{2}$) moles of gas disappear; hence steeper line. (c) See §9.7.

9.9

1. Approx. (i) $-15, -6, +2$ kJ, (ii) $+105, +40, -25$ kJ, (iii) $+45, +15, +10$ kJ. At 300 K reaction (i) is feasible (but kinetically unlikely), while (ii) and (iii) are unfeasible.

2. The reduction of Na_2O by C is possible at 1473 K, but the gaseous sodium would re-oxidize on cooling by reversal of the reaction. In any case, Na_2O is not an available raw-material.
3. (i) All temperatures, (ii) above 1300 K, (iii) not at all.
4. If the student has difficulty with this exercise, it may help him if the four relevant lines are re-drawn, with the intersection temperatures written in. (i) Above about 1050 K, (ii) above 900 K, but reaction (i) becomes the more favoured above 1100 K, and it is then followed by (iii) at a distance from the carbon, (iii) any temperature up to about 1600 K, (iv) above about 1800 K.
5. See also §9.10 and Additional Exercises, Part II.
6. (i) $\Delta G^{\ominus}$ = about $2 \times +50$ kJ so equilibrium lies far to the left. However, some SO_2 might be obtained from the cooled mixture by absorption in alkali. (ii) $\Delta G^{\ominus}$ = about $+60$ kJ, so equilibrium lies well to the left. The equilibrium mixture must be cooled rapidly if the small yield of NO is not to become even smaller. (iii) Reaction would be undetectable.

9.11

1. (i) Up to 900 K, (ii) up to 1230 K, (iii) if $p_{O_2} = 1$ atm, not feasible at all, (iv) not at all, (v) strictly, only up to about 500 K, since above this the reaction $2SnO \rightarrow SnO_2 + Sn$ is exergonic.
2. It is possible energetically, but not likely except below the surface of the CuO layer, because the free-energy for the further reduction of Cu_2O is too negative.
3. (i) $6FeO + SnO_2 \rightarrow 2Fe_3O_4 + Sn$; $\Delta G_{973} = c. -50$ kJ
   (ii) $3FeO + FeO$ (i.e. $4FeO$) $\rightarrow Fe_3O_4 + Fe$; $\Delta G = c. -45$ kJ
   (iii) No, the Fe_3O_4 line is the lower.
4. See §9.8.
5. Hg_2O disproportionation is feasible; $\Delta G^{\ominus} = -5$ kJ.

10.7

1. Several possible answers; e.g. react $PbBr_2$ solution or suspension with zinc, giving $Pb + ZnBr_2$. Filter and pass in Cl_2, giving Br_2. In this way the reaction has been coupled to the strongly exergonic reaction

$$Zn + Cl_2 \longrightarrow Zn^{2+}(Cl^-)_2$$

2. $C_{57}H_{104}O_6 \text{ (s)} + 80O_2 \text{ (g)} \longrightarrow 57CO_2 \text{ (g)} + 52H_2O \text{ (l)}; \quad \Delta H = -33\ 700 \text{ kJ}$

Efficiency = $c.$ 46%, slightly higher than that for glucose. 'Calorific value' (kcal per *gram*): lipid 9, glucose $3\frac{1}{2}$. Fat has about $2\frac{1}{2}$ times as much energy, weight for weight.
3. See §4.2 and §10.4.
5. Alcohols can be dehydrated or dehydrogenated at the same temperature by the choice of different catalysts.
7. (i) Energy absorbed $= \dfrac{350 \times 8}{100}$ J m^{-2} s$^{-1} \times 10 \times 10$ cm$^2 \times 10^{-4} \dfrac{\text{m}^2}{\text{cm}^2} \times t$

Energy used $= \dfrac{2890 \text{ kJ mol}^{-1} \times 1.8 \text{ g}}{180 \text{ g mol}^{-1}} \times 10^3 \dfrac{\text{J}}{\text{kJ}}$

Equating these gives $t = 1.03 \times 10^5$ s (about 29 hours).

(ii) $\quad E = \dfrac{hc}{\lambda} = \dfrac{4.0 \times 10^{-10} \text{ J s mol}^{-1} \times 3.0 \times 10^8 \text{ m s}^{-1}}{6600 \times 10^{-10} \text{ m}}$

$= 1.82 \times 10^5$ J mol^{-1} = 182 kJ mol^{-1}

$\therefore$ Minimum amount of photons to provide 2892 kJ = 16 mol.

(iii) Two different approaches give upper and lower limits.
(a) Considering the statement from 10.5 that one pair of H atoms lead to 3 high-energy phosphate bonds,

$$4 \times 182 \text{ kJ} \longrightarrow 2\text{H} \longrightarrow 3 \times 34 \text{ kJ}$$

$$\therefore \text{ efficiency} = \frac{3 \times 34}{4 \times 182} \times 100 = 14\%$$

This has ignored the active H atoms which become incorporated into the glucose molecule.
(b) If $6CO_2 + 24H \rightarrow C_6H_{12}O_6 + 6H_2O$, 48 photons provide the energy for the synthesis of 1 molecule of glucose,

$$\therefore \text{ efficiency} = \frac{2892 \times 100\%}{48 \times 182} = 33\% \text{ overall}$$

8. The conversion of chemical energy to heat can be 100% efficient, but even with zero heat losses the maximum efficiency of conversion of heat to work, by flow of heat from, say 310 K to 293 K, is

$$\frac{310 - 293}{310} \times 100\% = 5.5\%$$

This is far below the observed 20%, so the proposal must be rejected.

Appendix A

Energies of formation

$\Delta H_{f298}^{\ominus}$ = Standard enthalpy of formation of one mole of the compound at 298 K from the elements in the forms which are stable at that temperature under a pressure of 1 atm. $\Delta H_{f298}^{\ominus}$ differs little from ΔH_f for non-standard concentrations or other temperatures as long as the compound is in the state specified.

$\Delta G_{f298}^{\ominus}$ = Standard free-energy of formation at 298 K, the concentration being 1 atm (gas) or 1 molal (dissolved). $\Delta G_f^{\ominus}$ will usually differ greatly for other temperatures, and ΔG_f for other concentrations will differ from $\Delta G_f^{\ominus}$, although this difference may be unimportant if the deviation from standard concentration is not large.

$\Delta H_r^{\ominus}$ = Standard enthalpy of reaction. It is calculated by subtracting the algebraic sum of ΔH_f for the reagents from the sum of ΔH_f for the products.

$\Delta G_r^{\ominus}$ = Standard free-energy of reaction at specified temperature, with reactants and products in standard states.

$$\Delta G_r^{\ominus} = \Delta G_f^{\ominus} \text{ (products)} - \Delta G_f^{\ominus} \text{ (reactants)}$$

$\Delta H_{f298}^{\ominus}$ and $\Delta G_{f298}^{\ominus}$ = 0.00 for *any element* (in its standard state), and for H^+ (aq).

Energies of formation at 298 K (in kilojoule)

Substance	$\Delta H_f^{\ominus}$ kJ mol^{-1}	$\Delta G_f^{\ominus}$, kJ mol^{-1}	Substance	$\Delta H_f^{\ominus}$ kJ mol^{-1}	$\Delta G_f^{\ominus}$, kJ mol^{-1}
Aluminium			$Ba(OH)_2$ (s)	−946	−856
Al^{3+} (aq)	−525	−482	BaO (s)	−558	−528
$AlCl_3$ (s)	−695	−637	BaO_2 (s)	−630	−568
Al_2O_3 (s)	−1670	−1576	$BaSO_4$ (s)	−1465	−1353
$Al(OH)_3$ (s)	−1280	−1147			
			Bismuth		
Arsenic			$BiCl_3$ (s)	−379	−319
AsH_3 (g)	+172	+174	BiOCl (s)	−365	−322
As_2O_3 (s)	−657	−576			
			Bromine		
Barium			Br_2 (g)	+31	+3.1
Ba^{2+} (aq)	−538	−561	Br_2 (aq)	−4.6	+3.8
$BaCO_3$ (s)	−1218	−1139	HBr (g)	−36	−53
$BaCl_2$.			Br^- (aq)	−121	−103
$2H_2O$ (s)	−1462	−1296	OBr^- (aq)	−96	−34

Substance	$\Delta H_f^\ominus$ kJ mol^{-1}	$\Delta G_f^\ominus$ kJ mol^{-1}	Substance	$\Delta H_f^\ominus$ kJ mol^{-1}	$\Delta G_f^\ominus$ kJ mol^{-1}
Calcium			$C_{12}H_{22}O_{11}$ (s)	-2220	-1554
Ca^{2+} (aq)	-543	-553	sucrose		
CaC_2 (s)	-63	-68	CN^- (aq)	$+151$	$+166$
$CaCO_3$ (s)	-1207	-1129	CS_2 (l)	$+88$	$+64$
$CaCl_2$ (s)	-795	-750	$COCl_2$ (g)	-223	-210
$CaCl_2 . 6H_2O$ (s)	-2610				
CaF_2 (s)	-1214	-1162	*Chlorine*		
CaH_2 (s)	-189	-150	Cl_2 (aq)	-34	
$Ca(OH)_2$ (s)	-987	-897	Cl^- (aq)	-167.4	-131.1
CaO (s)	-635	-604	HCl (g)	-92.3	-95.3
$CaSO_4$ (s)	-1433	-1320	Cl_2O (g)	$+76$	$+94$
$CaSO_4 . \frac{1}{2}H_2O$ (s)	-1575	-1435	OCl^- (aq)	-108	-37
$CaSO_4 . 2H_2O$ (s)	-2021	-1796	*Copper*		
			Cu^+ (aq)	$+52$	$+50$
			Cu^{2+} (aq)	$+64$	$+65$
Carbon			Cu_2O (s)	-167	-146
C (graphite)	0.0	0.0	CuO (s)	-155	-127
C (diamond)	$+1.9$	$+2.9$	$Cu(OH)_2$ (s)	-448	-357
C (g)	$+718$	$+673$	$CuCl$ (s)	-135	-119
CO (g)	-110.5	-137.3	$CuCl_2$ (s)	(-206)	(-176)
CO_2 (g)	-393.6	-394.6	$CuCO_3$ (s)	-595	-517
HCO_3^- (aq)	-691	-588	$CuSO_4$ (s)	-769	-661
CO_3^{2-} (aq)	-676	-528	$CuSO_4 . 5H_2O$ (s)		
CH_4 (g)	-75	-51		-2278	-1880
CH_3Cl (g)	-82	-59	$Cu(NH_3)_4^{2+}$ (aq)		
$CHCl_3$ (l)	-132	-72		-339	-132
CCl_4 (g)	-107	-64			
CCl_4 (l)	-139	-69	*Fluorine*		
CF_4 (g)	-680	-636	F^- (aq)	-329	-276
CBr_4 (g)	$+50$	$+36$	HF (g)	-269	-271
CH_3OH (l)	-239	-166			
C_2H_5OH (l)	-278	-175	*Gold*		
C_2H_2 (g)	$+226$	$+209$	Au_2O_3 (s)	$+81$	$+163$
C_2H_4 (g)	$+52$	$+68$	$Au(OH)_3$ (s)	-418	-290
C_2H_6 (g)	-85	-32			
C_3H_8 (g)	-104	-23	*Hydrogen*		
C_6H_6 (g)	$+83$	$+130$	H^+ (aq)	0.0	0.0
C_6H_6 (l)	$+49$	$+125$	H_2O (g)	-241.8	-228.7
$HCHO$ (g)	-116	-110	H_2O (l) and H_3O^+ (aq)		
$HCOOH$ (g)	-363	-336		-285.9	-237.2
$HCOOH$ (l)	-409	-346	OH^- (aq)	-230.0	-157.3
$HCOO^-$ (aq)	-410	-334			
CH_3COOH (l)	-487	-392	*Iodine*		
$CH_3CO_2^-$ (aq)	-489	-372	I_2 (g)	$+62$	$+19$
$C_2O_4H_2$ (s)	-826	-698	I_2 (aq)	$+21$	$+16$
oxalic acid			I_2 (as KI_3, aq)	$+4$	$+2$
$C_2O_4^{2-}$ (aq)	-824	-675	I^- (aq)	-56	-52
oxalate			HI (g)	$+26$	$+1.4$
$C_6H_{12}O_6$ (s)	-1256	-898	ICl (g)	$+18$	-6
glucose			ICl_3 (s)	-88	-22

Substance	$\Delta H_f^{\ominus}$ kJ mol^{-1}	$\Delta G_f^{\ominus}$ kJ mol^{-1}	Substance	$\Delta H_f^{\ominus}$ kJ mol^{-1}	$\Delta G_f^{\ominus}$ kJ mol^{-1}
Iron			N_2O (g)	+82	+104
Fe^{2+} (aq)	−88	−85	N_2O_4 (g)	+10	+98
Fe^{3+} (aq)	−48	−10	HNO_3 (l)	−173	−80
'FeO' (s)	−266	−244	NO_2^- (aq)	−106	−35
Fe_2O_3 (s)	−822	−741	NO_3^- (aq)	−206	−110
Fe_3O_4 (s)	−1118	−1015	NH_3 (g)	−46	−16.6
$FeCl_2$ (s)	−341	−302	NH_3 (aq)	−81	−27
$FeCl_3$ (s)	−405	−336	NH_4^+ (aq)	−133	−79
$Fe(CN)_6^{4-}$ (aq)	+497	+772	NH_4Cl (s)	−315	−204
			NH_4NO_3 (s)	−365	−183
			$(NH_4)_2SO_4$ (s)	−1178	−900
Lead					
Pb^{2+} (aq)	+2	−24			
PbO (s, red)	−219	−189	*Oxygen*		
PbO_2 (s)	−277	−219	O_3 (g)	+142	+163
Pb_3O_4 (s)	−735	−618	OH^- (aq)	−230.0	−157.3
$PbBr_2$ (s)	−277	−260	H_2O (g)	−241.8	−228.7
$PbCO_3$ (s)	−700	−626	H_2O (l)	−285.9	−237.2
$PbCl_2$ (s)	−359	−314	H_2O_2 (aq)	−191	−132
PbI_2 (s)	−175	−174			
$Pb(NO_3)_2$ (s)	−449	−250			
$PbSO_4$ (s)	−918	−811	*Phosphorus*		
PbS (s)	−94	−93	P (s, red)	−17.6	−12
			P (s, white)	0.0	0.0
Lithium			P_4 (g)	+55	+24
Li^+ (aq)	−278	−293	PH_3 (g)	+9	+18
Li_2O (s)	−596	−560	PH_4I (s)	−70	+1
Li_2CO_3 (s)	−1215	−1132	P_4O_{10} (s)	−2984	−2698
LiH (s)	−91	−69	H_3PO_4 (s)	−1280	
			PO_4^{3-} (aq)	−1284	−1020
			PCl_3 (g)	−306	−286
Magnesium			PCl_3 (l)	(−339)	(−291)
Mg^{2+} (aq)	−462	−456	PCl_5 (g)	−400	−324
MgO (s)	−602	−570	PCl_5 (s)	(−463)	(−322)
$MgCO_3$ (s)	−1113	−1030			
Mg_3N_2 (s)	−462	−401			
Manganese			*Potassium*		
Mn^{2+} (aq)	−219	−223	K^+ (aq)	−251	−282
MnO (s)	−385	−363	K_2O (s)	−363	−322
MnO_2 (s)	−521	−466	KO_2 (s)	−280	
MnO_4^- (aq)	−518		KOH (s)	−425	
			KBr (s)	−392	−379
Mercury			$KBrO_3$ (s)	−332	−244
Hg (g)	+61	+32	KCl (s)	−436	−408
HgO (s, yellow)	−90	−58	$KClO_3$ (s)	−391	−290
Hg_2O (s)	−91	−54	$KClO_4$ (s)	−434	−304
$HgCl_2$ (s)	−230	−177	KI (s)	−328	−322
Hg_2Cl_2 (s)	−265	−211	KIO_3 (s)	−508	−426
			KNO_2 (s)	−370	
Nitrogen			KNO_3 (s)	−493	−393
NO (g)	+90	+87	$KMnO_4$ (s)	−813	−714
NO_2 (g)	+34	+52	K_2SO_4 (s)	−1434	−1316

Substance	$\Delta H_f^\ominus$ kJ mol^{-1}	$\Delta G_f^\ominus$ kJ mol^{-1}	Substance	$\Delta H_f^\ominus$ kJ mol^{-1}	$\Delta G_f^\ominus$ kJ mol^{-1}
Silicon			*Sulphur*		
SiH$_4$ (g)	-62	-39	S (s, rhombic)	0.0	0.0
SiO$_2$ (s, quartz)	-859	-805	S (monoclinic)	$+0.3$	$+0.1$
SiF$_4$ (g)	-1550	-1510	S$_8$ (g)	$+102$	$+50$
			S^{2-} (aq)	$(+40)$	$(+80)$
			HS$^-$ (aq)	-18	$+13$
Silver			H$_2$S (g)	-20	-33
Ag$^+$ (aq)	$+106$	$+77.1$	H$_2$S (aq)	-39	-27
Ag$_2$O (s)	-31	-11	SO$_2$ (g)	-297	-300
Ag$_2$CO$_3$ (s)	-505	-437	SO$_2$ (aq)	-328	-300
AgF (s)	-203	-185	SO$_3^{2-}$ (aq)	-624	-496
AgCl (s)	-127	-110	SO$_3$ (g)	-395	-370
AgBr (s)	-100	-94	H$_2$SO$_4$ (l)	-811	(-680)
AgI (s)	-62	-66	HSO$_4^-$ (aq)	-886	-752
			SO$_4^{2-}$ (aq)	-908	-742
Sodium			*Tin*		
Na (g)	$+108$	$+77$	Sn^{2+} (aq)	-10	-27
Na$^+$ (g)	$+610$		SnO (s)	-286	-257
Na$^+$ (aq)	-240	-262	SnO$_2$ (s)	-580	-520
Na$_2$O (s)	-416	-377	SnCl$_4$ (l)	-545	-474
Na$_2$O$_2$ (s)	-505	-450			
NaH (s)	-57	-33	*Titanium*		
NaOH (s)	-426	-380	TiO$_2$ (s)	-912	-853
NaF (s)	-569	-541	TiCl$_4$ (l)	(-750)	(-675)
NaCl (s)	-411	-384			
NaBr (s)	-360	-346	*Xenon*		
NaI (s)	-288	-282	XeF$_2$ (s)	-134	-63
NaNO$_2$ (s)	-425	-366	XeF$_4$ (s)	-250	-123
NaNO$_3$ (s)	-416	-377	XeO$_3$ (s)	$+400$	
Na$_2$SO$_4$ (s)	-1385	-1267			
Na$_2$SO$_4$.10H$_2$O (s)			*Zinc*		
	-4323	-3643	Zn^{2+} (aq)	-152	-147
Na$_2$CO$_3$ (s)	-1131	-1047	ZnO (s)	-348	-318
Na$_2$CO$_3$.10H$_2$O (s)			ZnCl$_2$ (s)	-416	-370
	-4082		ZnI$_2$ (s)	-209	-209
NaHCO$_3$ (s)	-948	-852	ZnS (s, sphalerite)		
				-203	-198
			ZnSO$_4$ (s)	-979	-872
Strontium			ZnSO$_4$.7H$_2$O (s)		
Sr^{2+} (aq)	-546	-557		-3076	-2560
SrO (s)	-590	-560	ZnCO$_3$ (s)	-812	-731
Sr(OH)$_2$ (s)	-959	-870			

Appendix B

Standard reduction potentials at 298 K†

	E/volt
$Li^+ + e^- \rightleftharpoons Li$	-2.96
$K^+ + e^- \rightleftharpoons K$	-2.93
$Ca^{2+} + 2e^- \rightleftharpoons Ca$	-2.76
$Na^+ + e^- \rightleftharpoons Na$	-2.71
$Mg^{2+} + e^- \rightleftharpoons Mg$	-2.37
$Al(OH)_4^- + 3e^- \rightleftharpoons Al + 4OH^-$	-2.35
$Ti^{2+} + 2e^- \rightleftharpoons Ti$	-1.75
$Al^{3+} + 3e^- \rightleftharpoons Al$	-1.67
$Zn(OH)_4^{2-} + 2e^- \rightleftharpoons Zn + 4OH^-$	-1.22
$SO_4^{2-} + H_2O + 2e^- \rightleftharpoons SO_3^{2-} + 2OH^-$	-0.90
$Zn^{2+} + 2e^- \rightleftharpoons Zn$	-0.763
$Cr^{3+} + 3e^- \rightleftharpoons Cr$	-0.74
$Fe(OH)_3 + e^- \rightleftharpoons Fe(OH)_2 + OH^-$	-0.56
$S + 2e^- \rightleftharpoons S^{2-}$	-0.51
$2CO_2 \text{(g)} + 2H^+ + 2e^- \rightleftharpoons H_2C_2O_4$	-0.49
$Fe^{2+} + 2e^- \rightleftharpoons Fe$	-0.44
$Cr^{3+} + e^- \rightleftharpoons Cr^{2+}$	-0.41
$Cd^{2+} + 2e^- \rightleftharpoons Cd$	-0.40
$Pb^{2+} + 2e^- \rightleftharpoons Pb$	-0.126
$2H^+ + 2e^- \rightleftharpoons H_2 \text{(g)}$	0.00
$S + 2H^+ + 2e^- \rightleftharpoons H_2S \text{(aq)}$	$+0.14$
$Sn^{4+} + 2e^- \rightleftharpoons Sn^{2+}$	$+0.16$
$Cu^{2+} + e^- \rightleftharpoons Cu^+$	$+0.17$
$SO_4^{2-} + 4H^+ + 2e^- \rightleftharpoons H_2SO_3 + H_2O$	$+0.20$
$Cu^{2+} + 2e^- \rightleftharpoons Cu$	$+0.346$
$O_2 \text{(g)} + 2H_2O + 4e^- \rightleftharpoons 4OH^-$	$+0.401$
$Fe(CN)_6^{3-} + e^- \rightleftharpoons Fe(CN)_6^{4-}$	$+0.46$
$I_2 \text{(in KI aq)} + 2e^- \rightleftharpoons 2I^-$	$+0.54$
$I_2 \text{(aq)} + 2e^- \rightleftharpoons 2I^-$	$+0.62$
$O_2 \text{(g)} + 2H^+ + 2e^- \rightleftharpoons H_2O_2 \text{(aq)}$	$+0.68$
$Fe^{3+} + e^- \rightleftharpoons Fe^{2+}$	$+0.770$
$Ag^+ + e^- \rightleftharpoons Ag$	$+0.800$
$Hg_2^{2+} + 2e^- \rightleftharpoons 2Hg$	$+0.85$
$2Hg^{2+} + 2e^- \rightleftharpoons Hg_2^{2+}$	$+0.91$
$NO_3^- + 4H^+ + 3e^- \rightleftharpoons NO \text{(g)} + 2H_2O$	$+0.96$

† *Note*: Throughout the standard concentration for water is excess H_2O (l), not 1 m. Solids are in contact with their saturated solutions at 298 K, and gases are at 1 atm partial pressure. For E at other concentrations see §8.13.

$$HNO_2 + H^+ + e^- \rightleftharpoons NO\ (g) + H_2O \qquad +1.00$$
$$Br_2\ (aq) + 2e^- \rightleftharpoons 2Br^- \qquad +1.09$$
$$O_2\ (g) + 4H^+ + 4e^- \rightleftharpoons 2H_2O \qquad +1.229$$
$$MnO_2\ (s) + 4H^+ + 2e^- \rightleftharpoons Mn^{2+} + 2H_2O \qquad +1.23$$
$$C_2O_7^{2-} + 14H^+ + 6e^- \rightleftharpoons 2Cr^{3+} + 7H_2O \qquad +1.33$$
$$Cl_2\ (aq) + 2e^- \rightleftharpoons 2Cl^- \qquad +1.358$$
$$PbO_2 + 4H^+ + 2e^- \rightleftharpoons Pb^{2+} + 2H_2O \qquad +1.46$$
$$ClO_3^- + 6H^+ + 6e^- \rightleftharpoons Cl^- + 3H_2O \qquad +1.46$$
$$Au^{3+} + 3e^- \rightleftharpoons Au \qquad +1.50$$
$$MnO_4^- + 8H^+ + 5e^- \rightleftharpoons Mn^{2+} + 4H_2O \qquad +1.51$$
$$MnO_4^- + 4H^+ + 3e^- \rightleftharpoons MnO_2\ (s) + 2H_2O \qquad +1.70$$
$$H_2O_2\ (aq) + 2H^+ + 2e^- \rightleftharpoons 2H_2O \qquad +1.77$$
$$Pb^{4+} + 2e^- \rightleftharpoons Pb^{2+} \qquad +1.80$$
$$Ag^{2+} + e^- \rightleftharpoons Ag^+\ (4m\ HClO_4) \qquad +2.00$$
$$S_2O_8^{2-} + 2e^- \rightleftharpoons 2SO_4^{2-} \qquad +2.01$$
$$O_3\ (g) + 2H^+ + 2e^- \rightleftharpoons O_2\ (g) + H_2O \qquad +2.07$$
$$F_2\ (g) + 2e^- \rightleftharpoons 2F^- \qquad +2.87$$

Appendix C

Glossary of terms

Absolute entropy ($S^{\ominus}$), also known as 'Third Law Entropy', calculated from thermal data by the summation of Q/T from 0 K upwards. $\Delta S_r = S(\text{prod}) - S(\text{react})$, but $S^{\ominus}$ for elements is not zero. §5.4

Adiabatic conditions: conditions without transfer of energy to or from the system. §2.10

Avogadro constant (L): the number of atoms in 12.000 g of ^{12}C. ($= 6.023 \times 10^{23}$). See *Mole*.

Boltzmann constant (k): the gas constant per molecule, i.e. R/L. ($= 1.38 \times 10^{-23}$ J K^{-1}).

Closed system: one which does not gain or lose mass. §2.10

Endergonic: having a positive free-energy change; unfeasible unless external work is supplied.

Endothermic: taking in heat, and having ΔH positive.

Enthalpy: heat content at constant pressure. §§2.3, 5.9

Exergonic: having a negative ΔG, with the system losing free-energy; thermodynamically feasible.

Exothermic: giving out heat (when unharnessed), and having ΔH negative.

Faraday constant (F): the quantity of electricity equal to one mole of electrons ($= 96\,487$, or $96\,500$, coulomb).

Free-energy of formation: See Appendix A.

Gas constant (R): For an ideal gas $PV = nRT$, where $n =$ number of moles. ($R = 1.987$ cal K^{-1}, 8.314 J K^{-1}, or 0.082 litre-atm K^{-1}, per mole.)

Gram-equation: that amount of reaction involving the number of moles of reactants specified by the equation.

Heat capacity (molar): the amount of heat which raises the temperature of 1 mole of the substance through 1 K. C_p and C_v symbolize heat capacities at constant pressure and volume respectively. For solids and liquids they are approximately equal, but for gases (ideal) $C_p = C_v + R$.

Heterogeneous: consisting of two or more phases. E.g. solid and gases, liquid and solid, or immiscible liquids.

Homogeneous: consisting of one phase only. E.g. a mixture of gases, or miscible liquids, or unsaturated solutions.

Internal energy change (ΔU): heat change at constant volume. $\Delta H = \Delta U - nRT$, where $\Delta n =$ increase in number of moles of gas.

Isothermal: at constant temperature. §2.12

Logarithm: power to which the base must be raised to equal the number. If $N = a^y$, $\log_a N = y$. Negative logarithms can be converted as in the following example:

$$\log N = -2.699 = -3 + 0.301, \text{ written } \bar{3}.301, \text{ so } N = 2 \times 10^{-3}$$

Natural logarithms arise from the integration of $1/x$, since $\int \frac{1}{x}\,dx = \ln x +$ constant. The conversion factors are:

$\log x = 0.4343 \ln x$
$\ln x = 2.3026 \log x$

Mole: An Avogadro number of molecules, atoms, ions, electrons, etc. E.g. 32 g oxygen = 1 mole O_2 molecules, or 2 moles atoms.

Molal: a concentration of 1 mole solute per kg solvent.

Molar: a concentration of one mole per litre of solution.

Reversible conditions: See §5.7.

Specific heat capacity, concentration, density, volume etc. In these terms the adjective 'specific' means 'divided by mass' (rather than by amount).

Spontaneous: (specialized meaning) energetically feasible without supply of work; exergonic.

Temperature: the *thermodynamic temperature*, T of a system may be defined by $T = q/\delta S$, or by the ideal gas equation $PV = nRT$. The SI unit of temperature is the kelvin, K. Temperatures on the Celsius scale are actually temperature intervals, defined by: $\theta_c/°C = T/K - 273.15$. Temperatures on the Fahrenheit scale are related to the thermodynamic temperature by: $\theta_F/°F = \frac{9}{5} T/K - 459.67$.

Temperature intervals, ΔT are also measured in kelvins. Even if the initial and final temperatures are given in °C it is easily shown that $(\theta_{c,2} - \theta_{c,1})/°C = (T_2 - T_1)/K$, and so °C should not be used as the unit for a temperature *interval*. In the case of Fahrenheit, $\Delta\theta_F/°F = \frac{9}{5} \Delta T/K$.

Bibliography

Suggestions for further reading

Campbell, J. Arthur, *Why Do Chemical Reactions Occur?* Prentice-Hall, London, 1965.
   A monograph on the micro-reaction approach.
Pimentel, G. C. (Ed.), *Chemistry. An Experimental Science*. W. H. Freeman & Co., San Francisco, 1963.
   The CHEM Study textbook. Chapter 8 is a useful introduction to reaction rates; Chapter 12 gives simple experiments with cells; Chapter 24, 'Energy sources in nature', would supplement the last chapter of this book.
Chemical Bond Approach Project, *Chemical Systems*. McGraw-Hill Book Co., New York and Maidenhead, 1964.
   The CBA textbook. Chapter 14 gives an approach to free-energy and the equilibrium constant through consideration of electrochemical cells. A helpful model to illustrate entropy appears a little later.
Strong, L. E. and Stratton, W. J., *Chemical Energy*. Chapman and Hall, London, 1965.
   A very readable account of enthalpy, bond energies and free-energy.
Moore, Walter, J., *Physical Chemistry*. Longmans, Green & Co., London, 1965.
   A University textbook which presents the rigorous 'mathematical' development of thermodynamics.
Asimov, Isaac, *Energy and Life*. Dobson, London, 1963.
   Written for the non-specialist, with infectious enthusiasm.

For teachers and course supervisors

Chemistry Today. OECD.
   Chapters 8 and 11 are particularly relevant.
Spice, J. E., *Teaching Thermodynamics to Sixth-formers*, Education in Chemistry (R.I.C.), **3**, 1966.
Halliwell, H. F., *The Teaching of Chemical Energetics in Introduction and Intermediate Courses*. OECD.
Ives, D. J. G., *Principles of the Extraction of Metals*, Royal Institute of Chemistry Monographs for Teachers.

Sources of data

Hodgman, C. D. (Ed.), *Handbook of Chemistry and Physics*, Blackwell Scientific Publications, 1961.

Rossini, F. D. *et al.*, *Selected Values of Chemical Thermodynamic Properties*. U.S. National Bureau of Standards, Circular 500.
Latimer, W. M., *Oxidation Potentials*, 2nd edition. Prentice-Hall, London, 1952.
Stark, J. G. and Wallace, H. G., *Chemistry Data Book*, 51 edition. John Murray, London, 1970.
John Wiley & Sons.
   Selected physical and thermochemical properties, redox potentials, dissociation and instability constants, etc., in a convenient 109-page book, designed for the student's own use.

Symbols

A	ampere	t	time
Å	Ångstrom unit of length, 10^{-10} m	T	temperature
		u	velocity
A	Arrhenius frequency factor (kinetics)	U	internal energy
		V	volume
aq	aqueous	$+w$	work done on system
c	concentration	$+W$	work done on system, per mole
°C	degree Celsius ($= T - 273.15$) K	Ω	thermodynamic probability
C	heat capacity	Z	collision frequency; atomic number
e^-	electron		
E_a	energy of activation, $\equiv \Delta H^{\ddagger}$	$\sum$	sum of
E	electrode potential, cell potential	$\prod$	product of
		[ ]	molar concentration of
F	Faraday constant		
g	gas		
ΔG_r	free-energy of reaction	*Superscripts*	
ΔG_f	free-energy of formation	$\ominus$	standard
h	Planck's constant	$\ddagger$	activated
ΔH	enthalpy change		
J	joule		
kJ	kilojoule	*Subscripts*	
k	rate constant, specific reaction rate	at	atomization
		b	boiling
K	equilibrium constant	c	with units of concentration
K	kelvin (unit of temperature)	D	dissociation
l	liquid	eq	equilibrium
ln	natural (base e) logarithm	ext	external
log	common (base 10) logarithm	f	formation
n	number of moles, electrons, etc.	fus	fusion
p	pressure, partial pressure	m	melting
P	steric factor (kinetics)	obl	obligatory (work)
$+q$	heat absorbed	opt	optional (work)
$+Q$	heat absorbed, per mole	ox	oxidation
Q	quotient $\dfrac{\prod [\text{products}]}{\prod [\text{reactants}]}$	p	at constant pressure; with units of pressure
R	gas constant	r	reaction
s	solid	rev	reversible conditions
S	absolute entropy	sol	dissolution
ΔS	entropy change	v	at constant volume
		vap	vaporization

Frequently used data

Gas constant $(R) = 8.314$ J K^{-1} mol^{-1}, or 1.987 cal K^{-1} mol^{-1}, or
$\qquad$ 0.0824 litre-atm. per mol-kelvin
Faraday constant $(F) = 96\ 487$ (or 96 500) coulomb per mol electrons
Specific heat capacity of water $= 4.18 \times 10^{-3}$ J kg^{-1} K^{-1}
Conversion of joules to calories 4.184 J = 1 cal
0°C (ice point) = 273.15 K
$\ln N = 2.3026 \log N$
$2.303 \times 8.314 \times 298/1000 = 5.706$
$2.303 \times 8.314 \times 298/96\ 487 = 0.0591$

	CO_2	H_2O (g)	H_2O (l)
ΔH_f/kJmol^{-1}	-393.6	-241.8	-285.9
$\Delta H_f^{\ominus}$/kJmol^{-1}	-394.6	-228.7	-237.2

Selected atomic weights

Name	Symbol	Atomic weight	Name	Symbol	Atomic weight
Aluminium	Al	27.0	Lithium	Li	6.9
Antimony	Sb	121.8	Magnesium	Mg	24.3
Arsenic	As	74.9	Manganese	Mn	54.9
Barium	Ba	137.3	Mercury	Hg	200.6
Bismuth	Bi	209.0	Nickel	Ni	58.7
Boron	B	10.8	Nitrogen	N	14.0
Bromine	Br	79.9	Oxygen	O	16.0
Cadmium	Cd	112.4	Phosphorus	P	31.0
Caesium	Cs	132.9	Platinum	Pt	195.1
Calcium	Ca	40.1	Potassium	K	39.1
Carbon	C	12.0	Rubidium	Rb	85.5
Chlorine	Cl	35.5	Selenium	Se	79.0
Chromium	Cr	52.0	Silicon	Si	28.1
Cobalt	Co	58.9	Silver	Ag	107.9
Copper	Cu	63.5	Sodium	Na	23.0
Fluorine	F	19.0	Strontium	Sr	87.6
Gold	Au	197.0	Sulphur	S	32.1
Helium	He	4.0	Tin	Sn	118.7
Hydrogen	H	1.0	Titanium	Ti	47.9
Iodine	I	126.9	Vanadium	V	50.9
Iron	Fe	55.8	Zinc	Zn	65.4
Lead	Pb	207.2			

LOGARITHMS

	0	1	2	3	4	5	6	7	8	9	1	2	3	4	5	6	7	8
10	0000	0043	0086	0128	0170	0212	0253	0294	0334	0374	4	8	12	17	21	25	29	33
11	0414	0453	0492	0531	0569	0607	0645	0682	0719	0755	4	8	11	15	19	23	26	30
12	0792	0828	0864	0899	0934	0969	1004	1038	1072	1106	3	7	10	14	17	21	24	28
13	1139	1173	1206	1239	1271	1303	1335	1367	1399	1430	3	6	10	13	16	19	23	26
14	1461	1492	1523	1553	1584	1614	1644	1673	1703	1732	3	6	9	12	15	18	21	24
15	1761	1790	1818	1847	1875	1903	1931	1959	1987	2014	3	6	8	11	14	17	20	22
16	2041	2068	2095	2122	2148	2175	2201	2227	2253	2279	3	5	8	11	13	16	18	21
17	2304	2330	2355	2380	2405	2430	2455	2480	2504	2529	2	5	7	10	12	15	17	20
18	2553	2577	2601	2625	2648	2672	2695	2718	2742	2765	2	5	7	9	12	14	16	19
19	2788	2810	2833	2856	2878	2900	2923	2945	2967	2989	2	4	7	9	11	13	16	18
20	3010	3032	3054	3075	3096	3118	3139	3160	3181	3201	2	4	6	8	11	13	15	17
21	3222	3243	3263	3284	3304	3324	3345	3365	3385	3404	2	4	6	8	10	12	14	16
22	3424	3444	3464	3483	3502	3522	3541	3560	3579	3598	2	4	6	8	10	12	14	15
23	3617	3636	3655	3674	3692	3711	3729	3747	3766	3784	2	4	6	7	9	11	13	15
24	3802	3820	3838	3856	3874	3892	3909	3927	3945	3962	2	4	5	7	9	11	12	14
25	3979	3997	4014	4031	4048	4065	4082	4099	4116	4133	2	3	5	7	9	10	12	14
26	4150	4166	4183	4200	4216	4232	4249	4265	4281	4298	2	3	5	7	8	10	11	13
27	4314	4330	4346	4362	4378	4393	4409	4425	4440	4456	2	3	5	6	8	9	11	13
28	4472	4487	4502	4518	4533	4548	4564	4579	4594	4609	2	3	5	6	8	9	11	12
29	4624	4639	4654	4669	4683	4698	4713	4728	4742	4757	1	3	4	6	7	9	10	12
30	4771	4786	4800	4814	4829	4843	4857	4871	4886	4900	1	3	4	6	7	9	10	11
31	4914	4928	4942	4955	4969	4983	4997	5011	5024	5038	1	3	4	6	7	8	10	11
32	5051	5065	5079	5092	5105	5119	5132	5145	5159	5172	1	3	4	5	7	8	9	11
33	5185	5198	5211	5224	5237	5250	5263	5276	5289	5302	1	3	4	5	6	8	9	10
34	5315	5328	5340	5353	5366	5378	5391	5403	5416	5428	1	3	4	5	6	8	9	10
35	5441	5453	5465	5478	5490	5502	5514	5527	5539	5551	1	2	4	5	6	7	9	10
36	5563	5575	5587	5599	5611	5623	5635	5647	5658	5670	1	2	4	5	6	7	8	10
37	5682	5694	5705	5717	5729	5740	5752	5763	5775	5786	1	2	3	5	6	7	8	9
38	5798	5809	5821	5832	5843	5855	5866	5877	5888	5899	1	2	3	5	6	7	8	9
39	5911	5922	5933	5944	5955	5966	5977	5988	5999	6010	1	2	3	4	5	7	8	9
40	6021	6031	6042	6053	6064	6075	6085	6096	6107	6117	1	2	3	4	5	6	8	9
41	6128	6138	6149	6160	6170	6180	6191	6201	6212	6222	1	2	3	4	5	6	7	8
42	6232	6243	6253	6263	6274	6284	6294	6304	6314	6325	1	2	3	4	5	6	7	8
43	6335	6345	6355	6365	6375	6385	6395	6405	6415	6425	1	2	3	4	5	6	7	8
44	6435	6444	6454	6464	6474	6484	6493	6503	6513	6522	1	2	3	4	5	6	7	8
45	6532	6542	6551	6561	6571	6580	6590	6599	6609	6618	1	2	3	4	5	6	7	8
46	6628	6637	6646	6656	6665	6675	6684	6693	6702	6712	1	2	3	4	5	6	7	7
47	6721	6730	6739	6749	6758	6767	6776	6785	6794	6803	1	2	3	4	5	5	6	7
48	6812	6821	6830	6839	6848	6857	6866	6875	6884	6893	1	2	3	4	4	5	6	7
49	6902	6911	6920	6928	6937	6946	6955	6964	6972	6981	1	2	3	4	4	5	6	7
50	6990	6998	7007	7016	7024	7033	7042	7050	7059	7067	1	2	3	3	4	5	6	7
51	7076	7084	7093	7101	7110	7118	7126	7135	7143	7152	1	2	3	3	4	5	6	7
52	7160	7168	7177	7185	7193	7202	7210	7218	7226	7235	1	2	2	3	4	5	5	6
53	7243	7251	7259	7267	7275	7284	7292	7300	7308	7316	1	2	2	3	4	5	6	6
54	7324	7332	7340	7348	7356	7364	7372	7380	7388	7396	1	2	2	3	4	5	6	6

LOGARITHMS

0	1	2	3	4	5	6	7	8	9	1 2 3 4	5	6 7 8 9
7404	7412	7419	7427	7435	7443	7451	7459	7466	7474	1 2 2 3	4	5 5 6 7
7482	7490	7497	7505	7513	7520	7528	7536	7543	7551	1 2 2 3	4	5 5 6 7
7559	7566	7574	7582	7589	7597	7604	7612	7619	7627	1 2 2 3	4	5 5 6 7
7634	7642	7649	7657	7664	7672	7679	7686	7694	7701	1 1 2 3	4	4 5 6 7
7709	7716	7723	7731	7738	7745	7752	7760	7767	7774	1 1 2 3	4	4 5 6 7
7782	7789	7796	7803	7810	7818	7825	7832	7839	7846	1 1 2 3	4	4 5 6 6
7853	7860	7868	7875	7882	7889	7896	7903	7910	7917	1 1 2 3	4	4 5 6 6
7924	7931	7938	7945	7952	7959	7966	7973	7980	7987	1 1 2 3	3	4 5 6 6
7993	8000	8007	8014	8021	8028	8035	8041	8048	8055	1 1 2 3	3	4 5 5 6
8062	8069	8075	8082	8089	8096	8102	8109	8116	8122	1 1 2 3	3	4 5 5 6
8129	8136	8142	8149	8156	8162	8169	8176	8182	8189	1 1 2 3	3	4 5 5 6
8195	8202	8209	8215	8222	8228	8235	8241	8248	8254	1 1 2 3	3	4 5 5 6
8261	8267	8274	8280	8287	8293	8299	8306	8312	8319	1 1 2 3	3	4 5 5 6
8325	8331	8338	8344	8351	8357	8363	8370	8376	8382	1 1 2 3	3	4 4 5 6
8388	8395	8401	8407	8414	8420	8426	8432	8439	8445	1 1 2 2	3	4 4 5 6
8451	8457	8463	8470	8476	8482	8488	8494	8500	8506	1 1 2 2	3	4 4 5 6
8513	8519	8525	8531	8537	8543	8549	8555	8561	8567	1 1 2 2	3	4 4 5 5
8573	8579	8585	8591	8597	8603	8609	8615	8621	8627	1 1 2 2	3	4 4 5 5
8633	8639	8645	8651	8657	8663	8669	8675	8681	8686	1 1 2 2	3	4 4 5 5
8692	8698	8704	8710	8716	8722	8727	8733	8739	8745	1 1 2 2	3	4 4 5 5
8751	8756	8762	8768	8774	8779	8785	8791	8797	8802	1 1 2 2	3	3 4 5 5
8808	8814	8820	8825	8831	8837	8842	8848	8854	8859	1 1 2 2	3	3 4 5 5
8865	8871	8876	8882	8887	8893	8899	8904	8910	8915	1 1 2 2	3	3 4 4 5
8921	8927	8932	8938	8943	8949	8954	8960	8965	8971	1 1 2 2	3	3 4 4 5
8976	8982	8987	8993	8998	9004	9009	9015	9020	9025	1 1 2 2	3	3 4 4 5
9031	9036	9042	9047	9053	9058	9063	9069	9074	9079	1 1 2 2	3	3 4 4 5
9085	9090	9096	9101	9106	9112	9117	9122	9128	9133	1 1 2 2	3	3 4 4 5
9138	9143	9149	9154	9159	9165	9170	9175	9180	9186	1 1 2 2	3	3 4 4 5
9191	9196	9201	9206	9212	9217	9222	9227	9232	9238	1 1 2 2	3	3 4 4 5
9243	9248	9253	9258	9263	9269	9274	9279	9284	9289	1 1 2 2	3	3 4 4 5
9294	9299	9304	9309	9315	9320	9325	9330	9335	9340	1 1 2 2	3	3 4 4 5
9345	9350	9355	9360	9365	9370	9375	9380	9385	9390	1 1 2 2	3	3 4 4 5
9395	9400	9405	9410	9415	9420	9425	9430	9435	9440	0 1 1 2	2	3 3 4 4
9445	9450	9455	9460	9465	9469	9474	9479	9484	9489	0 1 1 2	2	3 3 4 4
9494	9499	9504	9509	9513	9518	9523	9528	9533	9538	0 1 1 2	2	3 3 4 4
9542	9547	9552	9557	9562	9566	9571	9576	9581	9586	0 1 1 2	2	3 3 4 4
9590	9595	9600	9605	9609	9614	9619	9624	9628	9633	0 1 1 2	2	3 3 4 4
9638	9643	9647	9652	9657	9661	9666	9671	9675	9680	0 1 1 2	2	3 3 4 4
9685	9689	9694	9699	9703	9708	9713	9717	9722	9727	0 1 1 2	2	3 3 4 4
9731	9736	9741	9745	9750	9754	9759	9763	9768	9773	0 1 1 2	2	3 3 4 4
9777	9782	9786	9791	9795	9800	9805	9809	9814	9818	0 1 1 2	2	3 3 4 4
9823	9827	9832	9836	9841	9845	9850	9854	9859	9863	0 1 1 2	2	3 3 4 4
9868	9872	9877	9881	9886	9890	9894	9899	9903	9908	0 1 1 2	2	3 3 4 4
9912	9917	9921	9926	9930	9934	9939	9943	9948	9952	0 1 1 2	2	3 3 4 4
9956	9961	9965	9969	9974	9978	9983	9987	9991	9996	0 1 1 2	2	3 3 3 4

Index

Acetylene, 47, 48
activated complex, 81, 83
activation energy, *see* energy of activation
aluminium extraction, 155, 156
ammonia synthesis, 30, 102–3
Arrhenius equation, 80, 82, 84, 86
atomic hydrogen torch, 43
ATP., 165
autocatalytic reactions, 4

Barium peroxide, 90, 109
benzene, 47, 48–9
bismuth chloride, 95
bond, energy (strength), 40, 43–6
  enthalpy, transferable, 45–6
  length, 48
bromine solution, 94

Cadmium cell, 34
calcium oxide, 25
calorie, 9
calorimeter, 17–18, 171
carbon–carbon bonds, 47
carbonyl chloride, 105
Carnot factor, 144
catalyst, 2, 4, 87, 163
cell, electrochemical, 33, 34, 39
cell potential, 34, 35, 38, 125, 140, 141–2
collision frequency, 84
concentration cell, 37, 137–8
copper sulphate, 7, 29, 37, 38, 94

Degradation of energy, 65, 67
delocalization energy, 48
dipole, 50
disorder, 58–9, 60, 67, 69, 70
disproportionation, 132, 157–8, 159
dissociation constants, 115, 116, 117
distribution of energy, 81

Electrical energy (work), 8, 125
electrode potential, 126
electron affinity, 53, 54
electronegativity, 50
Ellingham diagram, 148, 149, 151–4
endothermic reaction, 3, 7, 24–5, 26, 100
energy, of activation, 73, 80, 81, 82–3, 87, 113
  of initiation, 2
enthalpy, of atomization, 14, 54
  of combustion, 13, 14, 15, 17, 21, 48, 144, 172
  of formation, 10, 14, 20–22, 52, 192
  of fusion, 10
  of hydration, 53, 55
  of neutralization, 13, 15, 23
  of reaction, 9, 11, 12, 83
  of solution, 13, 55, 56
  of vaporization, 26, 50–51, 52
  summation, 11–13
entropy, (ΔS), 28–31, 60–4, 67, 72, 89, 90
  absolute (S), 59–63, 70, 198
  of activation, 84

entropy, $\Delta(S)$—*contd.*
  of hydration, 116, 119
  of mixing, 180–2
enzymes, 162–4
equilibrium, 5, 85, 86, 89–120
  constant, 86, 95–7
escape velocity, 88
ester, hydrolysis of, 74, 94, 101
exothermic reaction, 7, 83

Feasibility, 69
First Law, 18, 19, 58, 68
free-energy, non-standard, 89, 91
  of activation, 85
  of expansion and dilution, 40, 105–7
  of formation, 32, 147, 152, 192
  standard, 31–2, 89, 91, 108
fuel cells, 144–5

Gas constant, 9
glucose, 160–5
gram-equation, 9

Harnessed reactions, 34, 68
heat, 67
  capacity, 8, 15, 61
heat of . . ., *see* enthalpy of . . .
heterogeneous reaction, 3
hydrogen, bond, 162, 180
  electrode, 127, 129
  iodide, 77, 81, 99, 101

Internal energy (ΔU), 17, 18, 19, 68
ionization energy, 52–4
iron (III) chloride, 12
isotherm, van't Hoff, 86, 96, 108–14, 142

Kinetic energy, 59, 81–3

Lactic acid, 160–2
latent heat, *see* enthalpy of . . .
lattice energy, 53, 55
Le Chatelier's Principle, 90, 97–104, 178

lorry and balls analogy, 111

Maxwell distribution, 82
metal extraction, 146, 154–6
micro-reversibility, 85–6, 178
mitochondria, 167
mixing, 51, 180
molecularity, 76–7, 85
muscle, 162, 167

Nernst equation, 138–9, 141
nitrogen dioxide, 64, 102
nitrosyl halides, 84, 109
non-reactions, 5

Order of reaction, 74–7
osmosis, 107
ozone, 30, 88, 103, 104

Permanganate, 124, 129–30, 139
phosphorus chlorides, 108, 110
photosynthesis, 166–7, 169
potential diagrams, 130, 136
potentiometer, 36, 179
probability (thermodynamic), 59–60, 106, 113

Rate, constant, 74, 80, 84
  of reaction, 3, 73–6, 78
reversible, conditions, 34, 66, 69, 70, 106, 125
  reactions, 4–5, 7, 25, 29–30, 90

Salt bridge, 37
Second Law, 58, 65, 67, 160
selenate ion, 104
sodium thiosulphate, 71, 78
solubility product, 117–20, 142
spontaneous process (see also feasibility), 25, 26, 57
standard (state, concentrations), 13, 14, 31–2, 91, 127
steric factor, 84
system (closed, isolated), 18, 58

Temperature, 81, 82, 89–90
thermal, decompositions, 24
    entropy, 61, 63
thermite reaction, 147
thermodynamic probability, *see*
    probability
Third Law, 61–2
Trouton's Rule, 51, 61, 71, 179

Units of energy, 7–9

Van der Waals forces, 49–50
van't Hoff isotherm, *see* isotherm
velocity, *see* rate

Water-gas reaction, 27–8, 91
weak acids, 115–17
work, 19, 64–5
    obligatory, 19, 68–9
    optional, 19, 34, 68–9, 106, 125,
      164